ISOELECTRIC FOCUSING

ISOELECTRIC FOCUSING

Edited by

J. P. ARBUTHNOTT, PH.D., M.I.BIOL.

Department of Bacteriology
The University of Glasgow Royal Infirmary

J. A. BEELEY, M.SC., PH.D.

Department of Oral Biology
The University of Glasgow Dental School

BUTTERWORTHS

LONDON - BOSTON

Sydney - Wellington - Durban - Toronto

THE BUTTERWORTH GROUP

ENGLAND

Butterworth & Co (Publishers) Ltd
London: 88 Kingsway, WC2B 6AB

AUSTRALIA

Butterworths Pty Ltd
Sydney: 586 Pacific Highway, Chatswood,
   NSW 2067
Also at Melbourne, Brisbane, Adelaide
   and Perth

SOUTH AFRICA

Butterworth & Co (South Africa) (Pty) Ltd
Durban: 152–154 Gale Street

NEW ZEALAND

Butterworths of New Zealand Ltd
Wellington: 26–28 Waring Taylor Street, 1

CANADA

Butterworth & Co (Canada) Ltd
Toronto: 2265 Midland Avenue,
   Scarborough, Ontario, M1P 4S1

USA

Butterworths (Publishers) Inc
Boston: 19 Cummings Park,
   Woburn, Mass. 01801

First Published 1975
Second Impression 1976

©

Butterworth & Co. (Publishers) Ltd., 1975

ISBN 0 408 70659 7

Printed in England by Page Bros. Ltd., Norwich

This volume is dedicated to Professor
Harry Rilbe (previously Harry Svensson)
whose pioneering work laid the foundation
for current developments in isoelectric
focusing.

PREFACE

Ampholine carrier ampholytes, a mixture of
synthetic polyamino-polycarboxylic acids, possess
properties such as good conductance and buffering
capacity which are required for the formation of
natural pH gradients in an electrical field. This
has allowed biochemists to exploit the extraordinary
resolving power of isoelectric focusing for the
separation of proteins according to their
isoelectric points. The technique has proved of
great value in the purification and characterisation
of proteins and its popularity is emphasised by the
fact that the LKB Company have, to date, sold over
5,000 sets of isoelectric focusing equipment.
    Although first introduced as a preparative
technique, several workers soon realised the
potential for analytical separation of complex
protein mixtures and modified existing electrophoretic
methods for performance of isoelectric focusing in
thin layers or rods of polyacrylamide gel. By 1973
several new developments had been made in both
preparative and analytical isoelectric focusing.
With the object of providing a forum for discussing
these new developments and of allowing experienced
users to describe applications of isoelectric
focusing to specific problems, a meeting entitled
'Electrofocusing '73' was arranged jointly by Dr
John P Arbuthnott, University of Glasgow and Mr Peter
Cox, LKB, Instruments Ltd and was held in Glasgow in
September 1973.
    Contributors to Electrofocusing '73 subsequently
submitted written accounts of the methods, apparatus
and applications described at the meeting. These we
have edited and arranged in four sections in the
present volume. The first and longest section deals
with theoretical and technical aspects. It includes
a discussion of the properties of Ampholine,

descriptions of new developments in preparative isoelectric focusing and several chapters on isoelectric focusing in polyacrylamide and granulated gels. The advantages and limitations of the methods together with a detailed description of the apparatus needed for their performance are described. Two chapters deal specifically with the factors affecting rapid resolution of protein mixtures at high voltage. Also the theory of transient state isoelectric focusing and its value in determining fundamental properties of proteins are described.

Section II comprises chapters on the application of isoelectric focusing to specific problems of protein chemistry. These serve to illustrate the value of the technique in isolating purified proteins and resolving mixtures containing multiple biologically active forms of enzymes, toxins and virus components. Some deal with practical problems encountered with proteins which are difficult to focus and some show the potential value of isoelectric focusing as a means of studying protein structure.

Section III deals with the application of analytical and preparative methods to the study of immunoglobulins and complement. Here isoelectric focusing has already proved of considerable value in investigating the genetics of immunoglobulin formation. Also it has considerable potential in the diagnosis of immunological abnormalities.

In Section IV there is a chapter on the application of isoelectric focusing to problems in the brewing industry and there are two contributions indicating the value of the technique in the field of isolation and characterisation of biological membranes.

The editors take pleasure in expressing their appreciation and thanks to the Editorial Staff of Butterworths for their help and guidance, and to Mrs Anne Strachan for typing the 'camera-ready' copy. Dr ER Arbuthnott and Dr JG Beeley provided invaluable support throughout.

In the course of preparing the book we have encountered certain unexpected problems; perhaps the most unusual was destruction of part of the manuscript by an author's cat!

JP Arbuthnott
JA Beeley

1 September 1974

CONTENTS

SECTION I - THE TECHNIQUE OF ISOELECTRIC FOCUSING

1   Properties of Ampholine   3
        H. Haglund

2   Some Recent Developments in Preparative   23
     Isoelectric Focusing
        J.S. Fawcett

3   Preparative Isoelectric Focusing in Short   44
     Density Gradient Columns with Vertical
     Cooling
        H. Rilbe and S. Pettersson

4   Transient State Isoelectric Focusing   58
        N. Catsimpoolas

5   A Horizontal Trough Apparatus for   74
     Isoelectric Focusing
        P. Talbot and I.S. Caie

6   Some Aspects of Isoelectric Focusing in   78
     Polyacrylamide Gel
        O. Vesterberg

7   Thin-layer Gel Isoelectric Focusing   97
        H. Davies

8   High Voltage Analytical and Preparative   114
     Isoelectric Focusing
        P. Righetti and A.B.B. Righetti

9   High Voltage Thin-layer Isoelectric   132
     Focusing in Polyacrylamide Gel with
     Automatic Constant Wattage
        J. Söderholm and T. Wadström

10 A Regulator Maintaining Constant Wattage   143
    with Constant Voltage or Constant Current
    Power Supplies
        J. Söderholm and P.-A. Lidström

11 Determination of pH Gradients in   147
    Isoelectric Focusing Gels
        J.A. Beeley, S.M. Stevenson and
        J.G. Beeley

12 Some Applications of a Zymogram Method in   152
    Combination with Isoelectric Focusing in
    Polyacrylamide Gels
        T. Wadström and C.J. Smyth

13 ^{14}C-Labelled Carrier Ampholytes Designed   178
    for Preparative Peptide Separations
        V. Gasparić and Å. Rosengren

14 Some Aspects of Preparative Isoelectric   182
    Focusing in Layers of Granulated Gels
        B.J. Radola

SECTION II - APPLICATIONS IN PROTEIN STRUCTURE
          STUDIES

15 Isoelectric Focusing as an Aid to other   201
    Techniques for the Separation and
    Characterisation of Proteins
        D.H. Leaback

16 Multiple Forms of Bacterial Toxins in   212
    Preparative Isoelectric Focusing
        J.P. Arbuthnott, A.C. McNiven and
        C.J. Smyth

17 Fractionation of Human Salivary Proteins   240
    by Isoelectric Focusing
        J.A. Beeley

18 Isoelectric Focusing Studies of   248
    β-Lactamases
        M. Matthew

19 The Use of Isoelectric Focusing in the   254
    Analytical and Preparative Fractionation
    of Chromatin Nonhistone Proteins
        A.J. MacGillivray and D. Rickwood

20 The Behaviour of Gelatin Preparations in   261
    the Acidic Region of the pH Gradient
        C.R. Maxey and M.R. Palmer

21 pH-Dependent States of a Viral Component   270
   from Foot-and-mouth Disease Virus
      P. Talbot

22 Clues to Protein Structures from   275
   Isoelectric Focusing
      M.J. Hobart

23 Heterogeneity of Hepatitis B Antigen   281
      C.R. Howard and A.J. Zuckerman

SECTION III - APPLICATIONS IN IMMUNOLOGY

24 Antibody Isoelectric Spectra   291
      A.R. Williamson

25 Polymorphism of the Sixth Component of   306
   Complement
      C.A. Alper, M.J. Hobart and P.J. Lachmann

26 Examination of Anti-D IgG Immunoglobulin   313
      J.G. Templeton and G.R. Milne

27 Isoelectric Patterns in IgG Myeloma   319
   Proteins: Possible Biochemical and
   Clinical Inferences
      M.T. Cwynarski, J. Watkins and
      P.M. Johnson

SECTION IV - MISCELLANEOUS APPLICATIONS

28 Towards an Understanding of Beer Haze   329
   Formation
      D.J. Savage, C.C. Thompson and
      S.J. Anderson

29 Characterisation of Cell Surfaces by   338
   Isoelectric Equilibrium Analysis
      G.V. Sherbet and M.S. Lakshmi

30 Isoelectric Focusing of Biological   347
   Membranes
      J.C. Allen and C. Humphries

LIST OF CONTRIBUTORS   355

INDEX   359

SECTION I

The Technique of Isoelectric Focusing

1. PROPERTIES OF AMPHOLINE

H. Haglund

1.1 INTRODUCTION

In 1961, Svensson published a paper entitled
'Isoelectric Fractionation, Analysis and
Characterisation of Ampholytes in Natural pH
Gradients'. This publication was the first of a
series describing the conditions necessary for the
establishment of natural pH gradients. At that time,
suitable carrier ampholytes were not available, nor
had any experiments with natural pH gradients for
the separation of proteins been performed.

Seven years earlier, Kolin had described the
'Separation and Concentration of Proteins in a pH
Field Combined with an Electric Field'[2-4]. The
technique involved the layering of two buffers with
different pH values, one above the other, in a
column. In the pH gradient which developed in the
diffusion zone between the two buffers, Kolin
effected protein separations during the short
period in which the pH gradient existed. The
proteins migrated in this pH gradient and collected
at their isoelectric pH values. They became focused
in distinct narrow bands. Kolin pointed out that
uniform field strength depended on the use of
electrolytes with high and uniform conductivities.
He also stressed the necessity of having a pH
gradient of sufficient buffering capacity.

Ikeda and Suzuki[5] made the first attempts
towards a natural pH gradient in 1912 when they were
granted a patent for a 'Method of Making a Nutritive
and Flavouring Substance'. The mixture of amino
acids in the plant-protein hydrolysate was
electrolysed in a three-chamber apparatus, the
chambers of which were separated by membrane walls.
The most acidic amino acids became concentrated near

3

to the anodic membrane and the most basic near to
the cathodic. The amino acids tended to arrange
themselves according to their isoelectric points
thus creating a natural pH gradient defined and
buffered by the amino acids themselves. Because of
convective forces in the primitive apparatus used,
and because of the lack of conductivity and
buffering capacity of some of the amino acids at
their isoelectric points, they could never develop a
stable and well defined pH gradient. These pioneer
workers were, however, able to isolate glutamic acid
as the glutamate of the cation of the anodic
solution (Figure 1.1). In spite of the limitation
arising from the instability of a diffusing pH
gradient, Kolin obtained remarkably good results
during the short observation times available.
Svensson called this type of pH gradient artificial
in contrast to a stable natural pH gradient buffered
by electrolytes in equilibrium with diffusion and
which is stationary in that the pH gradient remains
stable for a reasonable time. Electrolytes
fulfilling the requirements of the natural pH
gradient were ampholytes at their isoelectric
points. They are stationary in an electrical field
since their mobility at their isoelectric points is
zero. The conditions for isoelectric focusing in
artificial and natural pH gradients are shown
schematically in Figure 1.1. The requirement of
buffering capacity and conductivity at the
isoelectric point for a carrier ampholyte is
formulated as follows.

Consider a simple diprotic ampholyte where
$amph_o$ is the zwitterionic and unprotolysed form,
$amph^-$ and $amph^+$ are the anionic and cationic forms
respectively, and where C_{amph_o}, C_{amph^+} and C_{amph^-}
are the molar concentrations of these forms and
C_{amph} is the total concentration of both ionic and
unchanged forms. Two equilibria will occur in
solution:

$$amph_o \rightleftharpoons amph^- + H^+$$

$$amph_o + H^+ \rightleftharpoons amph^+$$

Applying the law of mass action but not considering
activity coefficients:

$$\frac{C_{amph^-} \times C_{H^+}}{C_{amph_o}} = K^-$$

and

$$\frac{C_{amph_o} \times C_{H^+}}{C_{amph^+}} = K^+$$

If α is the degree of protolysis and is defined as:

$$\alpha = \frac{C_{amph^+} + C_{amph^-}}{C_{amph}}$$

by taking logarithms and substituting pH for $-\log C_{H^+}$, and pK^+ and pK^- for $-\log K^+$ and $-\log K^-$ respectively, then:

$$pI = \frac{pK^+ + pK^-}{2}$$

and if pI = pH in the iso-ionic state, then after resolving C_{amph^+} and C_{amph^-} from the equations above and inserting in the expression for α:

$$\alpha = \frac{2}{2 + 10^{(pI - pK^+)}}.$$

α will be directly related to the conductivity of the ampholyte at its pH and hence the conductivity will have its maximum value when $(pI - pK^+)$ is at a minimum. For polyprotic ampholytes, this will be the case when the two pK values lying on either side of the pI are near to it and close together. However, a compound with two charged groups, as our ampholyte model, can never have a ratio between the two K values of less than 4 (ref. 6). Thus, if K^- is the most acidic of the two constants, $K^-/K^+ \geqslant 4$ and $pK^+ - pK^- \geqslant \log 4$.

Since pI = $(pK^+ + pK^-)/2$ then $pI - pK^- \geqslant \frac{1}{2} \log 4 \geqslant \log 2$. Obviously the minimum value for $pI - pK^+$ is $\log 2$. Hence,

$$\alpha_{max} = \frac{2}{2 + 10^{\log 2}} = \frac{1}{2} \quad (ref. 27)$$

The buffering capacity, $dQ/d(pH)$, where Q is the charge, also has its maximum when $(pI - pK^+)$ is at a minimum (Figure 1.2). (A more complete description of the mathematical treatment is given by Svensson[1] and Rilbe[28].)

In his early experiments in 1961, Svensson[1] used peptides obtained by partial hydrolysis of proteins as carrier ampholytes. These compounds reasonably fulfilled his theoretical postulates, namely that they must both retain good conductivity and have sufficient buffering power at their isoelectric points. Although the peptide system

has properties which are good enough for the
development of a stable natural pH gradient, it has
many disadvantages from a practical point of view.
The protein zones separated in such a pH gradient
cannot be detected by the photometric or
colorimetric methods used for the detection of
proteins, since a protein hydrolysate has the same
properties in these respects as proteins. Thus a
carrier ampholyte system which did not absorb light
at 280 nm and did not give colour with reagents used
for the detection of proteins was very much desired.
These and other requirements of a good carrier
ampholyte system stimulated Svensson and his
co-workers to investigate the conditions for

Figure 1.1   Four steps towards Ampholines.
(a): This shows an electrolysis cell containing
sodium sulphate. A totally unbuffered and unstable
pH gradient is formed.   (b): Preparation of glutamic
acid from plant protein hydrolysate (Ikeda and
Suzuki[5]).   This shows the same electrolysis
apparatus now loaded with a mixture of amino acids.
Amino acids are ampholytes and will order themselves
according to their isoelectric points so that the
most basic ones gather near the cathode, the neutral
ones towards the middle and the acidic ones near the
anode. Since some amino acids have low
conductivities and buffering capacities at their
isoelectric points, the pH gradient will be poorly
defined in those regions.   (c): Artificial pH
gradient (Kolin[2-4]). This shows a column apparatus
which is stabilised against convection by means of a
sucrose density gradient. An artificial pH gradient
is formed by a diffusion zone between two buffers
with different pH values. Such a pH gradient is
sufficiently stable to allow focusing of proteins in
sharp zones when an electric field is applied, but
is too unstable for prolonged experiments.   (d):
Natural pH gradient (Svensson[1]). This shows
essentially the same column apparatus similarly
stabilised against convection by means of a sucrose
density gradient. Instead of using amino acids as
carrier ampholytes (as in the experiments of Ikeda
and Suzuki[5]), ampholytes with adequate buffering
capacities and conductivities at their isoelectric
points are used. Under these conditions a stable
natural pH gradient comprised of ampholytes at their
isoelectric points can be formed. This pH gradient
will be well defined and with satisfactory buffering
capacity and conductivity at every point. Such a
natural pH gradient allows prolonged separation
              experiments and optimal resolution

Formation of pH gradients

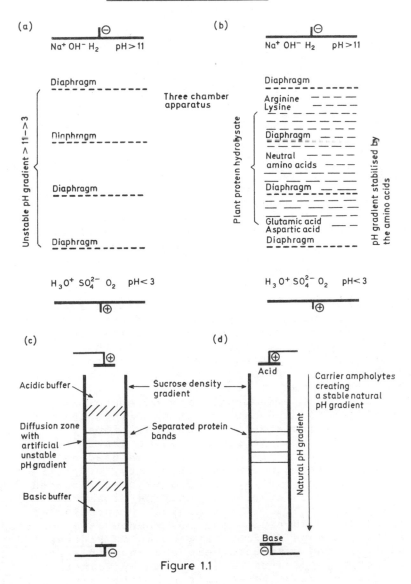

Figure 1.1

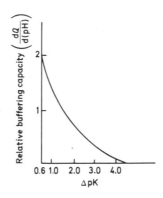

Figure 1.2 Buffering capacity dQ/d(pH) is at a
maximum when (pI - pK$^+$) is at a minimum which is
log 2. Hence, both conductivity and buffering
capacity are dependent on the same molecular
condition. The diagram shows the relationship
between the difference between the two pK values
nearest to the pI and the relative buffering
capacity. For more detailed information the reader
        is referred to original papers[1,8,28]

synthesising an ideal carrier ampholyte system. In
1966, Vesterberg and Svensson[7] synthesised a mixture
of polyaminopolycarboxylic acids which seemed to
fulfil most of the requirements. In the same year,
LKB started development work based on these results
which finally led to the product known as Ampholine.
This material was first marketed in 1967 on a
limited scale. The properties of Ampholine
conditioned by the natural pH gradient and by the
sample proteins are 'the classical properties of
Ampholine'[8]. In the seven ensuing years, during
which isoelectric focusing has been used as a
separation technique in biochemistry, properties
other than those first noted have been recorded. An
attempt to classify the properties of Ampholine is
made in Table 1.1. The classical properties of
Ampholine conductivity and absorbance as a function
of pH in the pH gradient are shown in Figures 1.3
and 1.4. The gradients were obtained in a zone
convection apparatus as described by Valmet[9].
     It should be noted that conductivities obtained
from experiments where the fractions were harvested

Table 1.1 Properties of carrier ampholytes and Ampholine

Fundamental 'classical' properties

   (a) buffering ion has a mobility of zero at isoelectric pH
   (b) good conductance
   (c) good buffering capacity

Performance properties

   (a) good solubility
   (b) no influence on detection systems
   (c) no influence on sample
   (d) separable from sample

'Phenomena' properties

   (a) 'plateau' effect; drift of the pH gradient
   (b) chemical change in sample
   (c) complex formation

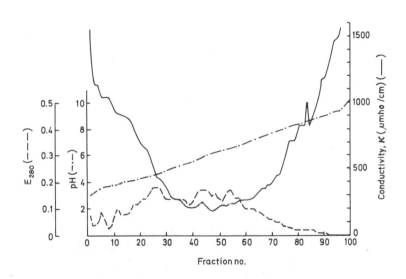

Figure 1.3 This diagram shows the conductivity (κ), absorbance (A) and pH of fractions obtained from pH 3 to 10 Ampholine by means of a one-hundred zone convection electrofocusing apparatus. A high concentration of Ampholine (8%, w/v) was used in order to obtain significant values, especially for the absorbance (Harlestram[29], personal communication)

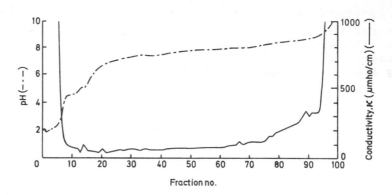

Figure 1.4   This diagram shows the conductivity (κ)
and pH from a 2% (w/v) Ampholine solution, pH 7 to
9, in fractions obtained in a one-hundred
compartment zone convection electrofocusing
    equipment (Harlestram[29], personal communication)

after the current had been disconnected differ from
the conductivities in the pH gradient <u>during</u>
isoelectric focusing. Immediately after the current
is switched off, the focused ampholytes will diffuse
and give the surroundings a higher conductivity than
in the focused state.
       The remainder of this chapter is concerned with
some of the properties of Ampholine which the author
has found to be of particular interest. For a
general review of isoelectric focusing, the reader
is referred to Catsimpoolas[10]. Some of the
properties of interest not referred to here are
described in detail by other authors. The
conditions for linear pH gradients are discussed
and treated mathematically by Almgren[11]. Resolution
and peak capacity in equilibrium-gradient methods of
separation are discussed by Giddings and Dahlgren[12].

1.2   INSTABILITY OF pH GRADIENTS: THE 'PLATEAU'
      PHENOMENON

Kolin's artificial pH gradient was unstable because
of both diffusion and the electrophoretic forces
acting upon the buffering ions. These problems were
a severe limitation in obtaining optimal resolution
of proteins as a function of their isoelectric
points. As proteins approach their isoelectric pH

values, their mobilities decrease; hence prolonged
times are required for the final stages of focusing.
The natural pH gradient made possible by carrier
ampholytes and by Ampholine, was believed to be the
final solution to this problem. In most cases, the
natural pH gradient has also been sufficiently
stable for optimum resolution.

Soon after the introduction of Ampholine, it
became evident that the pH gradient in column
density gradient experiments had a tendency to
migrate slowly towards the cathode: isoelectric
focusing in polyacrylamide gels showed similar
phenomena. Extensive studies of such changes of the
pH gradient have been reported[13,14], and it appears
that the changes are the result of the formation of
a pH 'plateau'.

The work of Miles, Simmons and Crambach[13]
showed that:

(i)   The plateau phenomenon progresses with both
        time and voltage. The spreading of bands in
        the polyacrylamide gel proceeds towards both
        the cathode and the anode whereas earlier
        observations in sucrose density gradient
        columns indicated a drift towards the cathode
        only.
(ii)   Band resolution appears unaffected by time or
        voltage (within the limits of the
        experiments) once the equilibrium has been
        reached.
(iii)   The plateau phenomenon, at constant voltage
        and time, progresses as an inverse function
        of Ampholine concentration.
(iv)   The plateau phenomenon is not due to leakage
        of Ampholine from the system: gel plugs at
        the end of the separation gel do not
        influence the effect.
(v)   The plateau phenomenon is independent of both
        the protein and the method by which the
        Ampholine solution is added to the gel.
(vi)   The conductivity in the region of neutrality
        decreases with time when compared with the
        acidic and the basic ends of the gradient.

The plateau phenomenon has been explained[13] by
the hypothesis that ampholytes at their isoelectric
points can reach a state of temporary 'transient
charge' which causes a temporary electrophoretic
migration. Before such a metastable transient ion
has been discharged again it will meet another
Ampholine molecule of a different pI with which it
forms a complex. In such a way, transient charged
ampholytes with excess carboxylic groups could
interact with ampholytes of a lower pI to give

stable complex forms. This will impoverish the
neutral zone of carrier ampholytes and enrich the
more acidic part of the gradient. Similarly,
ampholytes at their isoelectric points in the
presence of excess amino groups will tend to form
complexes with ampholytes of higher isoelectric
points, a process which would tend also to
impoverish the neutral parts but this time enrich
the zone of the gradient of higher pH. In this way
the gradients would begin to plateau as a result of
Ampholine molecules gradually migrating away from
the neutral region and complexing with other
ampholytes towards the ends of the gradient.
However, one experiment in particular contradicts
this hypothesis. A pH gradient of 3.5 to 6.0
should, according to the hypothesis, be flattened
in the neutral region only. In fact this is not the
case; the pH gradient gradually becomes more and
more acidic. Electro-osmotic flow or other effects
which might cause the ampholytes to leak out into
the electrode regions have also been suggested as
causes of the plateau phenomenon. However, our
work indicates that electro-osmotic flow will cause
a broadening and blurring of zones but not the
transport of zones out of the pH gradient or the
loss of ampholytes.

It has been shown[14] that the composition of the
polyacrylamide gel does not influence the rate of pH
gradient flattening. Thus it can be assumed that
different accelerators or different concentrations
of accelerators have no effect on the pH gradient.
The way in which the sample or the ampholytes were
introduced into the gel also had no effect on the
flattening of the pH gradient. The addition of
phenolic free radical inhibitors of polymerisation
and other substances which influence the
polymerisation also had no effect. Thus the plateau
effect is not the result of complex formation
between ampholytes and the acrylamide gel matrix.

Another explanation for the pH drift would be
hydrolytic or other chemical changes in the carrier
ampholytes at the basic and acidic ends of the pH
gradient. In this way, the isoelectric points of
the Ampholine molecules would gradually change
during isoelectric focusing and make the acidic end
still more acidic and the basic end still more
basic. Since the only functional groups in the
carrier ampholytes are carboxylic and amino groups,
and because they all are bound to aliphatic
structures, such changes seem very unlikely.

Electrode vessels that are too large can
result in flattening and loss of the pH gradient by

causing leakage of ampholytes out of the separation compartment, e.g. when disc gel electrophoresis apparatus[15] is used. Under these conditions, the pH gradient gradually flattens and may finally be totally lost. Such flattening of a pH gradient can be attributed to unsuitable experimental conditions and is not an explanation of the plateau phenomenon observed in the types of equipment normally employed for isoelectric focusing.

Table 1.2 Features of the 'plateau' phenomenon

1. Progresses with time and voltage

2. The spreading of bands in polyacrylamide gel proceeds both towards the cathode and anode in pH range 3 to 10. Early observations in density gradients indicated a drift towards the cathode only

3. Band resolution seems unaffected by time or voltage

4. Progresses in inverse relation to Ampholine concentration

5. Is not due to ampholyte leakage in the ends of the gel

6. The conductivity decreases in the region of neutrality, not at the ends

7. The composition of the polyacrylamide gel does not influence the progress of the flattening of the pH gradient. This is also true of added accelerators and the way in which the sample or the Ampholine is introduced

8. Addition of phenolic and other free radical polymerisation inhibitors has no effect. Thus complex formation between ampholytes and gel matrix seems unlikely

9. Chemical change in the ampholytes resulting in loss of carboxylic or amino groups seems unlikely

To date, no reasonable explanation of the plateau phenomenon exists. Fortunately, however, the pH drift or the plateau phenomenon do not normally adversely affect the resolution or reproducibility of isoelectric focusing. The drift is most pronounced after a 20-40 h run in a thin-layer gel experiment by which time the separation has already been completed. Furthermore,

the separated bands in thin-layer gel experiments do
not seem to lose resolution as a result of the pH
drift. However, a pH gradient that could be
maintained as a stable gradient independent of time
and voltage, would allow at least thin-layer gel
experiments to be completed more rapidly by using
higher voltage and field strength. The possibility
of using a higher field strength without losing the
pH gradient should also lead to improved resolution.
Further investigations into the causes of the
plateau phenomenon are also essential in order to
increase the understanding of the formation of
natural pH gradients. Sometime after the
Electrofocusing '73 Symposium, held in Glasgow,
Dr. Bjarne Beck (B. Beck, Rikshospitalet Copenhagen,
personal communication) reported that the pH drift
and the plateau phenomenon can be eliminated or to a
great extent diminished by choosing electrolytes
other than the traditional ones. The experimental
conditions for these experiments and his results
will be published elsewhere.

1.3 AMPHOLINE-PROTEIN INTERACTION

1.3.1 Chemical Interaction
Under normal circumstances, carrier ampholytes do
not cause chemical changes in proteins. Ampholine
carrier ampholytes consist of amino and carboxylic
acid groups linked to aliphatic structures which
normally have no chemical influence on proteins.
Most published results support this view. For
example, Hayes and Wellner[16] studied amino oxidases
in snake venom which electrophoretic experiments had
shown to contain three distinct bands. In
isoelectric focusing experiments, however, 18
readily distinguishable bands were observed. Since
it was first believed that the observation was the
result of artefacts, a thorough investigation was
carried out in which results from thin-layer and
density gradient separations, using Ampholines of
different pH ranges and using different methods of
Ampholine and sample application, were compared.
The results proved to be reproducible and enzyme
activity was recovered in all 18 bands. Most other
reports also support the conclusion that isoelectric
focusing has no detectable influence on the proteins
separated.
     However, negative results are less frequently
reported than are positive findings. Indeed, there
are cases known where isoelectric focusing failed
because the proteins under observation were either
denatured or had lost activity. Such findings have

usually been explained in terms of protein
instability at the isoelectric point giving rise to
irreversible denaturation. Reversible changes such
as loss of charged prosthetic groups have also been
observed; these changes can also result in enzyme
inactivation. In some cases, however, activity can
be restored by addition of the missing ion.

Changes in proteins resulting from the
splitting of protein complexes during isoelectric
focusing have also been reported. Valmet[17] showed
that albumin fatty acid complexes were gradually
dissociated during a prolonged focusing experiment.
The fatty acids from the complex migrated
electrophoretically out of the system. After a week
in the density gradient column, the albumin was
totally devoid of fatty acids and the original
albumin band had shifted to a position one pH unit
higher in the gradient. Such effects are now
accepted to be due to the physical-chemical
conditions of the pH gradient.

Oxidative changes in proteins have recently
been reported. Wadström and Vesterberg[18]
demonstrated that enzyme activity after isoelectric
focusing was higher when an anti-oxidant, such as
dithioerythritol, was present in the pH gradient.
Ascorbic acid was also used for the same purpose and
ascorbic acid consumption during the isoelectric
focusing was determined by titration before and
after the experiment. The position of application
of the sample to a gel slab also had an influence on
the oxidation: enzyme samples applied close to the
anode lost more activity than samples applied
further away from the anode.

Jacobs[19] made a thorough quantitative study of
the change in amino acid composition of proteins
during isoelectric focusing; bovine ribonuclease was
studied in particular. This somewhat basic protein
showed changes in amino acid composition during
isoelectric focusing; the sulphur-containing amino
acids, cystine and methionine, were shown to be
partially oxidised. By adding ascorbic acid (10%,
w/v) as an anti-oxidant, the changes in the amino
acid composition could be controlled and were
considerably diminished. It was observed that the
solution in the anodic electrode compartment
showed a considerable increase in absorbance at
280 nm, indicating the presence of reaction products
from sucrose, proteins, or carrier ampholytes.

Quinn[20] has reported unexpected reduction of
bovine methaemoglobin to haemoglobin when focused in
polyacrylamide gels of pH gradient 6 to 8. The
reduction was observed with both riboflavine- and

persulphate-polymerised gels. Prior to this,
persulphate-polymerised gels had been suspected to
be a cause of artefactual bands[21]. In the former
case, however, Ampholine was thought to be directly
involved in the reduction reaction.

It is difficult to accept that Ampholine in a
pH gradient can directly cause either oxidation or
reduction. The Ampholine molecules, being
aliphatic compounds with only amino and carboxylic
acids as functional groups, are unlikely to
participate in this type of reaction. Reactions
occurring in the electrode compartments, however,
are a more likely cause of this phenomenon. In
sucrose density gradient isoelectric focusing, it is
well known that dark coloured products result from
the oxidation of sucrose at the anode. Ionic
compounds which are oxidised by the anode solution
to positively charged compounds, would migrate into
the separation compartment and cause the oxidation
of protein bands focused there. Proteins sensitive
to oxidation, especially when focused in the
alkaline regions of the pH gradient, should be
prevented from contacting atmospheric oxygen by
performing the separation in oxygen-free nitrogen.

Although most isoelectric focusing experiments
do not appear to be subject to oxidation or
reduction or other chemical changes, it is advisable
to check the isoelectric focusing procedure by the
application of the sample at several different
points on the gel in the case of thin-layer
isoelectric focusing. Such an experiment will
usually provide a check on changes in the protein
that occur during isoelectric focusing. It should
be noted that if the sample is applied at the
extreme ends of the gel, chemical change might occur
due to exposing the sample to extremes of pH at the
beginning of the run before the pH gradient has
stabilised.

Information on limitations of mobility which
can occur in the polyacrylamide gel are obtained
simultaneously. Refocusing of separated zones is
also to be recommended if there is doubt as to
whether a protein is changed during isoelectric
fractionation.

1.3.2 Complex Formation

Proteins in solution will interact with any
electrolyte ion in its surroundings. This is also
the case for ions of carrier ampholyte type. For
Ampholine, however, these interactions with proteins
are reversible equilibria in the majority of cases.
Such reversible equilibria will not disturb the

isoelectric focusing and will not influence the
final result. In some cases, however, artefactual
components have been reported, possibly arising
from the formation of metastable complexes between
proteins and carrier ampholytes. In one case, a
protein which focused initially as one single band
became split into several bands when refocused in a
second experiment (Wadström, personal
communication[22]). This phenomenon could be
explained in terms of the formation of a metastable
protein-protein complex which is stable at the
isoelectric pH but which dissociates when exposed to
a pH different from that of the pI.

1.4   THE MOLECULAR WEIGHT OF AMPHOLINES

Early attempts to estimate the size of the Ampholine
molecules by means of gel filtration on Sephadex G25
and G50 indicated an average molecular weight of
around 700 (unpublished observations made during
development of Ampholine). Osmotic experiments gave
similar values. Recently, however, Aminkemi AB have
extended their investigations, the results of which
indicate that substances of higher molecular weight
and larger molecular size exist in the Ampholine
mixture. A more detailed account of this work is
described by Gasparic and Rosengren[23] who found
that the 'molecular weights' obtained by gel
filtration using various defined polyethylene
glycols as standards gave lower values for Ampholine
than those estimated by other methods. Since the
possibility of separating peptides from carrier
ampholytes by gel filtration is dependent on their
behaviour in the gel and not strictly on their
molecular weights, these authors introduced the
expression 'apparent molecular weight' instead of
attempting more precise molecular weight
estimations. In this way, they emphasised that
their results did not show the true molecular
weights of the carrier ampholytes but gave
information helpful in choosing experimental
procedures for the separation of Ampholines from
protein and peptide samples. From their
publication, it is evident that the apparent
molecular weight distribution curve for ampholine
reaches values in the regions of 5000. The apparent
molecular weight of the mean is approximately 400.
This value is obviously lower than the true mean of
the molecular weight which is probably between 600
and 900. Aminkemi AB have produced experimental
batches of ^{14}C-labelled carrier ampholytes with the
same primary structure as the ordinary Ampholine

carrier ampholytes but with limited apparent
molecular weights, the highest being less than
2000.   Only O.2% of the total radioactivity is above
1000.   The distribution of these Ampholines after
gel filtration on Sephadex G25 indicates that
Sephadex G50 should give better resolution and
therefore is preferential for the separation of
carrier ampholytes from protein fractions.   A more
detailed account of the optimal conditions for the
separation of proteins from carrier ampholytes by
means of gel filtration is given by Gasparic and
Rosengren[23] (see Chapter 13).

1.5   THE pI DISTRIBUTION OF AMPHOLINE

The pH ranges of Ampholines produced from 1967 up to
and including 1972 were extended at the acidic and
basic ends by the addition of acidic and basic amino
acids; aspartic and glutamic acids were added for
the acidic end and arginine for the basic.   It then
became possible to use the pH gradients obtained
from pH 3.5 up to pH 10.0.   Since 1973, no more
amino acids have been added.   Improved control of
the synthetic procedure has made it possible to
cover the ends of the entire pH gradient with
molecules of the normal Ampholine type without any
further additions.
        Extension of the pH gradient below pH 3 and
above pH 10 by means of artificial gradients has
been reported.   This was facilitated by the addition
of free acids and free bases without ampholytic
properties[25,26].
        Pettersson[24] has described the behaviour of
acids during isoelectric focusing.   He considered
that the equilibrium was determined by an
electrical mass flow towards the anode and by a
diffusion flow in the opposite direction.   To get an
evenly distributed pH gradient below pH 3 a mixture
of weak acids with different pK_a values was chosen.
In effect an artificial pH gradient was used.
Stenman and Gräsbäck[25] used such gradients for the
fractionation of vitamin B_{12}-binding protein of
human amniotic fluid.   In a similar way certain
bases were used to demonstrate the separation of
cytochrome C in artificial pH gradients above 10
(ref. 26).
        However, carrier ampholytes (Ampholines), are
now available with the pH ranges 2.5 to 4.0 and 9.0
to 11.0 (ref. 27).   Since they are of the same
amino-carboxylic acid aliphatic type as other
Ampholines, they form natural pH gradients.   The
buffering capacity of these ampholytes is about

twice that of the pH ranges of the normal range of
Ampholine regions. Accordingly, both the higher
and the lower ranges are supplied in 20% (w/v)
solutions and give about the same buffering capacity
per millilitre as the normal Ampholines which are
supplied as 40% (w/v) solutions. When working with
low or high pH gradients it is important to cover
the gaps between pH values of 4 and 7 or pH values
of 9 and 11 respectively with small amounts of
Ampholine of suitable intermediate pH range; pH 7 to
9 Ampholine is particularly useful for the latter
case in this respect. It is also important to
consider the high conductivity in the acidic region
and in the basic region when using low or high pH
gradient Ampholines. Extension of the gradients in
these regions is limited because differences between
the conductivity in the gradient and the field
strength will become too large. Problems such as
uneven heat distribution and bad focusing in regions
with too low a field strength limit the experimental
possibilities. Examples of the isoelectric focusing
of proteins at extreme pH values are shown in
Figures 1.5 and 1.6.

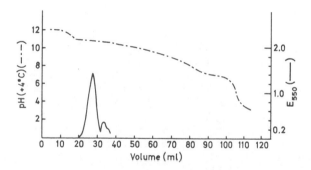

Figure 1.5   The fractionation of two subcomponents
of cytochrome C using pH 9 to 11 Ampholine. The
experiment was carried out in an LKB 8100-1
electrofocusing column (110 ml). In the experiment,
sorbitol was used instead of sucrose for the density
gradient since the latter shows slight dissociation
above 10.5. 2.2 ml (20%, w/v) Ampholine pH 9 to 11
was used. In order to increase the conductivity in
the neutral and anodic parts of the column, a small
quantity of Ampholine other than pH 9 to 11 was
added, i.e. 0.1 ml Ampholine pH 8 to 10 (40%, w/v)
and 0.3 ml Ampholine pH 6 to 8, (40%, w/v) were
added

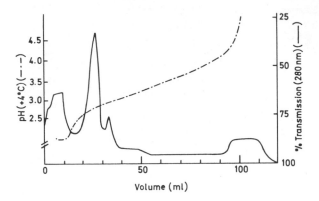

Figure 1.6   The separation of the two subcomponents
of a commercial pepsin preparation using Ampholine
of pH range 2.5 to 4.0 (ref. 27).   The experiment
was carried out in an LKB 8100-1 electrofocusing
column (110 ml) using sucrose as a stabilising
medium

REFERENCES

1. SVENSSON, H., 'Isoelectric Fractionation,
   Analysis and Characterisation of Ampholytes in
   Normal pH Gradients. I. The Differential
   Equation of Solute Concentration at a Steady
   State and its Solution for Simple Cases'.
   Acta Chem. Scand., 15, 325-341 (1961)
2. KOLIN, A., 'Separation and Concentration of
   Proteins in a pH Field Combined with an
   Electric Field'. J. Chem. Phys., 22,
   1628-1629 (1954)
3. KOLIN, A., 'Electrophoretic Line Spectra'.
   J. Chem. Phys., 23, 407-408 (1955)
4. KOLIN, A., 'Isoelectric Spectra and Mobility
   Spectra: A New Approach to Electrophoretic
   Separation'. Proc. Nat. Acad. Sci. (U.S.A.),
   41, 101-110 (1955)
5. IKEDA and SUZUKI, 'Method of Making a Nutritive
   and Flavouring Substance'. U.S. Pat. 1 015 891
   (1912)
6. McINNES, D.A., The Principles of Electro
   Chemistry, Reinhold, New York, pp. 396-397
   (1939)

7. VESTERBERG, O. and SVENSSON, H., 'Isoelectric
    Fractionation, Analysis and Characterisation of
    Ampholytes in Natural pH Gradients. IV. Further
    Studies on the Resolving Power in Connection
    with Separation of Myoglobins'. Acta Chem.
    Scand., 20, 820 (1966)
8. HAGLUND, H., 'Isoelectric Focusing in pH
    Gradients - A Technique for Fractionation and
    Characterisation of Ampholytes'. Methods of
    Biochemical Analysis, 19, 1-100 (1970)
9. VALMET, E., 'Zone Convection Electrofocusing, A
    New Technique for Fractionation of Ampholytes
    in Free Solution'. Protides of the Biological
    Fluids. Proc. 17th Colloq., Bruges, 1969,
    Pergamon Press, Oxford and New York,
    pp. 401-407 (1970)
10. CATSIMPOOLAS, N., 'Isoelectric Focusing and
    Isotachophoresis of Proteins'. Separation
    Science, 8, 71-121 (1973)
11. ALMGREN, M., 'Isoelectric Fractionation,
    Analysis and Characterisation of Ampholytes in
    Natural pH Gradients'. Chem. Scripta, 1,
    69-75 (1971)
12. GIDDINGS, J.C. and DAHLGREN, K., 'Resolution and
    Peak Capacity in Equilibrium Gradient Methods
    of Separation'. Separation Science, 6, 345-356
    (1971)
13. MILES, L.E.M., SIMMONS, J.E. and CRAMBACH, A.,
    'Instability of pH Gradients in Isoelectric
    Focusing on Polyacrylamide Gel'. Anal.
    Biochem., 49, 109-117 (1972)
14. BATES, L.S. and DEYOE, C.W., 'Polyacrylamide Gel
    Electrofocusing and the Ampholyte Shift'.
    J. Chromatog., 73, 296-297 (1972)
15. ORNSTEIN, L. and DAVIES, B.J., 'Disc
    Electrophoresis', Preprinted by Distillation
    Product Industries, Eastman Kodak Co. (1962)
16. HAYES, M.B. and WELLNER, D., 'Microheterogeneity
    of L-Amino Oxidase. Separation of Multiple
    Components by Polyacrylamide Gel
    Electrofocusing'. J. Biol. Chem., 244, 6636
    (1969)
17. VALMET, E., 'The Heterogeneity of Human Serum
    Albumin'. Protides of the Biological Fluids.
    Proc. of the 17th Colloq., Bruges, 1969,
    Pergamon Press, Oxford and New York,
    pp. 443-448 (1970)
18. WADSTRÖM, T. and VESTERBERG, O. 'Studies on
    Endo-β-N-Acetylglucosamidase, Staphylolytic
    Peptidase and N-Acetylmuramyl-alanine Amidase
    in Lysostaphin and from Staphylococcus aureus'.
    Acta Path. Microbiol. Scand., Section B, 79,
    248-264 (1971)

19. JACOBS, S., 'Effect of Isoelectric Focusing on the Amino-Acid Composition of Proteins'. Analyst, 98, 25-33 (1973)

20. QUINN, J.R., 'The Reduction of Ferric Myoglobin by Ampholine on Acrylamide Gel Electrofocusing'. J. Chromatog., 76, 520-522 (1973)

21. WRIGLEY, C.W., 'Protein Fractionation by Gel Electrofocusing : Importance of the Sample Application Procedure'. Protides of the Biological Fluids. Proc. of the 17th Colloq., Bruges, 1969, Pergamon Press, Oxford and New York, pp. 417-421 (1970)

22. WADSTRÖM, T., Statens Bakteriologiska Laboratorium, Lundagatan 2, 117 27 Solna, Sweden, personal communication

23. GASPARIC, V. and ROSENGREN, A., '14C Labelled Carrier Ampholytes Designed for Preparative Peptide Separations'. In: Isoelectric Focusing of Proteins and Related Substances, Butterworths, London (1974)

24. PETTERSSON, E., 'Isoelectric Fractionation, Analysis and Characterisation of Ampholytes in Natural pH Gradients. IX. A Method for Obtaining pH Gradients in the Region below pH 3, Stable enough to Permit Isoelectric Focusing of Ampholytes'. Acta Chem. Scand., 23, 2631-2635 (1969)

25. STENMAN, U. and GRÄSBÄCK, R., 'Gradients for Isoelectric Focusing at Low pH'. Biochim. Biophys. Acta, 286, 243-251 (1972)

26. VALMET, E., Lääketehdas, Onion Oy, P.O. Box 10019, Helsingfors, Finland, personal communication

27. KARLSSON, C. and ÖHMAN, J., LKB Application Notes No. 16 (1972) and No. 58 (1973)

28. RILBE, H., 'Isoelectric Fractionation, Analysis and Characterisation of Ampholytes in Natural pH Gradients. II. Buffering Capacity and Conductance of Isionic Ampholytes:A Correction'. Acta Chem. Scand., 25, 2768-2769 (1971)

29. HARLESTAM, R., LKB Produkter AB Fack S-16125 Bromma 1, Sweden, personal communication

2. SOME RECENT DEVELOPMENTS IN PREPARATIVE ISOELECTRIC FOCUSING

J.S. Fawcett

2.1 INTRODUCTION

In preparative separation techniques the success of any method is measured by the degree of resolution obtained, the loading capacity, the product yield and, in the case of biologically active compounds, the full recovery of activity. Over the past few years isoelectric focusing has been shown to be capable of high resolution in the separation of mixtures of proteins into many components. Theoretical limits of resolution by isoelectric focusing have been defined[1] and have been supported by results obtained from density gradient, polyacrylamide gel and Sephadex-stabilised systems.

In general the recovery of biological activity has been good. When activity is diminished it is often the result of removal of a co-factor or a similar phenomenon and is not due to any fundamental failure in the method.

The limits of loading capacity have not been fully exploited, either in respect of the maximum capacity of a density gradient column, or by the choice of other stabilising media.

In this report, ways of obtaining maximum resolution and maximum load will be discussed and alternative designs of density gradient columns will be presented. Isoelectric focusing in Sephadex[2], granulated polyacrylamide gels and by zone convection[3] have all shown considerable promise and the merits of these methods will be reported.

The steady-state condition in isoelectric focusing is an equilibrium between electrophoretic migration of the ampholyte towards its isoelectric point and the spread of the zone by diffusion (Figure 2.1). An increase in electrophoretic

23

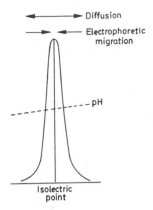

Figure 2.1 The focused zone at the steady state
condition where electrophoretic migration towards
the isoelectric point is in equilibrium with
diffusion in the opposite direction. Sharper zones
are obtained by applying a higher potential and by
use of ampholytes with a steep slope for mobility/pH
plot

migration obtained by applying a higher potential
will therefore give a sharper zone, but the gain is
only proportional to the square root of the
voltage[1]. Higher voltage gradients cause more heat
to be produced and, as with all forms of
electrophoresis, the ability of the apparatus to
dissipate heat sets an upper limit to any voltage
increase. Cooling is most favourable with
thin-film techniques when a high ratio of cooling
surface to total volume is provided.
     When high voltage is used in isoelectric
focusing, zones of high resistance are often formed
due to variation in the concentration and ionisation
of the various ampholytes along the pH gradient.
Heat produced within these zones must be efficiently
removed. This is particularly important in the case
of density gradient-stabilised systems where
localised heating will cause convection mixing with
the layers immediately above, thus destroying the
density stability. In Sephadex-stabilised systems,
local heating is less important provided that
thermally labile proteins are not present in the
heated zone. We have shown[4] that, with Sephadex
and polyacrylamide gels, a much higher voltage load
can be applied before zones become distorted. In
the zone convection apparatus localised heating will

give convective mixing within the compartment but
any disturbance will be confined and will not affect
the stabilisation of the system as a whole.

Another method of increasing resolution is with
the aid of shallow pH gradients[1]. This has the
effect of moving the zones further apart and also
allows an increase in load so that under ideal
conditions almost the whole volume of the pH
gradient is utilised. However, in a shallow pH
gradient the electrophoretic mobility towards the
isoelectric point is reduced and the resulting zones
will be wider. Also, due to the reduced
electrophoretic mobility, it will take longer to
establish steady-state conditions and the duration
of the experiment must be increased accordingly.

Surprisingly few applications of the use of
very shallow pH gradients have been reported. Some
experimental batches of Ampholines covering a range
of less than one pH unit have been made by the
manufacturer but are available only while stocks
last. In most of the work on narrow gradients
individual workers have prepared their own narrow
pH-range ampholytes by isoelectric fractionation of
Ampholine in the sucrose density gradient column.
By using a higher Ampholine concentration (4 to 5%),
sufficient ampholyte covering the required pH range
can be obtained. Narrow-range Ampholine prepared in
this manner will, of course, contain sucrose and,
where possible, should be collected from the less
dense section of the gradient. A high sucrose
content is inconvenient when using Ampholine for the
preparation of solutions for narrow-range gradients.
An alternative method is to fractionate the
Ampholine by isoelectric focusing in Sephadex in
which case the above complications may be avoided.

As stated by the manufacturers, it is important
when using narrow pH ranges to add a small quantity
(up to 10% by volume) of the wide-range Ampholine
(pH 3 to 10) to provide some conductivity throughout
the whole gradient, and especially in the region of
pH 7.

An example of the high resolution obtainable
with narrow-range pH gradients is described by
Albers and Scanu[5]. Separation of a mixture of
polypeptides from serum low-density lipoprotein in a
pH gradient of 4.35 to 4.85 gave excellent
resolution, completely separating two components
differing in isoelectric points by only 0.09 pH
units.

Full exploitation of this procedure requires
suitable adjustment of the components in the
Ampholine mixture in order that the pH gradient is

tailored to each particular separation problem.
Ideally, the mixture would give shallow gradients at
the appropriate pH where higher resolution or higher
sample load is required. Since the separate
components of Ampholines are not available, and very
few amphoteric substitutes are suitable, it is not
possible to prepare these specialised gradients
directly. An improved pH gradient can, however, be
prepared by a two-stage isoelectric focusing
procedure. After the first isoelectric focusing of
a protein mixture, fractions in regions where
incomplete separation has occurred are combined.
These fractions, together with additional Ampholine,
are subjected to further isoelectric focusing at a
second stage. There is now twice the amount of
Ampholine in the pH range, where originally the
components were incompletely separated, and the
resultant shallow pH gradient will give improved
resolution.

2.2   ISOLATION OF FOCUSED ZONES FROM DENSITY
       GRADIENT COLUMNS

Attempts to increase the resolution within the
isoelectric focusing apparatus are of little value
unless adequate precautions are taken to prevent
any re-mixing of the zones during the isolation
procedure when the column is drained and fractions
collected. With the density gradient column, this
is indeed a problem. Once the current is turned
off, zones rapidly begin to spread by diffusion and
additional spreading occurs due to wall effects and
turbulence as the zone moves down the column and
through the capillary tubing. An apparatus designed
by Svendsen[6], which allows elution of the column
while the potential is applied, has little practical
value since the fractions are diluted with
electrode solution.
    Another aspect, often neglected, is the ratio
of the volume of the fraction collected to the
volume occupied by individual protein zones. Minor
components may focus in zones only 1 mm thick, and
in the 110 ml LKB density gradient column this
represents a volume of 0.25 ml. It is customary to
collect 1 ml fractions and fractions of this volume
are thus inadequate to resolve these minor
components. It is therefore advantageous to monitor
the column effluent continuously. The method
normally adopted with the LKB column is to link the
flow cell of an ultraviolet monitor to the bottom
outlet and to maintain the density gradient by
downward liquid flow through the flow cell assembly.

This arrangement is not wholly satisfactory. We
find it causes further disturbance of the zones and
that sometimes gas bubbles collect in the flow cell
and interfere with the measurement of u.v.
absorption. The solution at the lower end of the
column is saturated with gas from the electrode and
if the temperature of this solution is allowed to
rise as it passes through the flow cell, a gas
bubble forms; this is not easily removed unless the
elution is interrupted. Bubble formation can be
avoided by thermostatically controlling the
temperature of the flow cell assembly[7].

We therefore decided to investigate other
methods of emptying density gradient columns. Our
first approach was to replace the lower Teflon
adapter of the LKB column by one incorporating a
quartz glass tube (Figure 2.2) as suggested by
Leuven[8]. This tube (7 mm o.d. x 80 mm long) was
filled with dense electrode solution and the column
filled and operated in the usual manner. For
monitoring the elution of the column we used a
modified detector head of a Uvicord II
(LKB-Produkter, Bromma, Sweden). The detector head
was placed on its side, front panel uppermost, and
the quartz tube passed through a hole made in the
back plate. A small plastic block, incorporating a
narrow slit, was held in position by a metal plate
that replaces the cell holder. The flow rate was
controlled by pumping water into the top of the
column and the density gradient solution passed
from the quartz tube directly into the fraction
collector without the use of plastic capillary
tubing.

This arrangement gave satisfactory
u.v.-monitoring and the disturbance of zones in the
quartz section was considerably less than that
experienced using the flow cell and capillary tube
attachments described above. However, there was
still some disturbance of zones as they left the
annular column and entered the bottom section above
the adapter.

The annular cross-section of the LKB column,
although providing excellent cooling by a high
'surface area to volume' ratio, does impose severe
conditions as the liquid is funnelled into a narrow
outlet tube. During this procedure a very slow flow
rate is preferable to allow the horizontal component
of the liquid flow to adjust itself to the density
gradient. However, very slow flow rates increase
the spreading of the zones by diffusion. For the
110 ml column a flow rate of 1 ml/min was chosen,
but it is possible that this was not optimal.

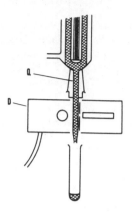

Q

D

<u>Figure 2.2</u> Alternative method of u.v. monitoring
when emptying an LKB density gradient column[8]. The
lower LKB adapter is replaced by one fitted with a
quartz glass tube (Q). The density gradient flows
down the quartz tube past the u.v. detector (D) and
          drips directly into a collecting tube

2.3   ALTERNATIVE DESIGNS OF DENSITY GRADIENT COLUMNS

The most exciting and important development in
column design is the introduction of short density
gradient columns[9] cooled from the top and bottom
surfaces. This technique is fully described by
Rilbe and Petterson (see <u>Chapter 3</u>).
This method allows rapid isoelectric focusing, has
high loading capacity and is likely to set the
design of the next generation of density gradient
columns.
     Columns designed specifically for density
gradient zone electrophoresis[10], have been used for
isoelectric focusing. They consist of a vertical
cooled column with a 'built-in' u.v. monitor. The
column is fitted at both ends with membranes
connecting to electrode vessels. By pumping dense
solution into the base of the column, the density
gradient is displaced upwards past the u.v. monitor.
Two larger versions of this column, without
'built-in' u.v. monitors, are now commercially
available (Instrumentation Specialities Co.,
Lincoln, Nebraska 68504, U.S.A.). The suitability
of this apparatus for isoelectric focusing has been

investigated[11] and very good separation of a mixture
of haemoglobin A and haemoglobin F has been obtained.
Isoelectric focusing in the larger columns[12] has
also been reported.

It seemed to us that these columns were
unnecessarily complicated when used for isoelectric
focusing, since large separate electrode
compartments are not required and the top
electrode can dip directly into the upper layers of
the column. Three simplified versions have been
constructed[13]. The first apparatus (Figure 2.3a)
consists of a central quartz glass tube (15 mm i.d.
x 450 mm long) fitted with a perspex cooling jacket.
The bottom end of this tube fits into an electrode
vessel and is isolated from the electrode solution
by a membrane. We have found that porous
polyethylene tubing, of which the pores have been
plugged with polyacrylamide gel, makes a very
satisfactory membrane[14]. The membrane is prepared
by immersing porous polyethylene tubing in a
solution of acrylamide, bisacrylamide and catalyst.
A vacuum is applied to remove air trapped in the
pores of the polyethylene and to allow the solution
to impregnate the tube. After polymerisation,
surplus gel is scraped off the surface and the
membrane thoroughly washed. This type of membrane
has a number of advantages. It has negligible
electro-osmotic flow; it is robust and, if allowed
to dry out, may be regenerated by soaking in water
without any detrimental effect on the membrane. In
the dried state the membrane is easily glued into
position with epoxy adhesive thus simplifying
construction of the apparatus.

Further simplification of these columns is
shown in Figures 2.3b and 2.3c where the quartz
column is one limb of a U-tube. Preparative
isoelectric focusing in a simple U-tube has been
described by Weller, Heaney and Sjögren[15] and on a
micro-scale by Godson[16] and by Koch and Backx[17]. A
three-way tap fitted to the base of the U-tube
(Figure 2.3b) facilitates the filling and emptying
of the column. In our experience more reproducible
results are obtained if the density gradient is
formed by filling the column from the bottom end[18]
but this is not possible in the U-tube without the
tap (Figure 2.3c). The diameter of the bore of the
three-way tap should not be less than a third of the
diameter of the column and it should always contain
electrode solution during the period that the
voltage is applied. Very little heat is generated
within the tap as the conductance of the electrode
solution is very much greater than that of the

B*

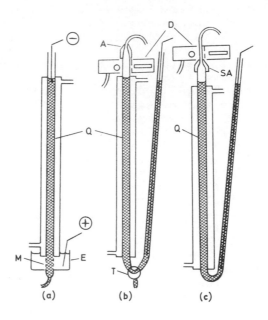

Figure 2.3 Three designs of density gradient
isoelectric focusing columns: (a) simplified version
of the design by Brakke, Allington and Langille[10]
with bottom membrane (M) and electrode compartment
(E); (b) U-tube fitted with three-way tap (T) to
facilitate filling and emptying the column; (c)
simple U-tube. All the columns consist of a central
quartz glass tube (Q) fitted with cooling jacket.
For emptying the column, the top electrode is
removed (Figures 2.3a and 2.3b) and dense solution
pumped into the bottom of the column to displace the
density gradient upwards past the u.v. detector (D)
which is placed around the tube top. The density
gradient leaves the column via an adapter (A). When
less sensitivity is required, a special adapter (SA)
is fitted incorporating a narrow quartz glass tube,
    and the detector is placed around this tube

Ampholine solution in the column. Columns of this
type without the inner cooling surface have a
limited cooling capacity and, if the internal
diameter is greater than 20 mm, the effect of
excessive heating becomes apparent. This sets an
upper limit of 100 ml for the total gradient volume.
    The columns are emptied by removing the upper
electrode and pumping dense sucrose solution into
the base of the quartz tube and displacing the

gradient upwards past the u.v. monitor. An adapter
moulded in silicone rubber, using a Silastic G RTV
mould-making rubber kit (Dow Corning Corporation,
U.S.A.) is attached to the column and allows
fractions to be collected. The monitoring device is
made by modifying a detector head of a Uvicord II
set for 280 nm absorption. The detector head is
placed on its side and fixed horizontally so that
the quartz tube projects through a 25 mm hole made
in the back plate. Used in this way the detector is
not immobilised to one single column but may be
moved in succession to monitor a number of different
columns.

The sensitivity of the u.v. monitor may be
increased by connecting the 100 mV output to a 10 mV
recorder (Vitatron type UR 401 fitted with
logarithmic amplifier). The upper limit of
sensitivity is set by the 280 nm absorption of the
Ampholines themselves and it is advisable to check
each batch of Ampholine by a blank run. When
decreased sensitivity is required, the detector head
is raised to a narrow quartz tube connected to the
column by a silicone rubber adapter (Figure 2.3c).

In conditions of bright sunlight it is
necessary to exclude external light from the quartz
tube adjacent to the detector head. A typical scan
obtained with this equipment is shown in Figure 2.4.
These columns give good analysis by u.v.-scanning
within the quartz tube, but the collection of
fractions, whilst an improvement on previous
methods, does result in some loss in resolution.
Other methods of fraction collection from these
columns are under investigation.

When pH measurements are required, a special
adapter fitted with electrodes is attached to the
top of the column and this allows continuous pH
monitoring of the effluent. The flow cell is
designed with the reference electrode fitted flush
with the cell wall and the glass electrode
projecting 3 mm into the liquid stream to give
minimum interference to the protein zones.
Continuous monitoring of the pH from isoelectric
focusing columns has been carefully studied by
Jonsson, Pettersson and Rilbe[7] who attached a pH
flow cell to the bottom outlet of an LKB column.
Two of the problems encountered by these workers,
namely the hydrostatic pressure on the reference
electrode and the gas-saturated electrodes acting as
a galvanic element, are avoided when monitoring pH
from the top of the columns as described in this
section.

One major difficulty is the slow response of the

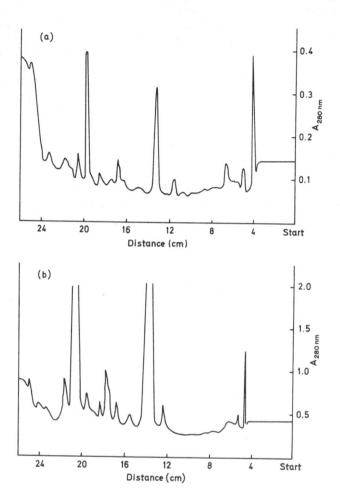

Figure 2.4   Absorption scan at 280 nm of a mixture
of whale and horse myoglobins fractionated by
isoelectric focusing in density gradient columns
shown in Figure 2.3.   Ampholine gradient pH 7 to 9,
final voltage 1200 V: (a) 300 µg of each protein
with u.v. detector set at maximum sensitivity; (b)
14 mg of each protein, detector positioned as in
Figure 2.3c.   Main peaks from right to left:
air-liquid interface, whale myoglobin, horse
         myoglobin, anode electrode solution

glass electrode which has made precise
measurements impossible at low temperatures. This
is a consequence of the small surface area of the
micro-electrode. In agreement with Jonsson,
Pettersson and Rilbe[7], we find it possible to obtain
accurate results only when using slow flow rates and
a narrow-range pH gradient.

2.4   INCREASING THE LOADING CAPACITY OF DENSITY GRADIENT COLUMNS

When impure protein extracts are subjected to
isoelectric focusing the protein to be purified is
often present as only a minor component. To obtain
sufficient material it is necessary to apply a high
protein load. During isoelectric focusing, extracts
of this type may form precipitates which aggregate
and sediment and disturb the subsequent
fractionation. Furthermore, components in high
concentration may exceed the limit of stabilisation
by the density gradient, forming wider zones which
spread into more dense regions of the column. One
way to increase the loading capacity at a particular
position in the column is to arrange for a steep
change in density in that region. This, of course,
necessitates a more shallow density change elsewhere
in the column. Complex density gradients of this
type can be readily produced with modern
gradient-forming apparatus.

By suitable choice of the polarity of the
electrodes, unwanted material can sometimes be
concentrated in the bottom section of the column
while separation in the upper part is undisturbed.
A fine example of this technique is described by
Janson[19], who loaded 7.3 g of Cytophaga johnsonii
cytoplasmic material on the 440 ml LKB column.
Heavy precipitates formed in the lower part of the
gradient, blocking the column and making a normal
elution procedure impossible. However, three
α-glucosidases focused in the upper part of the
gradient and were isolated by removing fractions
through a specially shaped capillary tube inserted
into the top of the column. Between each fraction
the capillary tube was lowered a further 5 mm into
the column.

We have investigated the separation of rabbit
carbonic anhydrase when high loads of red cell
haemolysates are applied to the 110 ml LKB column[20].
Using a narrow-range (pH 6.3 to 7.3) Ampholine, we
have applied up to 1 g of material and, using the
lower electrode as the cathode, found that the
haemoglobin formed a broad zone filling the bottom

third of the column. However, with such high loads
a precipitate formed in the upper part of the
gradient, sedimenting in the region where the
carbonic anhydrase is focused.

2.5 MULTIPLE DENSITY GRADIENT COLUMNS

In the example described above it is advantageous to
use a double gradient apparatus. This consists of
two vertical U-tubes joined together 20 mm from one
end (Figure 2.5a). Tubes B and C are each filled
with gradient while the limb A is filled with dense
cathode solution and limb D with dense anode
solution. Cooling is effected by immersing the
apparatus in a cooling tank. When the red cell
haemolysate was subjected to isoelectric focusing in
this apparatus, the haemoglobin concentrated in tube
B and almost occupied the entire volume. The
precipitate spread over the lower half of tube C
while the carbonic anhydrase, free from precipitated
material, focused in the upper half. Initially we
collected fractions by manually pipetting aliquots
from the upper half of the column. More recently,
we have constructed an adapter which fits into the
top of the column and enters below the
interconnecting section. A seal is made with the
side of the tube by compression of a silicone ring
as described by Vere[21]. The column is eluted by
pumping into the adjacent electrode limb and
displacing the gradient upwards analogous to the
column techniques already described.
    If, during isoelectric focusing, any
precipitated material should fall into the
concentrated electrode solution where it might
dissolve and be degraded, it is important to ensure
that it does not migrate electrophoretically back
into the density gradients. In such cases, the
outer limb can also be filled with a density
gradient and the electrode positioned at the upper
end of the tube.
    A further development of this technique is
given by the apparatus shown in Figure 2.5b. This
apparatus is similar to that described above but has
an additional U-tube (fitted with a stop cock)
between the two sections. By this means density
gradients can be introduced into the four tubes B,
C, D and E. The formation of these multiple density
gradients is achieved in one simple operation by a
multi-channel peristaltic pump.
    This apparatus has proved useful in the
isoelectric focusing of crude extracts to obtain a

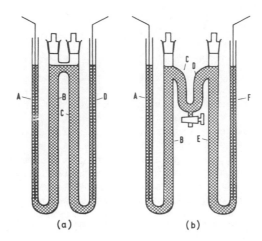

Figure 2.5 Multiple density gradient isoelectric focusing columns for use where precipitates or high concentration of impurities spread into focused zones.   (a) A density gradient is formed in tubes B and C; A and D (and F in diagram (b)) are filled with dense electrode solution.   The apparatus is cooled by immersion in a cooling tank.   The contents of B and C are emptied separately by upward displacement using a more dense solution and are collected through an adapter (not shown) lowered into the top of the column.   (b) Apparatus used for the preliminary fractionation into a narrow pH range.   Parts B, C, D and E are filled with density gradients.   After isoelectric focusing, when the pH is within the required range, the contents of C and
                D are collected as one fraction

isoelectric focusing, the pH of the solutions at the tops of B and E are measured and, if of the required pH range, the contents of tubes C and D are collected as one fraction.   The collection of a specific narrow pH range in the centre section requires careful selection of Ampholine solution and adjustment of the volumes of the density gradient in B and E.
     After focusing, if the pHs of the solutions at the tops of tubes B and E are not exactly of the required range, some adjustment is possible.   For example, by adding electrode solution to limbs A or F the pH gradient can be displaced in one direction or the other.   Another method is to continue the experiment for a longer period, when lower pH values

will be obtained due to the slow pH drift towards
the cathode.

2.6   SEPARATION OF PROTEIN FROM AMPHOLINES

There have been several reports suggesting that the
removal of Ampholines from proteins is an easy
separation but we have found it to be otherwise.
The process is made more difficult by the presence
of sucrose in fractions from the density gradient
column. We have found that high concentrations of
sucrose severely inhibit the removal of Ampholines
by dialysis, ultrafiltration or gel filtration.
Furthermore, traces of the high molecular weight
components of Ampholines are usually incompletely
separated from proteins by dialysis or
ultrafiltration. The separation of these components
is especially difficult from proteins of molecular
weight less than 20 000 where it is necessary to use
less porous membranes.
    A two-stage process has therefore been
developed[22] consisting of ion-exchange
chromatography followed by gel filtration.
    In the first stage the protein and Ampholine
are adsorbed onto the ion-exchange material, while
the sucrose passes through the column. Usually,
the conditions for adsorption and elution from an
ion-exchange material are known from previous
stages in the protein purification. For basic
proteins, the carboxylic acid cation-exchange resin
Amberlite IRC-50 (or the chromatographic grade
Amberlite CG-50 or Zeo-Karb SRC 44) is most
suitable, the spherical resin particles allowing
good flow rates with the viscous sucrose solution.
For other proteins the cellulose ion-exchangers are
preferable. In order to obtain good flow rates it
is important that all very fine particles be
removed by successive decantation before the column
is packed. Even so it may still be necessary to
apply a small hydrostatic pressure to increase the
flow rate and, depending upon the properties of the
adsorbant, it may also be necessary to dilute the
more highly viscous solutions by the addition of
water before passage through the column.
    Conditions of pH and ionic strength are chosen
such that the protein is readily adsorbed from
dilute solution, while a change in pH or an increase
in ionic strength elutes the protein in a small
volume. The size of the ion-exchange column is kept
as small as possible so that its capacity is just
sufficient to adsorb all protein from the solution.
In calculating the column dimensions, however, it

must be remembered that most if not all of the
Ampholines will also be adsorbed。
     In the second stage of the process, the
concentrated solution of protein and Ampholine from
the ion-exchange column is passed through a
Sephadex gel filtration column。 Where necessary,
additional sodium chloride is added to the sample
solution since a high ionic strength will aid the
dissociation of any Ampholine-protein complexes.
To effect maximum separation the porosity of the gel
should be as great as possible while still allowing
the protein to be eluted at the column void volume。
The total column volume is increased when low
molecular weight proteins are expected, since in
these separations maximum resolution will be
necessary for complete removal of the high molecular
weight Ampholines from the protein. With stable
proteins it is convenient to use Sephadex columns
equilibrated with 0。05 M ammonium bicarbonate (or
other volatile buffer) so that the product may be
obtained direct by lyophilisation。

2.7 SEPHADEX AND GRANULATED POLYACRYLAMIDE GELS

Details of isoelectric focusing in layers of
Sephadex or granulated polyacrylamide gel are
described by Radola (see Chapter 14)
and will not be discussed here。 It is surprising
that this method has not been more widely adopted as
it offers many advantages for both analytical and
preparative purposes. Thin-layer and slab
techniques, as developed by Radola[2], have
high-cooling efficiency, excellent stabilising
properties and a very high-loading capacity。 The
detection of focused zones by the filter paper print
technique is rapid and is particularly useful for
specific staining techniques。
     However, methods for specific detection of the
biological activity of some enzymes and hormones on
filter paper are not always available。 In these
cases it is necessary to divide the gel slab into
many segments in order to obtain an extract for
further testing. When a number of samples are to be
separated this procedure is somewhat laborious。
     We have attempted to overcome this problem by
using a vertical glass column packed with
Sephadex G-200。 The column design illustrated in
Figure 2。3a is suitable for this purpose。 After
isoelectric focusing, the upper electrode is removed
and, by pumping dense sucrose solution into the base
of the column, the Sephadex gel is displaced upwards
and into a fraction-collecting device (Figure 2.6)。

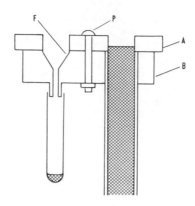

<u>Figure 2.6</u> Apparatus for collecting fractions after
isoelectric focusing in a tube filled with Sephadex
G-200. The fraction cutter has two Teflon discs (A)
and (B), the lower one (B) being fixed to the
column. A dense solution pumped into the bottom of
the column displaces the Sephadex up into the top
disc (A) which is then rotated about the pivot (P)
and the Sephadex fraction washed through the
    funnel-shaped hole (F) into the collecting tube

This fraction collector consists of a Teflon block
with a rotating Teflon disc pivoted at the centre.
The glass column is glued into a hole in the block
which also has a second funnel-shaped hole, with a
drain tube, on the opposite side of the centre
pivot. Sephadex gel is displaced up into the top
disc which is then rotated through 180° and the
Sephadex washed through the funnel into the
collecting tube. In this way fractions equivalent
to 3 mm sections of the Sephadex gel were obtained
with only moderate disturbance of the focused zones.

2.8   ZONE CONVECTION ISOELECTRIC FOCUSING

Zone convection isoelectric focusing was introduced
by Valmet[3] who used a special apparatus consisting
of a shallow rectangular trough with a ridged base.
A lid with similar ridges fits into this trough
forming a narrow zigzag channel which is cooled on
both sides by circulating coolant. The trough is
filled with Ampholine and protein mixture and when
the lid is lowered into position it displaces the
liquid giving rise to a continuous zigzag layer.
Electrodes are fitted at both ends and a high
potential applied. Zones focus and concentrate in

the bottom layer of the appropriate section and, on raising the lid, fractions are automatically trapped in each compartment. Valmet constructed his apparatus from perspex with a wall thickness of 1 mm; it is therefore difficult to make and at present no commercial models are available.

There are four main advantages claimed for this technique; these are:

(i)   high loading capacity,
(ii) rapid isolation of focused zones,
(iii) substances that precipitate at the
      isoelectric point are localised and do not
      spread,
(iv) the absence of added stabilising media
      simplifies the final separation of protein
      from Ampholine.

For some time little information on this technique was available but recently Bodwell and Creed[23], using a Valmet-type apparatus, have reported successful separation of a wide variety of proteins under various conditions, including the use of 10 M urea at 40°C. Elsewhere, Talbot describes an apparatus using the principle of zone convection isoelectric focusing for the separation of virus material (see Chapter 5).

We have constructed an apparatus (Figure 2.7) based on an earlier design[24]; it is made by machining two perspex blocks. One block forms the lid and the other has strips of 1 mm thick perspex cemented to its sides to form a narrow trough 450 mm long and 10 mm wide, containing 38 compartments. The base and the sides of the apparatus are cooled by inserting the unit in a cooling tank. When ovalbumin was focused in this apparatus, using a pH 3 to 10 gradient, the focused zone was contained in three compartments (76% in one), but when whale myoglobin was focused in a pH 7 to 10 gradient the components did not form such sharp zones. The failure to obtain sharply focused zones at the alkaline end of the pH gradient is probably due to a combination of poor cooling and electro-osmotic effects in the narrow channel.

Macko and Stegemann[25] have described a simply constructed apparatus suitable for zone convection isoelectric focusing, using a spiral tube made by winding plastic tubing round a metal rod. Each turn of the spiral represents one compartment of the Valmet apparatus. Fractions are isolated by plunging the spiral into a freezing bath and cutting the frozen tube into segments. Quite good results were obtained by these authors but in its present form the method is limited to small scale

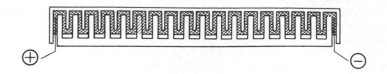

<u>Figure 2.7</u>   Zone convection apparatus based on the
design of Kalous and Vacik[24] consisting of long
narrow perspex trough with 38 compartments (only 18
    shown) and cooled by immersion in a cooling tank

preparative work as it is not practicable to form a
spiral from wider plastic tubing.

2.9   CONTINUOUS FLOW METHODS

The idea of continuous flow isoelectric focusing was
suggested by Rilbe[26] but Seiler, Thobe and Werner[27],
using their version of the Hannig Free Flow
apparatus, were the first to introduce this
technique to isoelectric focusing of proteins.
Quite recently this group[28] have extended the method
to include cells and cell particles. One of the
advantages of continuous flow isoelectric focusing
is that the zones are sharpened by the applied
potential right up to the time of removal from the
apparatus. They are, therefore, not subjected to
spreading by diffusion as encountered in the
isolation of focused zones from density gradient
columns. The method is capable of processing large
quantities of material, but applications in this
direction are obviously inhibited by the high cost
of Ampholine solution.
      We have investigated two types of continuous
flow apparatus. One uses a packed Sephadex bed with
vertical liquid flow. The other apparatus uses a
continuously flowing density gradient which flows
horizontally through a vertical trough. When
operated for several days both methods gave
excellent reproducibility, focused zones emerging at
the same position in the exit tubes during the whole
period. This has already been reported[29] last year
and will not be described here.

2.10   CONCLUSIONS

In isoelectric focusing maximum resolution is
obtained by the application of high applied
potential and shallow pH gradients.

Part of the resolution obtained by isoelectric focusing in the density gradient column is lost by some re-mixing of the focused zones during the emptying procedure.

An apparatus is required which can be emptied rapidly to limit zone spreading by diffusion, which incorporates u.v. and pH monitoring and which allows collection of fractions with minimum disturbance of separated zones. Although modifications in apparatus design have led to some progress, other methods of collection need to be developed.

Finally, the use of Sephadex as the stabilisation medium for isoelectric focusing should be further exploited, with special emphasis directed towards automatic collection of fractions.

ACKNOWLEDGEMENTS

The author is greatly indebted to Professor C.J.O.R. Morris for his invaluable advice and his many helpful suggestions in this project.

REFERENCES

1. SVENSSON, H., 'Isoelectric Fractionation, Analysis, and Characterization of Ampholytes in Natural pH Gradients. I. The Differential Equation of Solute Concentrations at a Steady State and its Solution for Simple Cases'. Acta Chem. Scand., 15, 325-341 (1961)

2. RADOLA, B.J., 'Isoelectric Focusing in Layers of Granulated Gels. I. Thin-Layer Isoelectric Focusing of Proteins'. Biochem. Biophys. Acta, 295, 412-428 (1973)

3. VALMET, E., 'Zone Convection Electrofocusing - A New Technique For Fractionating Ampholytes in Free Solution'. Science Tools, 16, 8-13 (1969)

4. FAWCETT, J.S., 'Direct Optical Scanning of Isoelectric Fractionations'. Protides of the Biological Fluids, Proc. of 17th Colloq., Bruges 1969, Pergamon Press, Oxford and New York, 409-412 (1970)

5. ALBERS, J.J. and SCANU, A.M., 'Isoelectric Fractionation and Characterization of Polypeptides from Human Serum Very Low Density Lipoproteins'. Biochem. Biophys. Acta, 236, 29-37 (1971)

6. SVENDSEN, P.J., 'A New Elution System for Isoelectric Focusing in Sucrose Gradients'. Protides of the Biological Fluids, Proc. of 17th Colloq., Bruges 1969, Pergamon Press, Oxford and New York, 413-416 (1970)

7. JONSSON, M., PETTERSSON, E. and RILBE, H.,
    'Isoelectric Fractionation, Analysis and
    Characterization of Ampholytes in Natural pH
    Gradients. VIII. Continuous Recording of pH and
    Light Absorbance of Column Effluent After
    Isoelectric Focusing'. Acta Chem. Scand., 23,
    1553-1559 (1969)
8. LEUVEN, M., cited by HAGLUND, H., 'Isoelectric
    Focusing in pH Gradients - A Technique for
    Fractionation and Characterization of
    Ampholytes'. In: Methods of Biochemical
    Analysis, Vol. 19, Ed. D. Glick, Interscience,
    New York, 1-104 (1971)
9. RILBE, H., 'Rapid Isoelectric Focusing in
    Density Gradient Columns'. Ann. N.Y. Acad.
    Sci., 209, 80-93 (1973)
10. BRAKKE, M.K., ALLINGTON, R.W. and LANGILLE, F.A.,
    'Mobility Measurements by Photometric Analysis
    of Zone Electrophoresis in a Sucrose Gradient
    Column'. Anal. Biochem., 25, 30-39 (1968)
11. GRANT, G.M. and LEABACK, D.H., 'The Use of ISCO
    Density Gradient Electrophoresis Columns for
    Isoelectric Focusing'. Shandon Instrument
    Applications, 31 (1970)
12. ALLINGTON, W.B. and ARON, C.G., 'Studies on
    Isoelectric Focusing in the Model 210 ISCO
    Density Gradient Electrophoresis Column'.
    ISCO Appl. Res. Bull., No. 4 (1971)
13. FAWCETT, J.S. unpublished observations
14. MORRIS, C.J.O.R., unpublished observations
15. WELLER, D.L., HEANEY, A. and SJÖGREN, R.E., 'A
    Simple Apparatus and Procedure for
    Electrofocusing Experiments: pI of Lactate
    Dehydrogenase and Isocitrate Lyase'. Biochem.
    Biophys. Acta, 168, 576-579 (1968)
16. GODSON, G.N., 'A Simple Apparatus for Rapid
    Isoelectrofocusing of Multiple Samples on a
    Micro Scale'. Anal. Biochem., 35, 66-76 (1970)
17. KOCH, H.J.A. and BACKX, J., 'A Miniature
    Electrofocusing Method'. Science Tools, 16,
    44-47 (1969)
18. FAWCETT, J.S., 'Isoelectric Focusing'. In:
    Methodological Developments in Biochemistry,
    Vol. 2, Ed. E. Reid, Longman, London, 61-80
    (1973)
19. JANSON, J.C., 'Studies on Dextran Degrading
    Enzymes from Bacteria and Molds'. Thesis
    Uppsala University, Almqvist and Wiksell,
    Uppsala, p. 121 (1972)
20. CARTER, N.J. and FAWCETT, J.S., unpublished
    observations

21. VERE, D.W., 'An Adjustable End-piece for Gel
    Filtration'. J. Chromatog., 24, 195-196 (1966)
22. FAWCETT, J.S., DEDMAN, M.L. and MORRIS, C.J.O.R.,
    'The Isolation of Bovine Thyrotrophins by
    Isoelectric Focussing'. FEBS Lett., 3, 250-252
    (1969)
23. BODWELL, C.E. and CREED, G.J., 'Separation of
    Proteins Using Horizontal Isoelectrofocusing'.
    Abstr. 9th Internat. Congr. Biochem.,
    Stockholm, p.25 (1973)
24. KALOUS, V. and VACÍK, J., 'Horizontal
    Preparative Electrophoresis Chamber Without
    Carrier'. Chem. Listy, 53, 35-37 (1959)
25. MACKO, V. and STEGEMANN, H., 'Free
    Electrofocusing in a Coil of Polyethylene
    Tubing'. Anal. Biochem., 37, 186-190 (1970)
26. RILBE, H., 'Trends in Instrumental and
    Methodical Development of Isoelectric
    Focusing'. Protides of the Biological Fluids,
    Proc. of 17th Colloq., Bruges 1969, Pergamon
    Press, Oxford and New York, 369-382 (1970)
27. SEILER, N., THOBE, J. and WERNER, G.,
    'Electrophoresis in a Carrier-Free Buffer
    Stream. I. Continuous Separation in Ampholyte
    Gradients'. Hoppe-Seyler's Z. Physiol. Chem.,
    351, 865-868 (1970)
28. JUST, W.W., LEÓN, J., WERNER, G., THOBE, J. and
    SEILER, N., 'Studies on Separations of Cells
    and Cell Organelles by Free Flow High Voltage
    Electrophoresis in a Natural pH Gradient'.
    Abstr. 9th Internat. Congr. Biochem.,
    Stockholm, p.30 (1973)
29. FAWCETT, J.S., 'Continuous Flow Isoelectric
    Focusing and Isotachophoresis'. Ann. N.Y.
    Acad. Sci., 209, 112-126 (1973)

3. PREPARATIVE ISOELECTRIC FOCUSING IN SHORT DENSITY GRADIENT COLUMNS WITH VERTICAL COOLING

H. Rilbe and S. Pettersson

3.1 INTRODUCTION

At the New York Academy of Sciences Conference on Isoelectric Focusing in 1972, a lecture entitled 'Rapid Isoelectric Focusing in Density Gradient Columns' was presented[1]. Philpot's[2] early suggestion of using short and thick columns in conjunction with vertical heat dissipation was then brought to renewed attention. If Philpot's suggestion is followed, the temperature gradient and the accompanying density gradient become vertical, and it is easy to realise an entirely stable, downward directed density gradient. The only limiting factor for the permissible electric load is then the maximum column temperature which cannot be allowed to rise to the vicinity of the denaturation temperature of proteins.

A cooled bottom plate in a short and thick column actually gives increased stability making heat convection virtually impossible. If the ceiling of the column is also cooled, the accompanying negative density gradient has to be compensated for by other means, e.g. an increased sucrose concentration gradient.

Columns for isoelectric focusing, if designed as originally suggested by Svensson[3], are characterised by electrodes in direct contact with the separation zone. If this principle is retained in a short and thick column, the electrodes necessarily must be as large as its cross-sectional area. A gas-escape tube for the bottom electrode is then impossible, and at least that electrode has to be of a non-gassing type. Such large electrodes can serve as excellent heat conductors for vertical heat dissipation from the column. A small column of

this type was described previously[1]. We have
continued our work with vertically cooled columns in
an effort to scale up preparative isoelectric
focusing in larger columns. The work has proceeded
along two different lines. Columns with large
noble-metal electrodes serving also as heat
conductors have been constructed. In order to save
precious material, we have also built large-scale
columns with quite small electrodes, the heat being
dissipated through cellophane membranes, and with
chilled, circulating acid and alkali solutions
bathing the electrodes. This article is a report of
results gained so far with columns of these types.

3.2   A 440 ml COLUMN WITH VERTICAL COOLING THROUGH LARGE PALLADIUM-SILVER ELECTRODES

The column shown in elevation in Figure 3.1 is an
extremely short and thick column. The distance
between electrodes is only 15.5 mm and the
cross-sectional area is 283.5 x 100 mm^2. It
contains three compartments: the central separation
column and one upper and one lower cooling
compartment. The cooling cylinders (1) are made of
brass, whereas the separation cell is enclosed
within a Plexiglass cylinder (6). The three
compartments are clamped together with the aid of a
number of bolts (2) which are electrically insulated
from the upper cooling compartment by Pertinax
sockets (3). Leakage is prevented by two O-ring
seals (5) round the upper and lower peripheries of
the Plexiglass cylinder. On two diametrically
opposite points of the latter, there are capillary
side tubes, not shown, attached to short rubber
tubes with pinch clamps. These rubber tubes allow
small volume changes which are unavoidable due to
temperature changes.
    The electrodes (7) and (8) are 0.1 mm thick
sheets of an alloy containing 75% palladium and 25%
silver. They are soldered with Wood's metal to the
big, circular brass plates being the bottom of the
upper and the roof of the lower cooling compartment.
Care was taken to get a uniform soldered joint all
over the surface because the volume increase on
charging palladium with hydrogen gives rise to a
considerable tension.
    The cooling was effected by circulating water
from a refrigerated tank. The two cooling
compartments were connected in parallel with the aid
of rubber tubing of 4 mm internal diameter and 1.5 m
in length. The potential difference between the
electrodes, about 100 V, gives rise to a creeping

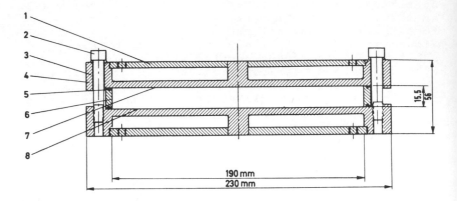

Figure 3.1 Short column with chilled
palladium-silver electrodes. 1, Brass compartment
for cooling medium; 2, bolt; 3, insulating socket;
4, cylindrical wall of cooling compartment; 5,
O-ring seal; 6, Plexiglass cylinder, vertical wall
of separation column; 7, palladium-silver electrode;
8, palladium-silver electrode

current in the µA range in these rubber tubes.
Corrosion and other effects of such a small current
are negligible.

A column with such a proportion between height
and diameter must be filled and emptied in an
orientation with a horizontal axis. The whole
assembly has thus been mounted in a mechanical
arrangement designed for cautious turning through
90° to a position in which the two side tubes of the
Plexiglass cylinder come at top and bottom of the
circle constituting the cross-section of that
cylinder. The turning motion has to be very slow
near the orientation with horizontal electrodes.

Prior to isoelectric focusing in a column with
palladium electrodes, the electrode intended to act
as anode has to be charged with a sufficient amount
of hydrogen. This can be done by filling the column
with dilute sulphuric acid and performing
electrolysis with the electrode in question as
cathode. The electrode should not be saturated with
hydrogen because this would expose the soldered
joint to undue stress. A quantity of hydrogen
corresponding to 1800 As (or coulomb) is sufficient.

The temperature within the column was
controlled with the aid of two thermocouples
inserted through small holes in the Plexiglass wall,
one situated midway between the electrodes, the

other 4 mm from one of them. The reference joints
were submerged in an ice/water mixture. The
temperature in the column was not allowed to rise to
more than 18°C.

The initial current was limited by the
available power supply to 1 A at an initial tension
of 60 V. In typical experiments the final potential
difference was 120 V and the final current 0.2 A.

Focusing was completed in 30 min in this
column. Figure 3.2 shows that the two subcomponents
of β-lactoglobulin, of pI 5.12 and 5.24, could be
just resolved. The focusing time is so short that
thermal equilibrium is probably never established in
the column.

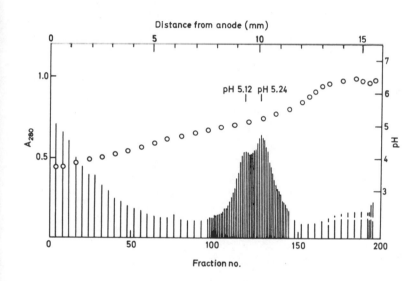

Figure 3.2   Separation of β-lactoglobulin into
subcomponents isoelectric at pH 5.12 and 5.24.
Average field strength: 75 V/cm; focusing time:
30 min; open circles, pH; vertical hatching, A_{280} nm

Because palladium is much cheaper than
platinum, the cost of these large electrodes is not
excessive (about £75). The resolution obtainable is
limited by the rapid diffusion from very narrow
zones during the time required for turning the
column through 90° after the current has been
switched off.

The palladium-silver electrode is not entirely
resistant to anodic oxidation. Special analyses
have shown that roughly 10^{-4} equivalents of

palladium and rather less silver go into solution on
passage of 1 F of electricity. The amount of
electricity required for focusing is about 1000 As,
roughly corresponding to 0.5 µmoles of palladium.
About the same number of moles of protein are
involved in the separation of, for example, 100 mg
of serum globulin. The number of Ampholine moles,
however, is in large excess, about 5000 µmoles, and
their complexing power is probably much greater than
that of proteins. The risk of contaminating
proteins with palladium and silver can thus be
regarded as rather small. Nevertheless, it was felt
worthwhile exploring an alternative column
construction with quite small platinum electrodes
and cooled through horizontal semipermeable
membranes.

3.3 A 110 ml COLUMN WITH VERTICAL COOLING THROUGH
MEMBRANES AND CHILLED CATHOLYTE AND ANOLYTE

The constructional principles of this column are
shown in Figure 3.3. It contains five compartments:
the central separation column (1), compartments (2)
and (3) for catholyte and anolyte, and compartments
(4) and (5) for circulating coolant. The separation
compartment is bounded against catholyte and anolyte
compartments by cellophane membranes (6) and (7).
The latter spaces have rotating magnets (8) and (9),
so heat is dissipated convectively through catholyte
and anolyte. The electrodes are quite small
platinum wires (10) and (11) situated in vertical
Plexiglass tubes (12) and (13). A uniform electric
field in the separation compartment is obtained by
using as catholyte and anolyte highly conducting
solutions of alkali and strong acid, respectively.
The handling of this apparatus is somewhat
complicated, and a detailed description is not
possible here.

This apparatus, too, is turned through 90° for
filling and emptying. Focusing requires 90 min
under standard conditions. The final potential
difference is about 125 V; the final current 20 to
25 mA.

The apparatus is suitable for preparative
purposes. In a run containing 4% Ampholine, pH 4 to
6, we isolated narrow-range Ampholine fractions
having pHs between 5.13 and 5.23. This was done in
order to increase the resolution of the
subcomponents of β-lactoglobulin which have pI
values of 5.13 and 5.23 respectively. Figures 3.4a
and 3.4b show the isoelectric spectra of 15 mg
β-lactoglobulin obtained without and with the

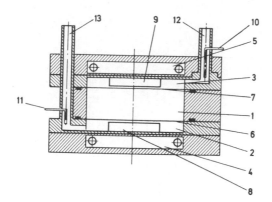

Figure 3.3 Short column with chilled semipermeable
membranes and small platinum electrodes. 1,
Separation column; 2 and 3, compartments for
catholyte and anolyte; 4 and 5, compartments for
circulating refrigerating medium; 6 and 7,
cellophane membranes; 8 and 9, rotating magnets;
10 and 11, platinum electrodes; 12 and 13,
                Plexiglass gas-escape tube

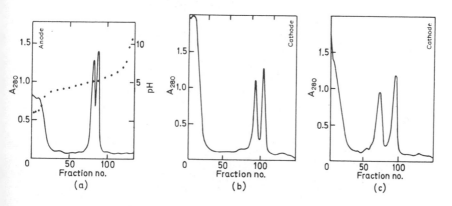

Figure 3.4 Separation of the subcomponents of
β-lactoglobulin. (a) Separation of 15 mg
β-lactoglobulin in a column with Ampholine pH 4 to
6. (b) As for (a) but enriched with Ampholine
components isoelectric in the same pH range as
β-lactoglobulin. (c) β-Lactoglobulin-containing
fractions from two experiments identical with (b)
were pooled and refocused; improved resolution was
obtained with a load of 30 mg protein. Open circles,
                pH; solid line, A_{280} nm

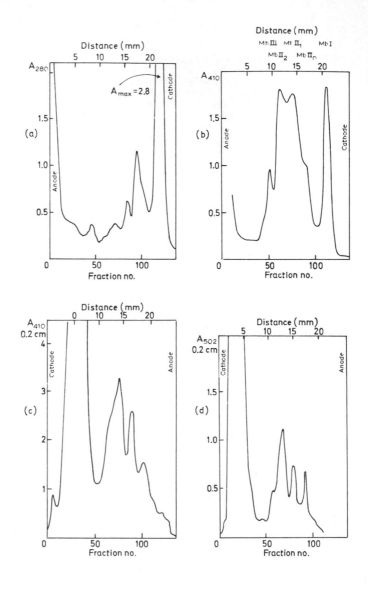

Figure 3.5 Separation of sperm whale myoglobin.
(a) 70 min focusing of 40 mg myoglobin in Ampholine
pH 6 to 9. (b) The second component from the right
(Mb II) in (a) was collected from two identical
experiments and re-run in Ampholine pH 7 to 9. (c)
2 h focusing of 0.25 g myoglobin in Ampholine pH 7
to 9. (d) 3 h focusing of 1.05 g myoglobin in
Ampholine pH 7 to 9

the addition of this preparation of narrow-range
Ampholine. The improved resolution obtained in the
narrow gradient is quite evident. When all
fractions containing β-lactoglobulin from two
identical experiments giving spectra shown in
Figure 3.4b were mixed and refocused together with
sufficient Ampholine, pH 4 to 6, to give an
unchanged total Ampholine concentration, the result
shown in Figure 3.4c was obtained. The still more
improved resolution is due to the continued
relative enrichment, effected by the procedure
described, of Ampholines isoelectric in the same
range as the β-lactoglobulins. It should be
especially noted that the higher resolution shown in
Figure 3.4c was obtained with twice as much protein
as in Figure 3.4b. Thus we encounter the unusual
situation of improved resolution being compatible
with increased capacity.

     Further examples of the usefulness of this
column for preparative purposes are given in
Figure 3.5. Figure 3.5a shows the isoelectric
spectrum obtained with 40 mg of sperm whale
myoglobin in an Ampholine pH 6 to 9 gradient during
70 min. One recognises, from right to left, the
three main components Mb I, Mb II, and Mb III
according to Theorell and Åkesson's nomenclature[4,5].
The Mb II fractions from two identical experiments
of this kind were mixed and refocused together with
enough Ampholine pH 7 to 9 to give a total
concentration of 1.1% (w/v). The result is shown in
Figure 3.5b, where the Mb II component has been
nicely resolved into a number of subcomponents.
The greatly increased area is due to the fact that
absorption measurements were made at 410 instead of
280 nm. Again, it has proved possible to improve
the resolution with an increased amount of protein.

     Figure 3.5c shows the isoelectric separation of
250 mg of sperm whale myoglobin focused for 2 h in
an Ampholine pH 7 to 9 gradient, whereas Figure 3.5d
shows the isoelectric spectrum of 1.05 g of the same
material, focused for 3 h in a pH 7 to 9 gradient.
Evidently, a density gradient is capable of carrying
quite appreciable amounts of protein. The following
theoretical investigation has been undertaken in
order to derive an upper limit for the capacity and
how it depends on zone thickness and resolving
power.

3.4   THE CAPACITY OF A DENSITY GRADIENT COLUMN

The concentration distribution in a gaussian protein
zone may be written:

$$C = C_o \exp \frac{-x^2}{2x_i^2} \tag{3.1}$$

where x is the column coordinate, x = O being the location of the maximum concentration C_o and $\pm x_i$ being the levels of the inflexion points. This zone has the mass content:

$$m = \int_{-\infty}^{+\infty} Cq \, dx = C_o q \int_{-\infty}^{+\infty} \exp \frac{-x^2}{2x_i^2} \, dx \tag{3.2}$$

where q is the cross-sectional area. With the aid of the well-known relation:

$$\int_{-\infty}^{+\infty} \exp \, (-t^2/2) \, dt = (2\pi)^{\frac{1}{2}} \tag{3.3}$$

one thus gets $m = C_o q x_i (2\pi)^{\frac{1}{2}}$ and consequently:

$$C = \frac{m}{q x_i (2\pi)^{\frac{1}{2}}} \exp \frac{-x^2}{2x_i^2} \tag{3.4}$$

If the contribution to density (ρ) of the carrier ampholytes is neglected, the density gradient $d\rho/dx$ can be expressed in terms of the sucrose concentration gradient dc/dx and the protein concentration gradient dC/dx as follows:

$$d\rho/dx = (\partial\rho/\partial c)_C (dc/dx) + (\partial\rho/\partial C)_c (dC/dx) \tag{3.5}$$

Stability requires the density gradient to be positive (for a downward-directed x axis) at all times and all levels in the column.
    Differentiation of (3.4) gives:

$$\frac{dC}{dx} = \frac{-mx}{q x_i^3 (2\pi)^{\frac{1}{2}}} \exp \frac{-x^2}{2x_i^2} \tag{3.6}$$

This derivative has its maximum negative value at the lower inflexion point, $x = +x_i$. Insertion of this value and subsequent substitution of equation 3.6 in equation 3.5 gives:

$$\frac{d\rho}{dx} = (\partial\rho/\partial c)_C (dc/dx) - (\partial\rho/\partial c)_c \frac{m}{qx_i^2 (2\pi e)^{\frac{1}{2}}} \qquad (3.7)$$

The requirement of a positive density gradient gives rise to the inequality:

$$m < \frac{(\partial\rho/\partial c)_C (dc/dx) qx_t^2 (2\pi e)^{\frac{1}{2}}}{(\partial\rho/\partial c)_c} \qquad (3.8)$$

With the aid of the relation $(\partial\rho/\partial c)_C (\partial c/\partial C)_\rho (\partial C/\partial\rho)_c = -1$, this inequality takes the form:

$$m < - (\partial C/\partial c)_\rho (dc/dx) qx_i^2 (2\pi e)^{\frac{1}{2}} \qquad (3.9)$$

where the derivative $(\partial C/\partial c)_\rho$ expresses that change in protein concentration that has to accompany a unit change in sucrose concentration in order to keep the density unchanged. The partial specific volume of sucrose in water solution is 0.6189 cm^3/g at a concentration of 0.25 g/cm^3, whereas most proteins have partial specific volumes between 0.70 and 0.75 cm^3/g, with an average of around 0.742 cm^3/g. The derivative can therefore be given the numerical value:

$$(\partial C/\partial c)_\rho = -0.742/0.6189 = -1.199 \qquad (3.10)$$

If this figure is lumped together with $(2\pi e)^{\frac{1}{2}}$, one gets the inequality:

$$m < 5qx_i^2 (dc/dx) \qquad (3.11)$$

We now introduce the volume V and the height h of the column and thus have $V = qh$. We also introduce the parameter r expressing the zone breadth, taken as $2x_i$, in units of the column height:

$$r = 2x_i/h \qquad\qquad x_i = rh/2 \qquad (3.12)$$

The inequality (3.11) can then be given in the form:

$$m < 1.25\, Vhr^2 (dc/dx) \qquad (3.13)$$

We shall further assume a linear sucrose concentration course from 0 to 0.5 g/cm^3 in agreement with general experimental practice. This

C

gives for the concentration gradient dc/dx the
numerical value:

$$dc/dx = (1/2h) \ g/cm^3 \qquad (3.14)$$

where h can be given in arbitrary length units.
Substitution in equation 3.13 gives:

$$m < 0.625 \ Vr^2 \ g/cm^3 \qquad (3.15)$$

For a 100 cm^3 column, one thus has:

$$m < 62.5 \ r^2 \ grammes \qquad (3.16)$$

The carrying capacity thus rises with the square of
the zone breadth. For zones as narrow as 1 mm in a
250 mm high column, equation 3.16 shows that the
mass content cannot be more than 1 mg, whereas a
2 mm broad zone can carry 4 mg. Such quantities of
protein per zone are commonly involved in
high-resolution isoelectric focusing in LKB's
110 ml column.
       If a protein zone is allowed to extend over one
tenth of the height of the column, (3.16) gives a
maximum protein content of 625 mg, whereas a zone
extending over one fifth of the column can take
2.5 g.
       Starting from inequality (3.11), one can also
introduce the following expression for the inflexion
point[6]:

$$x_i^2 = D/pE \qquad (3.17)$$

where E is the field strength, D the diffusion
coefficient of the protein, and p the gradient of
its mobility u:

$$p = - \frac{du}{dx} = - \frac{du}{d(pH)} \ \frac{d(pH)}{dx} \qquad (3.18)$$

Inequality (3.11) then takes the form:

$$m < \frac{5q \ D \ (dc/dx)}{E(-du/dpH)(dpH/dx)} \qquad (3.19)$$

If this expression is put in relation to the
resolving power[6]

$$\Delta pI = 3 \left\{ \frac{D(dpH/dx)}{E(-du/dpH)} \right\}^{\frac{1}{2}} \qquad (3.20)$$

elimination of the pH gradient between equations
3.19 and 3.20 gives:

$$m < \frac{45 \ q \ D^2 \ (dc/dx)}{E^2 \ (\Delta pI)^2 \ (du/dpH)^2} \qquad (3.21)$$

It is evident from this inequality that the capacity
of a density gradient column rises with the square
of the resolving power with which it operates for
one and the same protein system and for otherwise
unchanged experimental conditions. This means that
an experiment with a pH gradient favouring the
purity of protein fractions obtained also favours
the quantity of pure proteins that can be separated
in one run. This property places density gradient
isoelectric focusing in gaudy contrast to all other
separation techniques, in which a good yield
axiomatically excludes a high purity and vice versa.

The explanation of this unexpected result lies
in the fact that a high resolving power requires a
weak pH gradient, and that a weak pH gradient gives
rise to broad protein zones capable of holding
considerable amounts of protein. Isoelectric
focusing is dissimilar to other separation
techniques also in the respect that extremely sharp
bands in general indicate a relatively low resolving
power, whereas a very fine resolution within a
narrow pH range is characterised by comparatively
broad protein zones.

The result obtained does not imply that an
increased amount of protein, other conditions being
unchanged, leads to a better resolution. The
opposite is true as is well known to all workers in
this field. It does imply, however, that a
decreased pH gradient gives an improved resolution
and at the same time a possibility of having greater
quantities of protein in each zone. This conclusion
is experimentally verified by the experiments shown
in Figure 3.4 (b and c) and Figure 3.5 (a and b).
In both cases, the amount of protein was doubled,
but nevertheless the resolution was much improved.

Inequality 3.15 has never come into conflict
with experimental evidence. A stable protein zone
containing more protein than this critical value has
not been observed. In order to elucidate how close
to the critical limit we have come so far, we have
studied more closely the diagram in Figure 3.5d.
The main peak in this spectrum has an r value of
0.125, thus inequality 3.15 gives for a 110 ml
column a maximum protein content of 1074 mg. The
total amount of protein in this experiment was

1050 mg, but part of this material lies in the minor components. Integration of the complete spectrum has revealed that about 76% of the protein material is confined within the main peak. Consequently this zone contained 74% of the theoretical maximum.

3.5 SUMMARY

Two types of short and thick columns for isoelectric focusing with vertical cooling are described, one operating with large, horizontal noble-metal electrodes in direct contact with circulating cold water; the other with large, horizontal semipermeable membranes chilled by circulating acid and alkali solutions bathing small platinum electrodes. Some applications are reported, especially rapid separations of appreciable amounts of protein. A theoretical upper limit for the mass content of a protein zone is derived and shown to depend only on the volume of the zone. Because broad protein zones are compatible with a high resolving power, it is established that the separation capacity of a density gradient column rises as the resolving power is improved.

ACKNOWLEDGEMENTS

The financial support of the Swedish Board for Technical Development is gratefully acknowledged. The authors also wish to express their gratitude to Mr. Leif Hermansson for skilful performance of the measurements of anodically dissolved palladium and silver.

REFERENCES

1.   RILBE, H., 'Rapid Isoelectric Focusing in Density Gradient Columns'. Ann. N.Y. Acad. Sci., 209, 80-93 (1973)
2.   PHILPOT, J. St. L., 'The Use of Thin Layers in Electrophoretic Separation'. Trans. Faraday Soc., 36, 38-46 (1040)
3.   SVENSSON, H., 'Isoelectric Fractionation, Analysis, and Characterization of Ampholytes in Natural pH Gradients. III. Description of Apparatus for Electrolysis in Columns Stabilized by Density Gradients and Direct Determination of Isoelectric Points'. Arch. Biochem. Biophys., Suppl. 1, 132-138 (1962)
4.   THEORELL, H. and ÅKESON, Å., 'Reversible Splitting of a Homogeneous Horse Myoglobin'. Ann. Acad. Sci. Fennicae, Ser. A II, 60, 303-312 (1955)

5. ÅKESON, Å., and THEORELL, H.,
    'Microheterogeneity of Horse Myoglobin'.
    Arch. Biochem. Biophys., 91, 319-325 (1960)
6. RILBE, H., 'Historical and Theoretical Aspects
    of Isoelectric Focusing'. Ann. N.Y. Acad.
    Sci., 209, 11-22 (1973)

4. TRANSIENT STATE ISOELECTRIC FOCUSING

N. Catsimpoolas

4.1 INTRODUCTION

'Steady-state' isoelectric focusing based on
Svensson's theory[1] has been used extensively for the
separation of amphoteric macromolecules of
biological interest[2]. The method provides a single
concentration profile - distorted by diffusion in
the absence of electric field strength - at the end
of the experiment, and allows for the determination
of only one physical parameter, i.e. the isoelectric
point. However, the recent development of the
in situ direct optical scanning technique[3] and the
availability of a kinetic theory of isoelectric
focusing[4] has made possible the quantitative
measurement of several methodological parameters as
a function of time, and the estimation of apparent
physical constants related to the diffusion and
electric transport of amphoteric electrolytes in a
pH gradient[5-9]. This allows continuous assessment
of the kinetics of isoelectric focusing.
Exploration of the kinetic aspects of pH gradient
electrophoresis at the analytical level has been
called 'Transient State Isoelectric Focusing'
(TRANSIF)[10]. A brief description of the
capabilities, limitations, and desirable future
developments of this new technique will be presented
in this paper.

4.2 INSTRUMENTAL ASPECTS

Two main instrumental assemblies have been described
for TRANSIF experiments in density gradients or
gels[11-14]. In general, a micro-quartz column with
built-in electrolyte reservoirs is transported
linearly (in the vertical[11] or horizontal[12,13]

58

position) with the aid of a synchronously moving
mechanical stage in the path of a narrow light beam
(u.v. or visible). Narrow slits (50 to 100 μm) are
used in close proximity to the column. A recording
spectrophotometer or other similar instrumental
assembly is employed to record the u.v. absorbance
profile versus distance in the column. Scanning is
performed continuously throughout the isoelectric
focusing experiment. The analogue signal from the
spectrophotometer is digitised and the digital data
are processed with computing programmes applicable
to the use of desk-top programmable calculators[8].
All TRANSIF parameters are computed directly from
the digital output without any other experimental
manipulations. Such experiments can be carried out
either in polyacrylamide gels[5-7] or density
gradients[9].

4.3 DIGITAL DATA PROCESSING

An automatic digital integrator ('Infotronics',
Columbia Scientific Industries, Austin, Texas,
U.S.A.) is used in the 'digitising mode' to print the
amplitude of the photometer analogue voltage
(averaged over a fixed time period) multiplied by
the time of the integration interval (d_i) as a
function of the scanning time (t). The raw digital
data are converted to absorbance values (ordinate)
after i intervals (A_i) by

$$A_i = \frac{d_i F}{gfR} \qquad (4.1)$$

where F is the full-scale absorbance, g is the
digitising rate (in seconds), f is the integration
count rate (counts/mV/s), and R is the
millivoltage output at full scale (mV). In addition,
the coordinate values after i intervals (x_i) are
converted to distance (cm) by multiplying the
scanning time (s) by v/60, where v is the scanning
rate of the linear transport (cm/min). After
smoothing of the data and baseline correction (if
necessary) the m_0, m_1', and m_2 statistical moments of
the peak can be estimated[8] from

$$m_0 = \Sigma A_i g \qquad (4.2)$$

$$m_1' = \Sigma A_i x_i / \Sigma A_i \qquad (4.3)$$

$$m_2 = (\Sigma A_i x_i^2 / \Sigma A_i) - (\Sigma A_i x_i / \Sigma A_i)^2 \qquad (4.4)$$

where m_0 and m_2 are the zeroth and second central statistical amounts about the mean and m_1^* is the first statistical moment from an arbitrary origin.

Measurement of the zeroth (m_0), reduced first (m_1^*), and second (m_2) statistical moments of the zone concentration profile, which correspond respectively to the area, the position $(\bar{x})$, and the variance (σ^2) of the peak, are very important in the estimation of relevant methodological parameters and physical constants in TRANSIF. The experimental values of m_0, $\bar{x}$, σ^2 and σ (standard deviation of the concentration distribution of a focused zone = $(\sigma^2)^{\frac{1}{2}}$) in conjunction with $\bar{x}$ values of pI markers are the only parameters required to be measured in order to derive valuable quantitative information from a TRANSIF experiment as illustrated below.

4.4 SCANNING PATTERNS

A typical scanning isoelectric focusing pattern as a function of time is shown in Figure 4.1. The advantages of this technique over the conventional 'steady-state' method are several[5]. The progress of the isoelectric focusing experiment can be followed continuously by visual inspection of the recordings. Since the electric field is applied continuously, the resolution of the separated zones is excellent. The absorbance profile of each protein provides means for quantitative evaluation of results which is not possible when staining procedures are used for pattern identification. In addition, appropriate instrumentation allows the direct on-line acquisition and processing of data. Finally, either the total isoelectric focusing pattern can be scanned at different wavelengths, or a fixed position in a zone can provide a complete absorption spectrum as a function of wavelength, especially in the visible region.

4.5   METHODOLOGICAL PARAMETERS

4.5.1 Determination of Minimal Focusing Time
In the simple case of a single protein uniformly distributed in the column before the electric field is applied, the minimal time required to obtain complete focusing can be determined by following the position $(\bar{x})$ of the discernible peaks migrating from the two ends of the path (positive and negative) toward the isoelectric point position where they merge into one peak. At the steady-state and in the absence of significant pH gradient instability, the peak position at pI should remain constant with

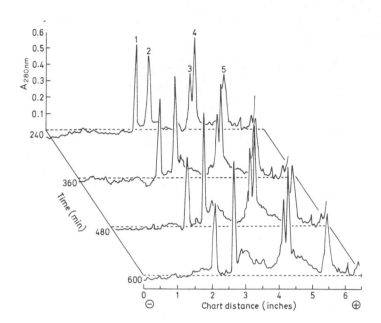

Figure 4.1 Representative scanning isoelectric spectra of lactoglobulin, ovalbumin and Bowman-Birk proteinase inhibitor in the pH 3 to 7 range. Final Ampholine concentration was 2% and 100 μg of each of the above proteins was distributed uniformly in the column at the beginning of the experiment[5]. 1, Lactoglobulin B; 2, lactoglobulin A; 3, ovalbumin II; 4, ovalbumin I; 5, Bowman-Birk proteinase inhibitor

time. Ideally the peak area (zeroth moment) and the variance (second moment about the mean) should also remain constant when the steady-state is reached. The latter two parameters can be employed in evaluating 'steady-state' conditions (and therefore minimal focusing time) of a mixture of proteins. It should be emphasised that depending on their individual pH-mobility relationships, proteins in a mixture may approach the 'steady-state' at different times. Other factors that affect the minimal focusing time of individual proteins are (a) molecular sieving effects in gels, (b) non-uniform distribution of electric field strength, and (c) presence of a viscosity gradient (e.g. sucrose density gradient). The minimal focusing time may also be affected by (a) Ampholine concentration,

C*

(b) electric field strength, (c) pH range of carrier ampholytes, (d) temperature, and (e) presence of additives, e.g. urea.

4.5.2 Segmental pH Gradient
This parameter, $\Delta(pH)/\Delta x(cm^{-1})$, is measured using two pI markers of closely spaced isoelectric points[5] from

$$\frac{\Delta(pH)}{\Delta x} = \frac{pI_A - pI_B}{\bar{x}_A - \bar{x}_B} \qquad (4.5)$$

where pI is the isoelectric point, $\bar{x}$ is the peak position, and subscripts (A) and (B) denote two pI markers. In using the above equation, it is assumed that species A and B have reached their isoelectric point, and that $\Delta(pH)/\Delta x$ is constant between pI_A and pI_B where $\bar{x}_A - \bar{x}_B$ represents a small segment of the separation path.

4.5.3 Apparent Isoelectric Point
If an 'unknown' protein (U) is included in the segmental pH gradient as described above, its apparent isoelectric point can be calculated by[5]

$$pI_U = pI_A + (\frac{\Delta(pH)}{\Delta x}) \; (\bar{x}_A - \bar{x}_U) \qquad (4.6)$$

All three species (A), (B) and (U) should be at their isoelectric pH, i.e. at the steady-state.

4.5.4 Resolving Power
In isoelectric focusing the resolving power has been defined[15] as:

$$\Delta pI = 3 \left[d(pH)/dx \right] \sigma \qquad (4.7)$$

Since $\Delta(pH)/\Delta x$ and σ can be obtained digitally in TRANSIF, the resolving power can be estimated directly[7].

4.5.5 Resolution
Arbitrarily assigning a resolution of unity to two species A and B which are just resolved, the resolution Rs has been defined[7] as:

$$Rs = \frac{\Delta \bar{x}}{1.5 (\sigma_A + \sigma_B)} \qquad (4.8)$$

where $\Delta \bar{x}$ is the peak separation of two zones A and B with standard deviations of σ_A and σ_B. Again, $\Delta\bar{x}$, σ_A and σ_B can be measured directly at any stage of fractionation.

4.6   DETERMINATION OF APPARENT PHYSICAL CONSTANTS

4.6.1 Theoretical Considerations

A TRANSIF experiment is characterised by three stages: focusing, defocusing and refocusing. In the focusing stage the sample (uniformly distributed or pulse-loaded) is subjected to an electrical potential in a pH gradient for a time t_1 until a nearly steady-state distribution of the focused zone is achieved. In the defocusing stage, the electrical field is removed for time t_2 allowing the zone to spread by diffusion. In the refocusing stage, the electrical field is applied once more for a time t_3 and the distribution again approaches the steady-state. The advantages of performing kinetic analysis of zone focusing during the refocusing period are: (a) focusing is carried out by starting with a (near) Gaussian distribution, (b) the zone is restricted to a narrow region of the pH (and mobility) spectrum near the isoelectric point, and (c) data are collected under conditions of nearly linear pH gradient [d(pH)/dx] and linear pH-mobility relationship [dM/d(pH)]. Thus, if the parameters d(pH)/dx and dM/d(pH) are constant, the experimentally measurable parameter p will also remain constant throughout the refocusing experiment, since

$$p = [dM/d(pH)] \quad [d(pH)/dx] \tag{4.9}$$

The parameter p is related to the standard deviation of the concentration distribution of a focused zone at the steady-state by

$$\sigma = \left(\frac{D}{pE} \right)^{\frac{1}{2}} \tag{4.10}$$

where D is the diffusion coefficient and E, the field strength (V/cm) is given by

$$E = \frac{i}{q\kappa} \tag{4.11}$$

where i is the applied current, q the cross-sectional area of the tube, and κ the zone conductance; pE therefore represents the slope of the pH-velocity curve.

   For experimental purposes, the kinetics of

defocusing and refocusing can be evaluated by following the changes of σ^2 which is the square of the standard deviation of the peak distribution versus elapsed time[6-9]. The equations derived theoretically[4] describing the behaviour of σ^2 during these two stages of the experiment have been shown to be:

(i)   Defocusing (where $\tau_1 \leqslant \tau \leqslant \tau_1 + \tau_2$ and $\tau = pEt$)

$$\sigma^2(\tau) = \sigma^2(0)e^{-2\tau 1} + \alpha(1 - e^{-2\tau 1}) + 2\alpha(\tau - \tau_1) \quad (4.12)$$

(ii)   Refocusing (where $\tau_1 + \tau_2 \leqslant \tau$)

$$\sigma^2(\tau) = \left[\sigma^2(0)e^{-2\tau 1} + \alpha(1 - e^{-2\tau 1}) + 2\alpha\tau_2\right]\exp$$

$$\left[-2(\tau - \tau_1 - \tau_2)\right] + \alpha\left\{1 - \exp\left[-2(\tau - \tau_1 - \tau_2)\right]\right\} \quad (4.13)$$

where α is given by D/L^2pE, L being the column length. In terms of real length and after 'linearisation'[9] the course of $\sigma^2(t)$ can be described by

(i)   Defocusing

$$\sigma^2(t) = \sigma^2(t_1) + 2D(t - t_1) \quad (4.14)$$

(ii)   Refocusing

$$\sigma^2(t) = \frac{D}{pE} + 2Dt_2 \exp(-2pEt_3) \quad (4.15)$$

or $\log_e\left[(\sigma_R^2 - \sigma_F^2)/\sigma_D^2\right] = -2pEt_3 \quad (4.16)$

Experimentally, a plot of σ^2 versus $2t_2$ should permit estimation of the apparent diffusion coefficient D (as the slope of the line) during the defocusing stage. Also a plot of $\log_e\left[(\sigma_R^2 - \sigma_F^2)/\sigma_D^2\right]$ versus $2t_3$ during the refocusing stage can be used to determine the parameter pE as the slope of the linear plot[4-9]. If $d(pH)/dx$ and E are known, the physical constant $dM/d(pH)$ can be estimated from equation 4.9.

4.6.2 Experimental Measurements of D and pE
Representative transient isoelectric focusing patterns of the dipeptide L-histidyl-L-tyrosine in a sucrose density gradient[9] during the defocusing and refocusing stages are shown in Figure 4.2. Both band spreading due to diffusion and band focusing following the re-application of the electric field can be easily seen. The time course

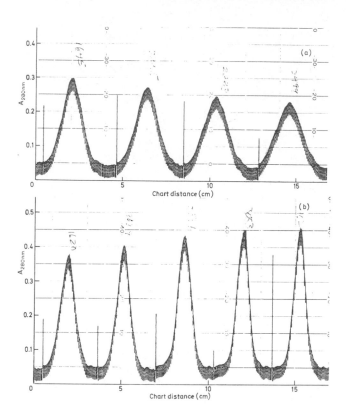

Figure 4.2 Scanning isoelectric spectra (not
retouched) of L-histidyl-L-tyrosine during the
stages of defocusing (A) and refocusing (B). The
event marks under the continuous curve profile
indicate the time at which absorbance readings were
taken[9]

of the change in peak variance (σ^2) as determined by
statistical second moment analysis is shown in
Figure 4.3. The defocusing stage involves a linear
increase of σ^2 as a function of time whereas the
refocusing stage exhibits an exponential decrease,
as predicted theoretically[4]. The steady-state is
characterised by (approximately) constant values of
σ^2 with time. The duration of the refocusing
period depends on the magnitude of the applied
voltage.
    It is of interest to note that the σ^2 as
determined at the start of the defocusing experiment
(first steady-state) may be smaller than the σ^2

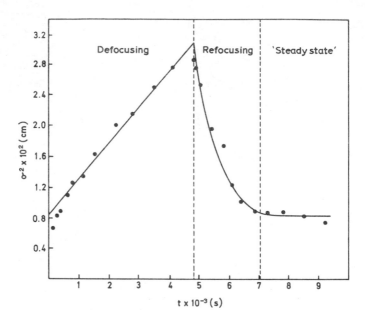

Figure 4.3 Plot of peak variance (σ^2) of
L-histidyl-L-tyrosine as a function of elpased time
during the stages of defocusing, refocusing, and the
steady-state[9]

estimated at the end of the refocusing experiment
(second steady-state). Theoretically, the system
after refocusing should return to the initial
conditions before defocusing and therefore the two
variances of the peak should be identical. However,
this may not occur for two main reasons. Firstly,
the applied voltage during refocusing may be
intentionally smaller than the voltage used for
focusing in order to allow adequate time for
multiple scanning of the refocused peak. Secondly,
the re-established pH gradient may be slightly less
steep than the original one. Both smaller voltage
and smaller pH gradient can result in a larger peak
variance.

      The slope of the line of the plot of σ^2 versus
t during defocusing (Figure 4.3) corresponds to
twice the value of the apparent diffusion
coefficient D. As estimated by linear regression
analysis, D can be determined with an error of
approx. ±5% by the present technique. The accuracy
of determining D may be improved by more elaborate

processing of the scanning data including smoothing
and baseline correction procedures. Determination
of the true diffusion coefficient may involve a
number of corrections including (a) considerations
on the effect of Ampholine concentration on apparent
D; (b) correction for possible concentration effects
of the compound of interest; (c) extrapolation to
zero zone load; and (d) viscosity and temperature
corrections[9]. The latter correction does not
present a serious problem since the viscosity of the
density gradient at the point of focusing can be
predicted mathematically from the shape of the
gradient curve. In addition, the statistical
second moment analysis eliminates errors due to the
slightly assymetric zone diffusion in a viscosity
gradient. With proteins a serious source of error
can be due to the so-called 'droplet sedimentation'
which can be recognised by excessive positive
skewness of the peak as determined by higher
statistical moment analysis[8].

As predicted by theory[4], the plot of log
$\left[(\sigma_R^2 - \sigma_F^2)/\sigma_D^2\right]$ versus 2t (where t is the elapsed time
of refocusing) should produce a straight line with
slope pE. Experimental verification of the
theoretical prediction is illustrated in Figure 4.4.

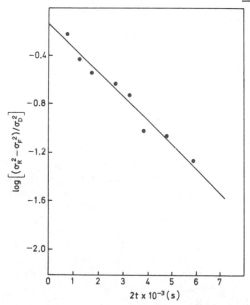

Figure 4.4   Kinetics of refocusing of
L-histidyl-L-tyrosine. The slope of the line
corresponds to the apparent value of the parameter
pE (ref. 9)

The slope of the line corresponds to the 'apparent' parameter pE of L-histidyl-L-tyrosine under the conditions of the experiment. Again, the true value of pE will require corrections similar in nature to those for the determination of true D (ref. 9). Experimental determination of the parameter pE may lead to the estimation of the slope of the pH-mobility curve $[dM/d(pH)]$ of the compound of interest which is a physical constant, since

$$dM/d(pH) \quad = \quad \frac{p}{d(pH)/dx} \qquad (4.17)$$

Estimation of the segmental pH gradient, $\Delta(pH)/\Delta x$, in the region of focusing can be carried out by the scanning isoelectric focusing technique with two marker compounds of known isoelectric point as described above.

Although p can be calculated from the parameter pE if E is known, some experimental difficulties are encountered at present in the accurate measurement of E at the region of focusing[9]. Equation 4.11 shows that E can be measured if i, q and κ are known. The final current i can be measured accurately with a digital micro-ammeter and therefore presents no problem. The cross-sectional area q can also be measured accurately (using equation 4.18) by weighing the electrofocusing tube empty (W_e) and filled with water (W_w).

$$q = \frac{W_w - W_e}{L} \cdot \frac{1}{\rho} \qquad (4.18)$$

where L is the tube length and ρ the density of water at the experimental temperature. However, because of the non-uniform distribution of the carrier ampholyte conductivity in the separation path, the conductance κ has to be measured at the region of focusing. Several experimental approaches are currently evaluated for the accurate measurement of κ. These involve either introduction of miniature electrodes in the column at the level of the zone position for in situ measurement of conductance, or withdrawal of a predetermined aliquot from the zone, while the current is on. It is imperative that the electric field is not removed because the distribution of carrier ampholytes will change by diffusion.

4.7 DIFFUSION IN POLYACRYLAMIDE GELS: DETERMINATION OF C_R

The apparent diffusion coefficient in polyacrylamide gels is related to the gel concentration by

$$\log(D) = \log(D_0) - C_R T \qquad\qquad (4.19)$$

where D_0 is the free diffusion coefficient, T is the gel concentration, D is the apparent diffusion coefficient at any gel concentration T, and C_R is the retardation coefficient obtained from diffusion data. C_R can be measured[6] during the defocusing stage of TRANSIF experiments from the slope of the plot $\log(D)$ against T. Thus, TRANSIF in polyacrylamide gels can provide a measure of molecular size. It is therefore possible that the effective molecular radius $\bar{R}$ and MW could be estimated by the present method from plots of C_R against $\bar{R}$, or against MW in analogy to the Rodbard-Chrambach plots[16].

4.8 ANOMALOUS BEHAVIOUR AT THE 'STEADY-STATE'

Ideally, a focused protein zone at the 'steady-state' should exhibit constant area (zeroth moment), peak position (reduced first moment), and variance (second moment) with time. However, a number of experimental factors and the physico-chemical properties of the protein itself may contribute to the anomalous behaviour that has been observed experimentally[5,6,9]. If the protein exhibits time-dependent conformational changes, dissociation, self-association, aggregation, or interactions with the chemical environment at the isoelectric point, it can be expected that the system will remain dynamic until each reaction reaches its own 'steady-state' within the duration of the experiment. However such systems may, for practical purposes, never reach 'steady-state'. For example, a time-dependent self-association of the protein at pI will lower its diffusion coefficient which may be reflected as a change in σ^2 of the focused peak. The area of the peak also may show some instability because of possible changes in the u.v. absorbance of the protein.

Transient or continuous disturbance of other factors such as temperature, conductance, viscosity, electric field strength, and pH gradient is likely to cause a corresponding change in the characteristics of the peak, even if pH equilibrium has been attained. The TRANSIF method therefore

70   Transient state isoelectric focusing provides the only feasible approach to the measurement of the deviations from the 'steady-state'. However, interpretation of any anomalous behaviour will require extensive and systematic experimentation with a particular system. In this respect, TRANSIF may open up a new era in the study of the physico-chemical behaviour of proteins under isoelectric conditions especially if carrier ampholytes with well defined physico-chemical properties become available.

4.9   GENERAL COMMENTS

The utilisation of u.v. absorption optics to follow the concentration profile of a zone in isoelectric focusing, and the ability to digitally measure the statistical moments of the peak have provided a new quantitative analytical method for the study of the behaviour of amphoteric electrolytes in a pH gradient. Although systems exhibit many non-ideal effects for the measurement of physical constants[9], it does appear promising in the sense that these problems may be solved by further refined experimentation and extension of the present theory. Specifically, improved instrumentation including a dual wavelength ratio recording system and direct coupling of the instrument to a computer will contribute to the precision of peak analysis. Precise temperature control and the development of methods for measurement of zone conductance and/or the production of carrier ampholytes with uniform conductivity will alleviate some of the problems encountered due to the non-uniform field strength.
    In conclusion, the TRANSIF method will be very useful in methodological and physico-chemical studies involving isoelectric focusing in a pH gradient and diffusion at the isoelectric point. In analogy to analytical density gradient centrifugation, the present method may provide an additional tool not only for evaluation of the degree of separation, but also for the physical characterisation of biological macromolecules.

4.10   APPENDIX

Symbol	Description
A_i	absorbance at the interval i
C_R	retardation coefficient (from diffusion data)
D	diffusion coefficient (cm^2/s)
D_0	free diffusion coefficient

Symbol	Description
d_i	average amplitude of the photometer analogue voltage times the time of the intergration interval
dM/d(pH)	slope of the pH-mobility curve
d(pH)/dx	pH gradient
E	field strength (V/cm)
F	full-scale absorbance
f	integration count rate (counts/mV/s)
g	digitising rate (s)
i	applied current (Amp)
L	column length (cm)
MW	molecular weight
m_o	zeroth central statistical moment about the mean
m_2	second central statistical moment about the mean
m_1'	first statistical moment from an arbitrary origin (reduced first moment)
p	$\left[dM/d(pH) \right] \left[d(pH)/dx \right]$
pE	slope of the pH-velocity curve
pI	isoelectric point
pI_A	pI of marker A
pI_B	pI of marker B
pI_U	pI of unknown protein
q	cross-sectional area of the tube
R	millivoltage output at full scale (mV)
$\bar{R}$	effective molecular radius
Rs	resolution
T	gel concentration
t	time (s)
t_1	focusing time
t_2	defocusing time
t_3	refocusing time
U	unknown protein
v	scanning rate of the linear transport (cm/min)
W_e	weight of electrofocusing tube (g)
W_w	weight of electrofocusing tube filled with water (g)
$\bar{x}$	peak position (cm)
x_i	coordinate at the interval i
$\bar{x}_A$	peak position of marker A
$\bar{x}_B$	peak position of marker B
α	$D/(L^2 pE)$
$\Delta(pH)/\Delta x$	segmental pH gradient (cm^{-1})
ΔpI	resolving power
$\Delta \bar{x}$	peak separation distance (cm)
κ	zone conductance
ρ	density of water at experimental temperature

Symbol	Description
σ	standard deviation of the concentration distribution of a focused zone $[(\sigma^2)^{\frac{1}{2}}]$ cm
σ_A	standard deviation of zone A
σ_B	standard deviation of zone B
σ^2	peak variance (cm^2)
σ_D^2	σ^2 at the end of defocusing
σ_F^2	σ^2 at the steady-state (refocusing)
σ_R^2	σ^2 at any time of refocusing
τ	pEt

REFERENCES

1. SVENSSON, H., 'Isoelectric Fractionation, Analysis, and Characterization of Ampholytes in Natural pH Gradients. 1. The Differential Equation of Solute Concentrations at a Steady-state and its Solution for Simple Cases'. Acta. Chem. Scand., 15, 325-341 (1961)

2. CATSIMPOOLAS, N., 'Isoelectric Focusing and Isotachophoresis'. Ann. N.Y. Acad. Sci., 209, (1973)

3. CATSIMPOOLAS, N., 'Analytical Scanning Isoelectrofocusing'. Ann. N.Y. Acad. Sci., 209, 65-79 (1973)

4. WEISS, G.H., CATSIMPOOLAS, N. and RODBARD, D., 'Theory of the Kinetics of Isoelectric Focusing'. Arch. Biochem. Biophys. (in press)

5. CATSIMPOOLAS, N., 'Transient State Isoelectric Focusing: Digital Measurement of Zone Position, Zone Area, Segmental pH Gradient, and Isoelectric Point as a Function of Time'. Anal. Biochem., 54, 66-78 (1973)

6. CATSIMPOOLAS, N., 'Transient State Isoelectric Focusing: Experimental Determination of Apparent Diffusion Coefficients in Polyacrylamide Gels'. Anal. Biochem., 54, 79-87 (1973)

7. CATSIMPOOLAS, N., 'Transient State Isoelectric Focusing: Resolving Power and Zone Resolution'. Anal. Biochem., 54, 88-94 (1973)

8. CATSIMPOOLAS, N. and GRIFFITH, A.L., 'Transient State Isoelectric Focusing: Computational Procedures for Digital Data Processing with a Desk-top Programmable Calculator'. Anal. Biochem. 56, 100-120 (1973)

9. CATSIMPOOLAS, N., YOTIS, W.W., GRIFFITH, A.L.
   and RODBARD, D., 'Transient State Isoelectric
   Focusing in Sucrose Density Gradients: Effects
   of Zone Load and Carrier Ampholyte
   Concentration on the Kinetics of Defocusing and
   Refocusing'. Arch. Biochem. Biophys. (in
   press)
10. CATSIMPOOLAS, N., 'Transient State Isoelectric
    Focusing'. Fed. Proc., 32, 625 (1973)
11. CATSIMPOOLAS, N. and WANG, J., 'Scanning Gel
    Isoelectrofocusing of Proteins'. Anal.
    Biochem., 39, 141-155 (1971)
12. CATSIMPOOLAS, N., 'Scanning Density Gradient
    Isoelectric Separation of Proteins on a
    Microscale'. Separ. Sci., 6, 435-442 (1971)
13. CATSIMPOOLAS, N., 'Analytical Scanning
    Isoelectrofocusing: Design and Operation of an
    in situ Scanning Apparatus'. Anal. Biochem.,
    44, 411-426 (1971)
14. CATSIMPOOLAS, N., 'Analytical Scanning
    Isoelectrofocusing: Design and Operation of a
    Column-filling Apparatus'. Anal. Biochem., 44,
    427-435 (1971)
15. VESTERBERG, O. and SVENSSON, H., 'Isoelectric
    Fractionation Analysis, and Characterization of
    Ampholytes in Natural pH Gradients. IV.
    Further Studies on the Resolving Power in
    Connection with Separation of Myoglobins'.
    Acta. Chem. Scand., 20, 820-834 (1966)
16. RODBARD, D. and CHRAMBACH, A., 'Unified Theory
    of Gel Electrophoresis and Gel Filtration'.
    Proc. Nat. Acad. Sci. (U.S.A.), 85, 970-977
    (1970)

5. A HORIZONTAL TROUGH APPARATUS FOR ISOELECTRIC FOCUSING

P. Talbot and I.S. Caie

Characterisation of a number of proteins by isoelectric focusing has been hampered by a tendency for the focused material to precipitate at its isoelectric point; this results in impaired resolution. The concept of zone convection electrofocusing, described by Valmet[1], offers an elegant solution to this problem and the apparatus described here embodies this concept and its advantages in an easily constructed design. Besides eliminating difficulties associated with precipitation of focused material, the design additionally provides for ready access to the pH gradient and incorporates a facility for auto-fractionation of the gradient at the end of the experiment.

Isoelectric focusing is performed in a pH gradient contained in a horizontal separation trough. The dimensions of the trough are critical to the design and its construction is described in detail. An exploded diagram of the apparatus is shown in Figure 5.1.

The separation trough (T) is machined into a block of Perspex 1 in. deep by 2½ in. wide by 24 in. long. By sequentially milling the upper face of this block 36 times, using a 0.625 in. diameter ball-end-mill, to a depth of 0.75 in. on centres 0.593 in. apart with a 0.625 in. traverse, a trough is formed with a corrugated base and sides. This is fitted with a lid (L) to minimise evaporation and with an electrode-locating plate (E) at each end of the trough.

A supporting framework is constructed of two Perspex end plates (P) spaced by three stainless

74

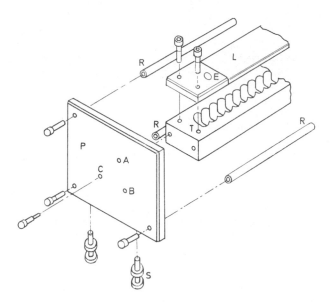

<u>Figure 5.1</u> Exploded diagram of part of horizontal
trough apparatus for isoelectric focusing.
T, separation trough;   L, lid;
E, electrode-locating plate;   P, end plate;
R, stainless steel tie rods;   S, levelling screws;
        C, pivot pin;   A, B, locking screws

steel tie rods (R) to form a rigid unit which is
levelled by adjustable screws (S). Within this
framework the separation trough is pivoted about
pin (C) in each end plate and can be locked in
either the 45° position by pin A or in the
horizontal position by pin B.
        To assemble the apparatus for use, the
supporting framework is levelled and the
separation trough locked in the 45° position by
pin A.   Then 1% (w/v) Ampholine carrier ampholytes
(30 ml) of the desired pH range are poured into the
trough and evenly distributed between its 36
corrugations by gently tilting the whole apparatus
from end to end.   With the trough in the 45°
position, this volume of ampholyte solution bridges
the corrugations and forms a continuous electrical
path along the length of the trough.   The circuit
is completed by inserting an electrode into each of
the electrode-locating plates (E).   Each electrode
consists of a Perspex tube filled with a plug of

synthetic fibre soaked in the appropriate
electrode solution. When using pH 3 to 10
Ampholine, the electrode solutions are 1% (v/v)
phosphoric acid for the anode and 1% (v/v)
N,N,N',N'-tetramethyl-ethylene diamine for the
cathode. When the electrode is positioned in the
electrode-locating plate (E), one end of it dips
into the Ampholine solution contained in the
separation trough. A platinum wire connected to the
power supply is inserted into the other end of the
electrode and penetrates the synthetic fibre plug.
This arrangement provides self-contained electrode
vessels and protects the contents of the separation
trough from the products of electrolysis.
Electrical contact between the platinum wire and the
Ampholine solution in the trough is made via the
synthetic fibre plugs soaked in electrode solution.
Before the start of isoelectric focusing, the
apparatus and its contents are cooled to 4°C in a
cold room and subsequent operations are carried out
at this temperature.
    The pH gradient is established before the
sample is inserted. An initial current of 1.0 mA is
passed through the apparatus, using a regulated
current power supply. This corresponds to a voltage
of approx. 450 V. As the pH gradient becomes
established, the electrical resistance of the
system (and consequently the voltage) increases.
It is desirable to limit the maximum power input to
the apparatus since any excess heat production
tends to disturb the pH gradient. This is
conveniently accomplished by using a power supply
fitted with a voltage-limiting device, so that at
an empirical maximum of 800 V it is automatically
switched to a regulated voltage mode. As the
electrical resistance of the apparatus further
increases with time, the applied voltage is
maintained at this figure and the current decreases
accordingly. Under these conditions a stable pH
gradient is formed after 16 h; samples are
routinely inserted after a further 8 h.
    On removal of the lid (L) the pre-formed pH
gradient is readily accessible and samples of up to
0.5 ml, in dilute buffer, are introduced into one
of the separation trough corrugations at the
desired pH. Focusing is then continued for a
further 72 h, after which the gradient is
fractionated.
    This is accomplished by releasing pin A and
lowering the trough to the horizontal position,
where it is locked by pin B. In the horizontal
position the trough contents no longer bridge the

corrugations and discrete fractions are located in
the bottom of each compartment. The pH of each
fraction is measured directly in the apparatus,
using a micro combined pH electrode, either at 4°C
or subsequently at room temperature.

The apparatus has been used for the isoelectric
focusing of viruses and their protein components
(see Chapter 21). When using microgram quantities
of radioactively labelled virus preparations,
sample recovery after focusing as measured by
radioactivity averages 80 to 100%.

REFERENCE

1. VALMET, E., 'Zone Convection Electrofocusing:
a New Technique for Fractionation of
Ampholytes in Free Solution'. Protides of the
Biological Fluids. Proc. 17th Colloq.,
Bruges 1969, Pergamon Press, Oxford, p. 401
(1970)

6. SOME ASPECTS OF ISOELECTRIC FOCUSING IN POLYACRYLAMIDE GEL

O. Vesterberg

6.1 INTRODUCTION

Even though the first applications of isoelectric focusing (IF) in polyacrylamide gel were quite successful, this technique has undergone various modifications: no review article covers all of them. It may, therefore, be difficult for a scientist who wants to start using the method to know which publication to follow. Furthermore, most papers omit technical details, some of which may be very essential for successful results. Moreover, in some cases, e.g. focusing in the alkaline pH range, problems still remain unsolved. Unfortunately this article cannot be the complete, critical and comprehensive review one might wish. It will deal with some fundamental aspects of the technique and point out problems. Practical hints and recipes will be described elsewhere[1].

In most of the earlier papers on isoelectric focusing in polyacrylamide gel, conventional equipment for disc electrophoresis in gel rods was used and this technique has been reviewed by Haglund[2], Wrigley[3] and Catsimpoolas[4]. Special equipment, better adapted for isoelectric focusing in gel rods, has also been described and this offers advantages mainly due to incorporation of small-volume electrode compartments. For the reasons mentioned below, the author has found the thin-layer or flat-bed procedure more generally useful than the gel rod procedure. This article will deal mainly with the thin-layer procedure although many comments apply equally to the gel rod technique. Another chapter in this volume (Chapter 7) also deals with aspects of isoelectric focusing in thin layers of polyacrylamide gel carried out with commercially available equipment.

6.2 WHICH GEOMETRY OF THE GEL IS MORE ADVANTAGEOUS?

The thin-layer or flat-bed procedure has many advantages, including:

(i)   Carrier ampholytes can be added to the gel by soaking after polymerisation.

(ii)   The electrolytes used at the electrodes and the concentrations of these are less critical.

(iii) There is no risk of the proteins coming in contact with the extreme pH of the electrode vessels during application.

(iv)   The proteins can be applied in many ways and at different points between the electrodes, e.g. at 'both ends' on the same lane. Joining of the proteins is an indication that the experiment has reached completion.

(v)   All samples are focused under identical conditions and, as they can be run side by side, direct comparison is possible.

(vi)   The time-consuming handling of many gel rods is avoided.

(vii) The flat bed is easier to handle during pH measurement, staining, destaining and sectioning.

(viii) The gels are less likely to become scratched or broken, e.g. during staining.

(ix)   The flat-bed gel can retain its original size even after destaining.

(x)   Flat-bed gels are well suited to zymogram (overlay) and autoradiographic procedures.

The reason why the thin-layer technique has not been used more widely is that a suitable instrument with efficient cooling has only recently become available (LKB-Multiphore).

6.3 OPTIMAL CONCENTRATION OF THE GEL AND DEGREE OF CROSS-LINKING

In contrast to disc electrophoresis, in gel isoelectric focusing it is desirable to have as little restriction on molecular migration as possible. A gel with the largest pores possible from a practical point of view should generally be used. The total concentration (T) of acrylamide and N,N'-methylenebisacrylamide (bis) can be expressed as follows[5]:

$$T = \frac{(a + b) \times 100}{V} \% \qquad (6.1)$$

and the cross-linking concentration (C) is given by

$$C = \frac{100 \times b}{a + b} \%$$
(6.2)

where a = weight of acrylamide (g), b = weight of bis (g) and V = volume of solution (ml).

It has been shown earlier[9] that by lowering T, there is an increase in pore size. However, the magnitude of the effect is only small when going from 5 to 3%. Available data also indicate that the concentration of bis (C) influences the pore size to a large extent[6,7]. At very low bis concentrations, e.g. C ≃ 2%, the gels become very weak and often tear when staining or destaining. By increasing the bis concentration above C = 8%, the size of the pores is enlarged[6,7]. This can probably be explained partly by the bis molecules acting merely as chain terminators rather than as cross-links. However, gels having C>15% appear opaque; this is undesirable if the gels are subsequently to be used for densitometry. Such gels may, however, be used with advantage when a very large pore gel is required. Further details on aspects of the properties of gels at various concentrations of T and C have been published elsewhere[6-9].

6.4 ADDITIVES

It is known that additives such as glycerol, ethylene glycol, sucrose and urea increase the mechanical stability of the gels. The use of urea or ethylene glycol also has other advantages, for example to keep less soluble proteins in solution. Ethylene glycol in concentrations up to 30% has been used with success in studies of lipoproteins[10,11]. Additives have another advantage, in that they provide an even level of osmolarity throughout the gel, that is superimposed on the uneven osmolarity caused by the more or less well focused zones of carrier ampholytes[12]. The additive can thus be thought of as an agent which counteracts the latter effect. This reduces the tendency for a wavy pattern to be formed, which can otherwise be seen on the surface of the gel. Also the additives, due mainly to the osmotic effect, reduce the risk of free-flowing water which is sometimes seen on the surface. This surface water is undesirable because protein, if present, might move about and be lost, for example during staining. If there is no reason for preferring a particular additive, sucrose in a concentration of about 12%

(w/v) is recommended. When working in the very alkaline region above pH 10, sucrose should be replaced by another solute, such as sorbitol[13].

6.5 CARRIER AMPHOLYTES* (CA)

It has been shown by others, including Finlayson and Chrambach[9] and Righetti and Drysdale[15] that too low a concentration of CA can introduce problems, for example 'the plateau phenomenon'. When working in the pH range 3.5 to 9.5, it would appear necessary to use a final concentration of at least 2% (w/v) in the gel. Even higher concentrations can be used to keep less soluble proteins in solution.

Should the CA be added before or after polymerisation of the acrylamide gel? Most experimenters have added the ampholytes before polymerisation for the sake of convenience. It should be mentioned that TEMED (N,N,N'N'-tetramethylethylene diamine) is unnecessary when Ampholine is present during polymerisation, but must be added when it is absent. When CA is added before polymerisation, there is a risk either that some CA molecules are altered by coupling of acrylamide molecules onto the amino groups, or that some CA could be coupled to or included in the gel matrix. The latter phenomenon could bring about electro-endosmosis, which in turn could contribute to a more rapid development of the 'plateau phenomenon'[9] and to an undesirable swelling of the gel in the vicinity of the electrodes. The pH profiles obtained with the two procedures can be somewhat different[13,14]. However, when using rapid focusing techniques in particular, there seems to be little disadvantage in adding CA before polymerisation.

One circumstance will now be mentioned, which can at least partially explain the development of the 'plateau phenomenon'. Because glass is negatively charged, especially above pH 5, this can cause an endosmotic waterflow against the cathode in the gel. In electrophoresis experiments it has been found that the endosmotic flow over glass can be higher than in paper. It is well known that the latter can be quite considerable.

What pH range should be used? Most users of the technique are interested in working in the pH range 3 to 10. It has been found, however, that in order to get a reasonably good pH gradient in the

*Unless otherwise stated 'carrier ampholytes' stands for 'Ampholine'.

alkaline region, one should fortify the pH 3.5 to
10 Ampholine mixture with Ampholines of pH 9 to 11.
A more favourable distribution of the field strength
is obtained if Ampholines of pH 4 to 6 and 5 to 7
are also added[12]. Supplementary Ampholines can be
added in an amount corresponding to about 10% (v/v)
of the total Ampholine concentration. It is
difficult to define the optimal proportions exactly
as there are many factors which need to be
considered.

It should also be mentioned that polymerisation
is not possible above pH 7.5 when riboflavin is used
as the initiator. Gels having an average pH above
7.5 should be polymerised with ammonium persulphate,
or should be prepared by polymerising the gel
before adding CA. Recommended recipes for different
pH ranges can be found elsewhere[1].

6.6   ELECTRODE SOLUTIONS

The type and concentration of electrode solution
preferred depends on many factors.
  (i)   When the volumes of the electrode vessels are
        large, more dilute solutions should be used.
        This also applies when the pH gradient ends
        at a pH in the region of 2 pH units on either
        side of pH 7. In these cases a rather weak
        electrolyte can be used, such as acetic acid
        instead of phosphoric acid, or ethylene
        diamine instead of sodium hydroxide.
        Alternatively, a carrier ampholyte solution
        can be used as an electrolyte (Figure 6.1).
  (ii) When the volumes of the electrode solutions
        are small (e.g. if carbon or another porous
        material is used for electrodes in the
        thin-layer procedure) stronger electrolyte
        concentrations should be used when the pH
        range ends at a pH outside the region of 2 pH
        units on either side of pH 7. More specific
        conditions can be found elsewhere[1].

6.7   APPLICATION OF PROTEIN SOLUTION

The presence of some salt in the protein solution is
not usually very critical during gel isoelectric
focusing. However, too high salt concentration can
impair the result. As a rule of thumb, the total
salt content in a sample should be less than 20
µmoles. If the content is higher, one could reduce
the sample volume or dialyse the material. When a
protein solution is to be diluted, a 2% (w/v) water
solution of Ampholine pH 7 to 9 or pH 6 to 8 is

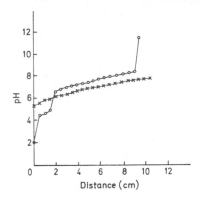

<u>Figure 6.1</u>   The influence on the pH course by using
strong and weak electrolytes at the electrodes,
respectively.   Ampholine of the pH range 5 to 7 was
used in the acrylamide gel.   The pH was measured
with a surface pH electrode at 20°C. (o---o), The pH
course obtained with 1 M H_3PO_4 and 1 M NaOH in the
anode and cathode strips respectively;(x---x), the
pH course obtained with 1% Ampholine pH 4 to 6 and
1% Ampholine pH 6 to 8 in the anode and cathode
                    strips, respectively

often suitable.   However, for serum it appears more
advantageous to dilute the sample tenfold with 0.1 M
NaCl and to apply a correspondingly larger volume.
This is preferable to applying a smaller volume of
undiluted serum.
      As is illustrated in <u>Figure 6.2</u> the protein
solution can be applied by several methods when
using thin layers of acrylamide:
  (i)   Directly to the surface, either as a small
           droplet (not more than 5 μl), or as a streak
           (up to 0.1 ml) on a line perpendicular to
           the electrodes, or spread over a
           rectangular area (up to 50 μl).   With this
           type of application it is especially
           important to work carefully and to apply the
           sample to a 'dry' surface.
  (ii)   Soaked into pieces of porous material such as
           filter paper or cellulose acetate.   (See
           also Smyth and Wadström, <u>Chapter 12</u>).
  (iii) In basins placed on the gel surface.
           Segments about 3 to 6 mm can be cut from
           rectangular or square-shaped glass tubes or
           plastic tubes measuring e.g. 10 x 10 mm.
           Such pieces can be placed with slight
           pressure on the gel surface, and filled with

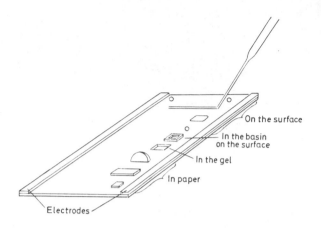

On the surface

In the basin
on the surface

In the gel

In paper

Electrodes

Figure 6.2 Different methods of applying protein
sample. From lower left to upper right the
different procedures indicated on the gel surface
diagrammatically illustrate samples applied on a
square piece of chromatography paper; on a
rectangular piece of chromatography paper; on a
semicircle of paper standing on the gel; in a basin
in the gel; in a basin on the gel surface; as a
droplet, spread over rectangular area; as a streak
on the gel; and finally application at two points on
the same lane at opposite ends and close to the
                  electrodes

        protein solution. In this way we have
        applied samples of up to 0.3 ml.
        Alternatively, squares or rectangles of soft
        plastic about 2 mm thick, in which
        rectangular holes are cut, can be placed on
        the gel surface and the holes filled with
        sample (K. Carlsson, personal
        communication). Results to date have
        indicated that some refinement of these
        techniques is necessary in order to obtain
        straight zones.
(iv)   In basins within the gel. Such basins can be
        formed during the making of the gel if
        pieces of plastic, e.g. Plexiglass
        (polyacrylate) are glued onto the
        siliconised glass plate; the pieces should
        not be as thick as the gel. According to
        Stegemann (unpublished observations)

improved results are obtained if a piece of
porous paper soaked in the protein solution
is placed over the basin after filling.
     Regardless of how the proteins are applied, it
is often valuable, in some experiments at least, to
apply the proteins at various positions between the
electrodes, as some proteins are less suitable for
application at a certain pH for reasons of
stability or low solubility. In general, however,
we apply the proteins in the vicinity of the
cathode, except for the pH range 9 to 11.

6.8 AMOUNT OF PROTEIN

Usually, isoelectric focusing in acrylamide gels is
used for analytical purposes. The total amount of
protein should be adjusted according to the
sensitivity of the method of detection of even the
minor components. In general, more protein per
volume of gel can be allowed with isoelectric
focusing than with disc electrophoresis. However,
there is a risk of overloading which may cause
precipitation in the gel; wavy protein zones after
staining indicate overloading. With Coomassie Blue
R250, usually 1 µg of protein or in some cases one
tenth thereof can be detected[12]. When immunological
or other biological methods such as zymogram
techniques are used, the limit of detection is in
most cases much lower (see Chapter 12).

6.9 VOLTAGE AND WATTAGE

The higher the voltage the shorter the time
necessary for the completion of an experiment. The
maximum voltage that can be applied merely depends
on how many watts can be allowed in the system being
used. Since $W = V \times I$, where W = watts, V = volts
and I = current in amperes, the following factors
must be considered:
  (i)   The efficiency of heat transfer per cm^2,
depends on the thickness of the glass plate on top
of the cooling plate, the thickness of the glass
plate on which the gel is located, and the rate of
heat transfer between these glass plates. It is
advisable to apply water (about 20 ml) containing
a small amount of detergent (preferably non-ionic,
e.g. Tween) between the glass plates, to give
optimal heat transfer[12].
  (ii) Provided the heat generation can be regarded
as approximately uniform for the whole of the gel
surface, it is evident that the larger the surface
area of the gel the higher the total heat formation

D

that can be allowed. Further information about heat
distribution over the gel surface is given by Davies
(Chapter 7).

(iii) Thickness of the gel layer. According to
Ohm's law, a thicker gel means a larger
cross-section area and higher current for a given
voltage: ($I = V/R$; where I = current, V = volts and
R = resistance in ohms). In practice it is
difficult to form gels of even thickness if they are
less than 1 mm thick. Skewed protein zones are
often obtained with such thin gels. There is also
increased risk of endosmosis (see section 6.5).

(iv) Distance between the electrodes. The longer
the distance between the electrodes the greater the
decrease in current as the total resistance
increases. Thus, with a certain heat production per
cm^2 of gel, the longer the distance between the
electrodes the higher the voltage that can be used.

(v)   Concentration of solutes. With regard
firstly to the concentration of Ampholine, the
higher the Ampholine concentration the lower will be
the resistance. The resistance also differs for
different pH ranges of Ampholine. Secondly, sucrose
and such uncharged additives increase the viscosity
and thereby increase the resistance. This means
that at a given voltage a lower current is obtained
in the presence of such uncharged additives.

(vi) Uneven distribution of the heat production.
After some time, there is a tendency for uneven
resistance to occur between the electrodes. This is
particularly noticeable with some types of
ampholytes, for example those of extreme pH ranges.
If no protein is to be found in such an area, a
higher temperature can be allowed to develop in
such zones than in the rest of the gel. For data on
temperature in the gel under various conditions the
reader is referred to Davies, Chapter 7.

(vii) The highest temperature allowed. Some data
indicate that the temperature of focusing is not as
critical as the temperature of pH measurement for pI
determination[16]. For theoretical reasons, however,
excessive temperature variations between the
electrodes during isoelectric focusing should be
avoided because the pI values of proteins may
differ in their temperature dependence. It is also
important that the proteins are not exposed to
temperatures which might cause partial or complete
denaturation. With rapid focusing procedures,
however, the reduction in time for focusing reduces
such a risk. This also means that a higher
temperature is permissible for rapid focusing. The
temperature in the gel is often up to $10^{\circ}C$ above

that of the coolant water (see Chapter 7).
     Perhaps the most important limitation is that
raised in point (i). Poor heat transfer is
indicated by loss of water from some parts of the
gel and condensation on the lid just above the
critical area. This means that the conditions for
equilibrium may change not only locally but also in
other parts of the gel in view of the fact that the
conditions in one part of the gel also influence
the pH equilibrium in other parts. When
condensation is observed the voltage should be
lowered.
     In general, one can say that the system is able
to stand higher wattage at the beginning than during
the final focusing due to the fact that the
conductivity is higher when the ampholytes are
distributed at random (Figure 6.3).

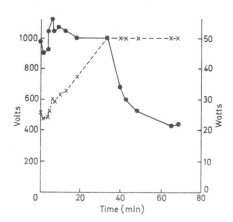

Figure 6.3 Changes in volts (x---x) and watts
(●---●) during isoelectric focusing in
polyacrylamide gel for the pH range 3 to 10. A
mixture of Ampholines, pH 3 to 10, 2.8 ml; pH 8 to
10, 0.4 ml; pH 5 to 7, 0.2 ml; pH 4 to 6, 0.2 ml;
was used in order to obtain a final average
concentration of 2% (w/v). The gel measured 245 x
112 x 2 mm. The distance between anode and cathode
was 100 mm. Haemoglobin samples applied near to
          both electrodes fused after 45 min

     Practical experience showed that a gel
containing 2% (w/v) Ampholine of the pH range 3 to
10 (ref. 11) and 12% (w/v) sucrose, measuring 115 mm
x 250 mm and 2 mm thick, can withstand 45 W at the
beginning of the experiment. The voltage was
increased gradually, without exceeding 45 W until

1000 V was reached after 35 min. The joining of
haemoglobin zones required 48 min. As indicated
above, a gel of the pH range 5 to 8 could withstand
50 W without adverse effect. 1000 V was reached
after 19 min and the joining of haemoglobin required
25 min. Gels in the pH range 5 to 9 can withstand
higher wattage than gels of other pH ranges[1].

6.10   FOCUSING TIME

The conditions for 'true' isoelectric focusing are
less favourable for isoelectric focusing in gels
than in density gradients. The 'plateau phenomenon'
has been mentioned earlier. A definitive
explanation for this has not yet been given. In any
case, for all experiments involving isoelectric
focusing in gels, at a certain time optimal
resolution is achieved. According to Sherins
et al.[17] optimal resolution was obtained at the end
of the period 'at which the pH gradient remained
linear'. Using this procedure, this time has to be
determined for each particular set of experimental
conditions.
      There is a simple way of determining the time
taken by observing when protein zones join when
samples have been applied at both electrodes.
Usually we allow about a 20% longer time than this
so that slower migrating proteins also have a chance
to be focused.

6.11   pH MEASUREMENTS

Many investigators want to measure the pH at various
points in the gel on a track between the anode and
the cathode in order to get an idea of the pH course
and to estimate the isoelectric points of their
proteins. With the thin-layer gel this can be done
in two different ways. Firstly, one can take out
small pieces of gel at regular intervals and soak
them in water (preferably free from dissolved carbon
dioxide). It is important not to use too large a
volume of water in relation to the volume of the gel
piece[12]. Secondly, one can measure the pH with a pH
electrode adapted for measurements on a surface
(Figure 6.4). These electrodes should have as small
a cross-sectional area as possible. These two
methods have often shown a good correlation when
used on the same gel. It is important to
standardise the conditions, e.g. the temperature at
which the pH is measured. It is difficult to
measure pH with a surface electrode at a
temperature much lower than room temperature unless

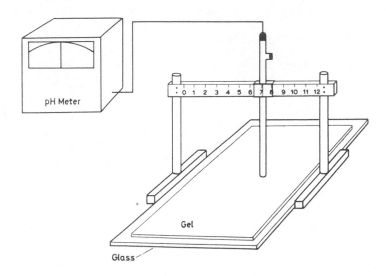

Figure 6.4   Apparatus and stand for pH electrode
   facilitating pH measurements on the gel surface

special precautions are taken to insulate and
stabilise the temperature of the whole pH electrode.
Successful use of an antimony pH electrode has been
reported by Beeley et al. (Chapter 11).

6.12   DETECTION OF PROTEIN

(i)   Staining procedures.   It is known that 0.1 μg
of protein can be detected by staining, using
Coomassie Blue directly without interference of the
carrier ampholytes[12,18,19].   It has been found that
in order to achieve such high sensitivity, it is
necessary to work with a hot staining solution[12].
However, it is not always easy to be successful with
the staining procedures described.   This is probably
due partly to the fact that the reactions at
staining and destaining involve complex adsorption
and solubility equilibria.   As the recipes described
have merely been found by trial and error, it is
expected that more successful results will be
obtained after thorough systematic studies.
    It has been found that it is possible to make a
reasonable quantitative evaluation of the amount of
protein in a zone by visual comparison with known
amounts of the same protein used as standards.   With
densitometric evaluation a high accuracy has been

obtained[20]. Selective staining of glyco- and
lipoproteins after isoelectric focusing in gels has
been described[19,10].

(ii) Enzymatic procedures, i.e. zymograms, have
been used in connection with gel isoelectric
focusing in many cases for the detection of very
small amounts of protein, e.g. fibrinolytic
activity[21], other proteolytic activities[22,23],
LDH[24], phosphatases[25], phospholipases and
amylases[26,27], esterases[28,29] and, recently,
cellulases[30]. Other biological activities e.g.
haemolysis, and haptoglobin[31] have been detected by
similar procedures. Examples of these techniques
will be described in more detail by Wadström and
Smyth (Chapter 12).

(iii) Immunologic procedures modified in different
ways have been used. These can be readily divided
into three categories:

   (a) Direct diffusion from the acrylamide of the
       protein antigens into agarose against
       antibodies to obtain precipitation lines[4].
   (b) Small sections of acrylamide gel are made,
       homogenised and placed in wells in agar for
       diffusion against antibodies[4].
   (c) Electro-immunoprecipitation which is
       obtained by a procedure analogous to the
       crossed electrophoresis procedure
       originally developed by Laurell[32] (Figures
       6.5a and 6.5b). However, difficulties
       have been encountered due to the different
       waterflow and endosmotic properties of
       acrylamide and agarose. One way to
       overcome this problem is to increase the
       viscosity of the agarose by incorporating
       such agents as acrylamide[33]. This
       technique still requires some refinement[34].

(iv) Radioactive procedures have recently been
described[35,36]. However, these procedures often
require that the protein can be labelled with a
suitable isotope such as H^3 or I^{131} before
separation. Some proteins which have a high
affinity for specific molecules can easily be
labelled if the corresponding molecules are
prepared in a labelled form[37]. A method of drying
the gels in a suitable way to permit good contact
with the film for autoradiography has recently been
developed[1,38].

(v)   Electrophoresis at right angles to the
isoelectric focusing separation and subsequent
staining (Figure 6.5c) has often given typical
patterns with a very high resolution, which can be
useful for diagnostic[39] and genetic[40] purposes.

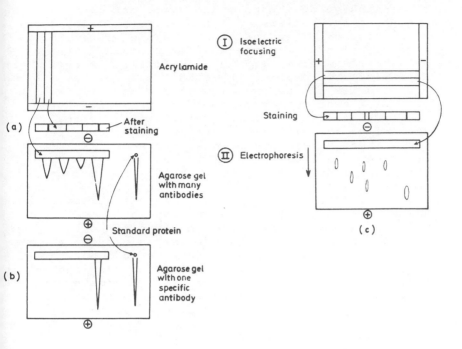

Figure 6.5   (a)   The principle of isoelectric
focusing in a strip (top slab) followed by
electrophoresis at right angles into a thin layer of
agarose gel (lower slab) containing antibodies
against many of the separated proteins.   The
precipitation arcs are detected by subsequent
staining.   Between the gel slabs, the result of
staining of the proteins in a strip of gel after
isoelectric focusing is also illustrated.   (b)
Procedure similar to that shown in Figure 6.5a but
with antibodies against only one of the separated
proteins.   (c) The principle for isoelectric
focusing (IF) in one strip (top slab) followed by
electrophoresis at right angles (to IF) in a thin
layer of acrylamide gel (lower slab), and
subsequent localisation of the protein spots by
staining.   Between the gel slabs the result of
staining of the proteins in a strip of gel after IF
is illustrated

6.13   A COMPARISON BETWEEN DISC ELECTROPHORESIS AND
         ISOELECTRIC FOCUSING IN POLYACRYLAMIDE GEL

It is known that proteins can be separated with high
resolution by disc electrophoresis.   In order to
optimise this procedure, however, various degrees of

cross-linkage of the gel, and different compositions and pH of the buffers, often need to be tried for each protein. When more than one protein is under investigation, as in the case of protein mixtures, in a single system, it may be difficult or even impossible to optimise the conditions for more than one or a few of the proteins at a time. Almost 5000 different compositions of buffers have been described[41]. The difficulty in finding optimal conditions for disc electrophoresis probably partly explains why more protein zones are sometimes detected with isoelectric focusing than with disc electrophoresis. In particular this appears to be the case as far as studies on crude protein mixtures are concerned. The method of isoelectric focusing has been found superior in the separation of some proteins showing only small charge differences, e.g. γ-globulins[35,42-46]. However, as is often the case, new methods do not replace older methods but rather tend to complement them. Isoelectric focusing in polyacrylamide gel appears to offer a simple direct approach to the high resolution of proteins. Furthermore, the possibility of estimating the isoelectric point (pI) of proteins by this technique is extremely valuable for characterisation and comparative purposes.

ACKNOWLEDGEMENTS

Thanks are due to Dr. Cyril Smyth for critical comments and for reviewing the English text. Thanks are due also to Mrs. Gun Nise and Mr. Lars Hansén for skilful technical assistance.

REFERENCES

1. VESTERBERG, O., 'Isoelectric Focusing of Proteins in Thin Layers of Polyacrylamide Gel'. Science Tools, 20, 22-29 (1973)
2. HAGLUND, H., 'Isoelectric Focusing in pH Gradients - A Technique for Fractionation and Characterization of Ampholytes'. In: Methods of Biochemical Analysis, Vol. 19, Ed. D. Glick, Wiley (Interscience), New York, 64-104 (1971)
3. WRIGLEY, C.W., 'Electrofocusing of Proteins'. In: Ann Arbor Science Publ. Inc., Ed. A. Niederwieser and G. Pataki, Ann Arbor, Michigan, 291-339 (1971)
4. CATSIMPOOLAS, N., 'Isoelectric Focusing and Isotachophoresis of Proteins'. In: 13th Eastern Analytical Symposium Articles, Separ. Sci., 8, 71-121 (1973)

5. HJERTÉN, S., '"Molecular Sieve" Chromatography on Polyacrylamide Gels, Prepared According to a Simplified Method'. Archives Biochem. Biophys., Suppl. 1, 147-151 (1962)

6. RODBARD, D., LEVITOV, C. and CHRAMBACH, A., 'Electrophoresis in Highly Cross-linked Polyacrylamide Gels'. Separ. Sci., 7, 705-723 (1972)

7. FAWCETT, J.S. and MORRIS, C.J.O.R., 'Molecular-Sieve Chromatography of Proteins on Granulated Polyacrylamide Gels'. Separ. Sci., 1, 9-26 (1966)

8. BLATTLER, D.P., GARNER, F., VAN SLYKE, K. and BRANDLEY, A., 'Quantitative Electrophoresis in Polyacrylamide Gels of 2-40%'. J. Chromatog., 64, 147-155 (1972)

9. FINLAYSON, G.R. and CHRAMBACH, A., 'Isoelectric Focusing in Polyacrylamide Gel and Its Preparative Application'. Anal. Biochem., 40, 292-311 (1971)

10. KOSTNER, G., DEPISCH, A., ALBERT, W. and HOLASEK, A., 'Isoelektrische Fokussierung und anschliesende immunochemische Charakterisierung der Lipoproteine des Humanserums'. Monatshefte Chemie, 103, 1695-1704 (1972)

11. RITTNER, Ch. and RITTNER, B., 'Variations in Human Serum Lipoprotein Detected by Isoelectric Focusing'. Z. Klin. Chem., Klin. Biochem., 9, 503-507 (1971)

12. VESTERBERG, O., 'Isoelectric Focusing of Proteins in Polyacrylamide Gels'. Biochim. Biophys. Acta, 257, 11-19 (1972)

13. VESTERBERG, O., 'Physico-chemical Properties of the Carrier Ampholytes and Some Biochemical Applications'. Ann. N.Y. Acad. Sci., 209, 23-33 (1973)

14. ROBINSON, H.K., 'Comparison of Different Techniques for Isoelectric Focusing on Polyacrylamide Gel Slabs Using Bacterial Asparaginases'. Anal. Biochem., 49, 353-366 (1972)

15. RIGHETTI, P. and DRYSDALE, J.W., 'Isoelectric Focusing in Polyacrylamide Gels'. Biochim. Biophys. Acta, 236, 17 (1971)

16. VESTERBERG, O. and SVENSSON, H., 'Isoelectric Fractionation, Analysis, and Characterization of Ampholytes in Natural pH Gradients. IV. Further Studies on the Resolving Power in Connection with Separation of Myoglobins'. Acta Chem. Scand., 20, 820-834 (1966)

D*

17. SHERINS, R.J., VAITUKAITIS, J.L. and CHRAMBACH,
    A., 'Physical Characterization of hFSH and Its
    Desialylation Products by Isoelectric Focusing
    and Electrophoresis in Polyacrylamide Gel'.
    Endocrinology, 92, 1135-1141 (1973)
18. SÖDERHOLM, J., ALLESTAM, P. and WADSTRÖM, T.,
    'A Rapid Method for Isoelectric Focusing in
    Polyacrylamide Gel'. Febs Lett., 24, No. 1,
    89-92 (1972)
19. GRAESSLIN, D., TRAUTWEIN, A. and BETTENDORF, G.,
    'Gel Isoelectric Focusing of Glycoprotein
    Hormones'. J. Chromatog., 63, 475-477 (1971)
20. VESTERBERG, O. and NISE, G., 'Urinary Proteins
    Studied by Use of Isoelectric Focusing. I.
    Tubular Malfunction in Association with
    Exposure to Cadmium'. Clin. Chem., 19,
    1179-1183 (1973)
21. VESTERBERG, O. and ERIKSSON, R., 'Detection of
    Fibrinolytic Activity by a Zymogram Technique
    after Isoelectric Focusing'. Biochim. Biophys.
    Acta, 285, 393-397 (1972)
22. VESTERBERG, O., 'Isoelectric Focusing of Acidic
    Proteins. Studies on Pepsin'. Acta Chem.
    Scand., 27, 2415-2420 (1973)
23. ARVIDSON, S. and WADSTRÖM, T., 'Detection of
    Proteolytic Activity after Isoelectric Focusing
    in Polyacrylamide Gel'. Biochim. Biophys.
    Acta, 310, 418-420 (1973)
24. CHAMOLES, N. and KARCHER, D.,
    'Isoelectro-Focusing en Acrylamide de la
    Lacticodés-Hydrogénase Hydrosoluble de Tissus
    Humains'. Clin. Chim. Acta, 30, 359-364 (1970)
25. SMITH, I., LIGHTSTONE, P.J. and PERRY, J.D.,
    'Isoelectric Focusing of Alkaline Phosphatases.
    A Focusing-Disc Electrophoresis Transfer
    Technique'. Clin. Chim. Acta, 35, 59-66 (1971)
26. WADSTRÖM, T. and SMYTH, C.J., 'Zymogram Methods
    applied to Thin-Layer Isoelectric Focusing in
    Polyacrylamide Gel'. Science Tools, 20 (1973)
27. ROBINOVITCH, M.R. and SREEBNY, L.M., 'Short
    Communication on the Nature of the Molecular
    Heterogeneity of Rat Parotid Amylase'. Archs
    oral Biol., 17, 595-600 (1972)
28. STEGEMAN, Manuscript in preparation
29. NAKAI, Y., 'Esterase Isozymes in Germinating
    Seeds of Brassica and Raphanus'. Japan J.
    Breeding, 20, 75-81 (1970)
30. ERIKSSON, K-E and PETTERSSON, B., 'A Zymogram
    Technique for the Detection of Carbohydrases'.
    Anal. Biochem., 56, 618-620 (1973)

31. ISHIMOTO, G. and KUWATA, M., 'Serum Protein Typing by Gel Electrofocusing'. Reports of National Inst. of Police Sciences, 25, 8-12 (1972)

32. LAURELL, C.B., 'Antigen-Antibody Crossed Electrophoresis'. Anal. Biochem., 10, 358-361 (1965)

33. SKUDE, G. and JEPPSSON, J-O., 'Thin Layer Electrofocusing Followed by Electrophoresis in Antibody Containing Gel'. Scand. J. clin. Lab. Invest., 29, Suppl. 124, 55-58 (1972)

34. VESTERBERG, O., HANSIN, L. and NISE, G., manuscript in preparation

35. WILLIAMSON, A.R., 'Antibody Isoelectric Spectra. Analysis of the Heterogeneity of Antibody Molecules in Serum by Isoelectric Focusing in Gel and Specific Detection with Hapten'. Eur. J. Immunol., 1, 390-394 (1971)

36. KECK, K., GROSSBERG, A.L. and PRESSMAN, D., 'Specific Characterization of Isoelectro-focused Immunoglobulins in Polyacrylamide Gel by Reaction with 125 I-labelled Protein Antigens or Antibodies'. Eur. J. Immunol., 3, 99-102 (1973)

37. SUGINAKA, H. et al., 'Multiple Penicillin-binding Components in Bacillus subtilis, Bacillus cereus, Staphylococcus aureus, and Escherichia coli'. J. Biol. Chem., 247, 5279-5288 (1972)

38. VAN DONGEN, C.A.M. and PEIL, P.S.M., 'An Improved Method for Preparing Polyacrylamide Gels for Autoradiography'. Anal. Biochem., 53, 654-655 (1973)

39. DALE, G. and LATNER, A.L., 'Isoelectric Focusing of Serum Proteins in Acrylamide Gels followed by Electrophoresis'. Clin. Chim. Acta, 24, 61-68 (1969)

40. WRIGLEY, C.W., 'Protein Mapping by Combined Gel Electrofocusing and Electrophoresis: Application to the Study of Genotypic Variations in Wheat Gliadins'. Biochemical Genetics, 4, 509-516 (1970)

41. JOVIN, T.M., 'Multiphasic Zone Electrophoresis. IV. Design and Analysis of Discontinuous Buffer Systems with a Digital Computer'. Ann. N.Y. Acad. Sci., 209, 477-496 (1973)

42. DRAWERT, F. and GÖRG, A., 'Comparative Measurements between Disc Electrophoresis and Isoelectric Focusing of Vegetable Proteins in Polyacrylamide Gels'. Chromatographia, 5, 268-274 (1972)

43. PETERSON, R.F., 'Testing for Purity in Proteins by Gel Electrophoresis'. J. Agr. Chem., 19, 595-599 (1971)

44. ROWLEY, P.T., JACOBS, M., ROSECRANS, C., WEITKAMP, L.R. and DOHERTY, R.A., 'High Resolution Analysis of Hemoglobins: Polyacrylamide Isoelectric Focusing'. Biochem. Med., 6, 553-560 (1972)

45. JEPPSSON, J.O. and BERGLUND, S., 'Thin-Layer Isoelectric Focusing for Haemoglobin Screening and its Application to Haemoglobin Malmö'. Clin. Chim. Acta, 40, 153-158 (1972)

46. SALUJA, P.G., GRONOW, M. and HAMILTON, J.M., 'Measurement of Canine Pituitary Prolactin'. J. Endocrinol., 56, 245-258 (1972)

7. THIN-LAYER GEL ISOELECTRIC FOCUSING

H. Davies

7.1 INTRODUCTION

The first use of thin-layer plates of polyacrylamide as the stabilisation medium for isoelectric focusing was described by Awdeh, Williamson and Askonas[1] and Leaback and Rutter[2] and the use of Sephadex was introduced by Radola[3]. These developments followed soon after the gel rod technique was first published by Wrigley[4] in 1968. Since then, both these techniques have been in use. However, the gel rod technique has been used more frequently because standard disc gel electrophoresis equipment can be utilised. Until recently, no commercial instruments especially designed for thin-layer gel isoelectric focusing have been available, and generally experiments have been performed with home-built equipment of different designs.
    The thin-layer technique has many advantages:
  (i)   Several samples can be compared simultaneously on the same plate and under identical conditions.
  (ii)   The gel matrix is able to support protein precipitates.
  (iii)   Efficient cooling of the gel is possible which means a considerable shortening of the experimental time.
  (iv)   Sample application is simple and can be done at alternative places in the pH gradient. It can also easily be carried out after the pH gradient has been established.
  (v)   Marker proteins or other reference samples can be run alongside the samples under investigation.
  (vi)   The cost of Ampholine per sample analysed is low.

(vii)   Determination of the pH gradient with a
        surface pH electrode placed directly on the
        gel is easily performed.
(viii) Samples can be subjected to different
        staining or zymogram techniques.
(ix)   Storage of stained polyacrylamide gels is
        simple.

7.2   THE MULTIPHOR APPARATUS

Based on the thin-layer acrylamide gel isoelectric
focusing apparatus described by others [1, 5], we have
designed an instrument, the LKB 2117 Multiphor.
This is a versatile instrument which can be used
for isoelectric focusing, electrophoresis and
isotachophoresis in thin-layer gels. The
separation is performed in either direction on a
125 x 260 mm cooled glass plate. The construction
and main features of this instrument, when used for
isoelectric focusing, as well as the technique and
difficulties of thin-layer gel isoelectric focusing
will be discussed in this article.
       The Multiphor as used for isoelectric
focusing is shown in Figure 7.1. A thin-layer
acrylamide gel moulded onto a thin glass plate is
put on the glass cooling plate with a film of water
in between, electrode filter paper strips soaked in
electrode solution having previously been placed at
the appropriate edges of the gel. The samples are
applied on small pieces of filter paper placed on
the gel surface. A lid designed for isoelectric
focusing, containing the platinum electrodes, is
placed over the gel and connected to the buffer
tank. Finally, the cover which contains the
electrical connections from the power supply is
hinged onto the buffer tank and, when closed,
completes the electric circuit.

7.2.1   The Electrode Strips
These strips should be absorbent, soft enough to
give good contact and have a very low resistance
when soaked. They should also be disposable. So
far we have found nothing better than thick filter
paper which, however, has a tendency to
disintegrate in strongly basic solutions. There
may also be a risk of electro-endosmosis with some
electrode solutions.

7.2.2   Isoelectric Focusing Lids
Two types of lid are available for isoelectric
focusing either across the length or width of the
gel. The platinum wires are stretched along a

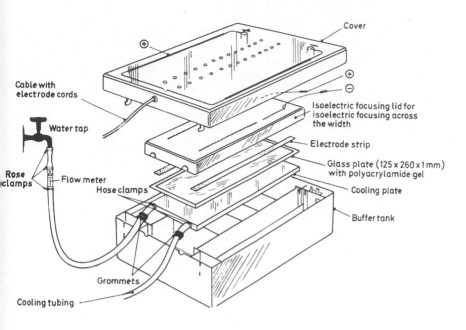

<u>Figure 7.1</u> The LKB 2117 Multiphor for thin-layer
  gel isoelectric focusing in polyacrylamide gel

saw-tooth ridge which ensures good contact with the
electrode strips and at the same time permits any
gas bubbles on the electrodes to escape easily.
The cooled gel surface should be shielded as much as
possible from the surrounding atmosphere in order to
minimise condensation of water on top of the gel,
and of course to prevent evaporation from the gel.
For this reason the lid is tight-fitting, close to
the gel and also covers the sides of the gel and the
cooling plate.

7.2.3   The Cooling Plate
Glass has been chosen as the best non-conducting
material in order to ensure high thermal efficiency.
Cooling water is circulated in channels through the
cooling plate. The 3 mm thick top glass plate is
glued to the bottom channelled piece with silicon
rubber glue, which gives a strong, flexible bond.
The cooling plate will withstand a water pressure of
at least 0.343 N/m^2 (= 3.5 kg/cm^2), permitting a
high flow of cooling water. A flow indicator shows
maximal flow for cooling with tap water.

7.3 COOLING CAPACITY

We have measured the temperature rise at different
power levels in a 2 mm acrylamide gel moulded on a
1 mm glass plate. The gel contained an acetate
buffer in order to obtain uniform heat production
over the whole gel. The temperature was measured
with a pin-point thermocouple inserted about 1 mm
into the gel. The results are shown in <u>Figure 7.2</u>,
where the power is presented as mW/cm^2. The cooling
plate was thermostatically controlled at 10°C.

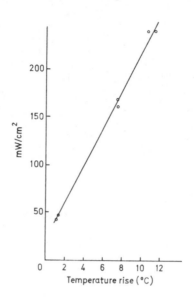

<u>Figure 7.2</u> Temperature rise in a 2 mm thick
polyacrylamide gel during electrophoresis at
different electrical loads. Cooling plate
                thermostated at 10°C

The total cooling capacity at different temperatures
can be obtained my multiplying the power per cm^2 by
the cooling plate area. One should, however,
remember that in isoelectric focusing the heat is
not evenly distributed over the entire pH gradient.
However, in an experiment with a pH gradient of 3.5
to 9.5, in which the gel was monitored with a
Thermovision camera, no irregularities due to
inadequate or uneven cooling were observed.

7.4   GEL MOULDING

The thin-layer polyacrylamide gel is moulded on a

1 mm thick glass plate. This is formed in a cell
which can be completely filled with the solution
to be polymerised so that it is unnecessary to have
an overlayer of water. The cell is assembled as
shown in <u>Figure 7.3</u>. Part of the gasket is pulled
out, so that the solution to be polymerised can be
introduced into the cell, and it is then replaced
to seal the cell. The cell is held together with
modified paper clips which also act as a stand for
the cell.

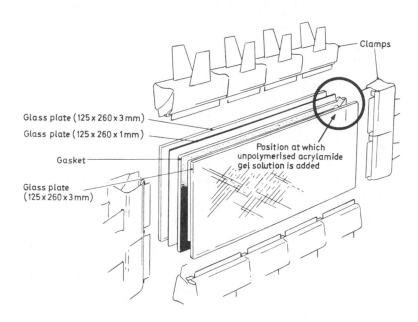

Glass plate (125 x 260 x 3mm)
Glass plate (125 x 260 x 1mm)
Gasket
Glass plate
(125 x 260 x 3mm)
Clamps
Position at which
unpolymerised acrylamide
gel solution is added

<u>Figure 7.3</u>   Polyacrylamide moulding cell for the
Multiphor apparatus

After photopolymerisation, which takes about
one hour at room temperature, the clamps are
removed and the cell is put into a refrigerator at
about 4°C for 15 min. This facilitates removal of
the thick glass plate from the gel.
To disassemble the cell it is placed
horizontally on a table and the short side of the
gasket is carefully pulled out. A thin spatula is
pushed in a little way between the gel and the thick
glass plate, allowing air to enter as the cell is
prised apart with another spatula. This manoeuvre
requires care but is soon learned! Many materials
were tested in order to find one that is suitable
for the gasket such that the gel would polymerise
all the way to the gasket, giving a good edge, but

would not stick to it. Many plastic or rubber
materials either inhibit polymerisation at their
surface or stick firmly to the gel. The gasket
supplied is made of natural rubber.

The upper glass plate, which is removed from
the gel after polymerisation, can be siliconised to
facilitate its removal. However, in our experience
this procedure is not always effective. Many
different plastic plates have been tried instead of
glass, but this has always resulted in a viscous
upper gel surface after photopolymerisation. The
focused bands have not been as sharp and distinct
as is the case when a dry gel surface is used.

7.5   PHOTOPOLYMERISATION

The gels were photopolymerised for one hour at room
temperature with the LKB 2114 Polylite which
contains two fluorescent lamps, Philips TL 20W/55.
The distance between the moulding cell and the
Polylite was about 100 mm. Polyacrylamide gel
plates can be stored, wrapped in thin polyethylene
sheet, at about 4°C. Gels have been stored under
these conditions for several weeks without any
noticeable deterioration.

7.6   SAMPLE APPLICATION

One of the many advantages of the thin-layer
technique is the variety of sample application
possibilities. Filter paper soaked in a sample
solution can be applied anywhere on the gel surface,
before or after the pH gradient is established.
This gives unique possibilities of studying whether
different Ampholine regions affect the focused
steady state of the sample. It is possible to
control the sample concentration and to obtain both
major or minor components by applying the sample on
pieces of filter paper of different sizes. We have
been using Whatman 3MM filter paper which has a
capacity to absorb about 25 μl/cm^2. The filter
paper technique is very simple and useful for many
samples. However, we have had reports of proteins
which were absorbed by the filter paper when very
dilute protein solutions have been used. Some
other possibilities include putting the sample
into slots formed in the gel while the gel is being
moulded, or making slots in a piece of plastic
which can be stuck on the gel surface and then
filling the slots with the sample solution. Both
these techniques have given quite good results, but
are somewhat more difficult to perform.

7.7 POLYACRYLAMIDE GEL FOR ISOELECTRIC FOCUSING

In general, the molecular-sieving effect in the stabilising medium for gel isoelectric focusing should be kept to a minimum. Proteins are then reasonably mobile as they migrate to their isoelectric pH values and thus the analysis time is decreased. Another factor that also influences the choice of polyacrylamide gel composition is the physical property of the gel. Some procedures are described here that give a polyacrylamide gel with T=5% and C=3%[5]. In our experience this has given good workable gels which we have found suitable for the analysis of many different proteins with a wide range of molecular weights.

We have always used photopolymerisation with riboflavin as the catalyst, except in the most basic pH ranges where the high pH inhibits photopolymerisation. Chemical polymerisation with ammonium persulphate catalyst has been used for such pH ranges.

The purity of acrylamide and N,N'-methylenebisacrylamide (bis) is an important factor in obtaining good reproducible gels. In all our experiments we have used chemicals from B.D.H. (British Drug Houses), Poole, England. The acrylamide and bis have not been recrystallised but were used directly. Several different batches have been used with equally good results.

7.7.1 Stock Solutions for Gel Preparation

A.	Acrylamide	29.1%	(w/v)
B.	N,N'-Methylenebisacrylamide	0.9%	"
C.	Riboflavin	0.004%	"
D.	Ammonium persulphate	1%	"
E.	Sucrose	25%	"
F.	Sorbitol	25%	"

All stock solutions should be filtered and stored in dark bottles in a refrigerator. The solutions should preferably be kept for not more than a week, when fresh solutions should be made.

7.8 COMPOSITION OF AMPHOLINE FOR GEL ISOELECTRIC FOCUSING[6]

Various Ampholine ranges should be mixed as indicated in Table 7.1 in order to obtain a stable and linear pH gradient as well as an even distribution of the field strength between the electrodes. The gradients formed are shown in

With the standard Ampholine range pH 3.5 to 10 (Figure 7.4a) a pH gradient which is not linear around pH 5 and extends only to pH 9 is obtained. Moreover, the pH gradient is very steep at both ends

Table 7.1   Gel compositions for different pH ranges

Stock solutions	Volume (ml) of stock solutions for gels having the following pH ranges			
	3.5-9.5	2.5-6	5-8.5	7.5-10.5**
A	10	10	10	10
B	10	10	10	10
C	0.4	0.4	0.4	
D*				0.8
E	30	30	30	
F				30
Ampholine pH 3.5-10	2.8			
Ampholine pH 2.5-4		1.2		
Ampholine pH 4-6	0.2	1.2		
Ampholine pH 5-7	0.2	0.6	1.5	
Ampholine pH 7-9			1.5	0.2
Ampholine pH 9-11	0.4			3.6
H_2O	6	6.6	6.6	5.4

The solutions should be mixed thoroughly followed by de-aeration for 1 or 2 min.
*   Solution D should be added after de-aeration.
** According to Vesterberg[6] a better gel is obtained in this pH region using T=6%, C=4.5% in which case the volumes given in Table 7.1 should be changed accordingly.

The pH gradients in Figure 7.4 were all determined with a surface pH electrode with the gel plate left on the cooling plate in the Multiphor. The cooling water from a thermostat had a temperature of +10°C.
One of the advantages of isoelectric focusing is that the degree of separation obtained can be controlled by the composition of the pH gradient. The pH gradient can be spread and flattened in

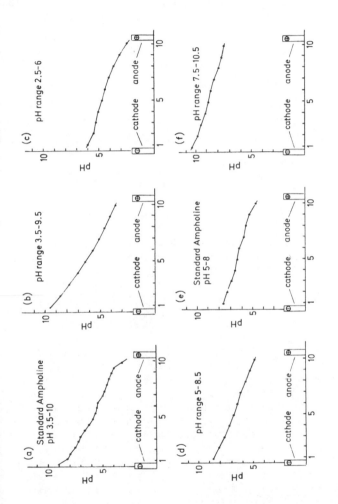

Figure 7.4   Different pH gradients obtained with standard Ampholine or with Ampholine compositions given in Table 7.1

Table 7.2   Suitable electrode solutions

pH Range	Cathode	Anode
3.5-9.5	1 M NaOH	1 M H_3PO_4
2.5-6	0.5% Ampholine pH 5-7	1 M H_3PO_4
5-8.5	0.1-1 M NaOH or 1% Ampholine pH 8-10	0.1-1.0 M H_3PO_4 or 1% Ampholine pH 5-7
7.5-10.5	1 M NaOH	0.1% Ampholine pH 7-9

different regions in order to obtain a better separation without losing the total separation picture over a wide pH range.

The concentration of Ampholine should be at least 2% (w/v). The appearance of a 'plateau phenomenon' as described by Finlayson and Chrambach[7] becomes marked at Ampholine concentrations below 1% (w/v), especially in the pH range 3.5 to 9.5. The 'plateau phenomenon' is a progressive flattening of the pH gradient from the centre of the gel.

7.9   FORMATION AND STABILITY OF THE pH GRADIENT

The formation of the pH gradient in the pH region 3.5 to 9.5 was followed by measuring the pH of the gel at different intervals. As seen in Figure 7.5, the formation of the pH gradient starts at the acidic and basic ends and develops towards the middle of the gel. A pH plateau can still be seen after 45 min. A linear pH gradient was formed after about one hour. If isoelectric focusing is continued for several hours the 'plateau phenomenon' becomes apparent, resulting in a drift of the pH gradient (Figure 7.6). In practice, this means that the pH gradient is shortened in the basic region and that the focused zones slowly migrate towards the cathode. The instability of the pH gradient seems to be proportional to the potential applied as well as to the length of the focusing time, and is more pronounced when Ampholine concentrations below 2% (w/v) are used.

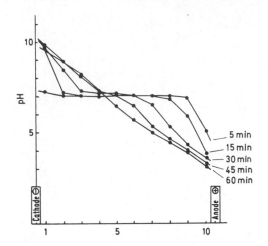

Figure 7.5   Formation of a pH gradient of 3.5 to
9.5   The pH was measured at the time intervals
shown

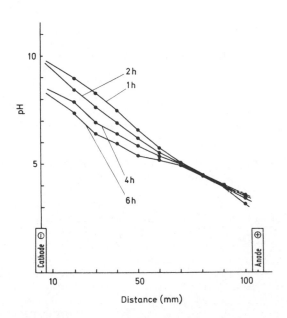

Figure 7.6   Changes in a pH gradient 3.5 to 9.5
after continued isoelectric focusing at 1100 V for
2, 4 and 6 h

Figure 7.7 shows the different phases of an isoelectric focusing run in a pH gradient of 3.5 to 9.5 using haemoglobin as the sample. The sample was applied at three different positions: in the middle and at 10 mm from the anodic and cathodic electrode strips respectively. After one hour, the haemoglobin zones from these different application points have reached the same position and have focused into sharp bands. The drift of the pH gradient becomes apparent after about two hours and was observed for several hours more. The focused haemoglobin zones remain fairly sharp and well resolved as they drift towards the cathode. This is due to the fact that the slope of the pH gradient around pH 7, where haemoglobin focuses, remains fairly constant (Figure 7.6). The drift of the pH gradient and the 'plateau phenomenon' have been reported and discussed in several papers[7-11]. However, an adequate explanation for all the experimentally observed facts is still lacking. In practice, however, the instability of the pH gradient is low when Ampholine concentrations of about 2% (w/v) or higher are used, and becomes apparent only some time after the gradient has formed and the proteins have focused.

Another phenomenon which we have observed after prolonged isoelectric focusing in the pH gradient 3.5 to 9.5 is that the gel shrinks and becomes very thin in the middle. At the same time, the gel swells considerably at the electrode strips. The swelling is greater at the anodic than the cathodic isoelectric focusing strip.

7.10   LINEARITY OF THE pH GRADIENT AT RIGHT ANGLES TO THE pH GRADIENT

Linearity of the pH gradient at right angles to the pH gradient can be checked by applying the sample on a long filter paper strip across the whole length of the gel. Zones usually focus as straight lines in the different regions of the pH gradient. However, we have observed a tendency for zones which focus in the acid pH region near the anode to be somewhat distorted and curved. This tendency does not always occur but is more pronounced when isoelectric focusing is run in the long direction of the gel plate, i.e. at longer focusing times with a higher electrical potential. One can observe this by looking at the gel just after focusing has been completed. The gel surface shows many waves running parallel to the pH gradient. These waves are then sometimes distorted at the acid end of the gel near

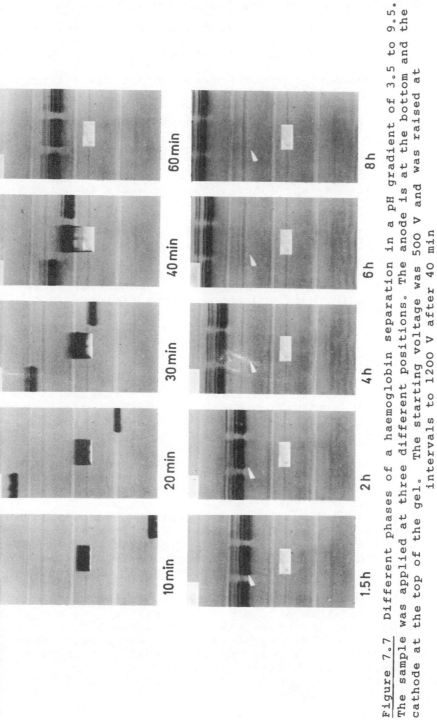

Figure 7.7 Different phases of a haemoglobin separation in a pH gradient of 3.5 to 9.5. The sample was applied at three different positions. The anode is at the bottom and the cathode at the top of the gel. The starting voltage was 500 V and was raised at intervals to 1200 V after 40 min

the anode. This wavy pattern on the gel surface is probably due to the different concentrations and conductivities of focused Ampholine bands.

7.11 VOLTAGE, MAXIMUM POWER, COOLING TEMPERATURE AND FOCUSING TIME

The Multiphor has an efficient cooling system which is very important for rapid and reproducible results. Even if tap water can be used, a cooling thermostat is to be preferred as both the temperature and the flow of water must be kept constant. We have used a cooling water temperature of +10°C. This temperature has been chosen to avoid protein denaturation or other inactivation and to avoid condensation of moisture on top of the gel. It is also important to remember that the mobility of proteins is decreased as the temperature is lowered.

In isoelectric focusing the electrical field and thus the heat evolved is never distributed evenly across the whole gel. This is because the conductivity varies along the pH gradient. By making up the Ampholine ranges as suggested in Table 7.1, the variation in conductivity can be compensated for in part but not completely ruled out. We have followed an isoelectric focusing run in a pH gradient of 3.5 to 10 with a Thermovision camera from AGA AB, Lidingö, Sweden in a preliminary experiment. At the beginning of the run, the temperature of the gel starts to rise close to the electrodes; the temperature rise is higher nearer to the anode than the cathode. During the run these warmer zones broaden and move towards the centre of the gel. At the end of the experiment there was a warmer zone in the middle of the gel with the temperature dropping towards the electrodes.

By running experiments at very high electrical loads, one can follow the heat evolved by observing the condensation of moisture inside the isoelectric focusing lid. The condensation areas inside this lid correspond to the warmer areas of the gel as shown by the Thermovision camera. We have measured the temperature of the gel in these regions and found the temperature rise to be about 8°C above the cooling plate temperature. These measurements were made with a very small, pin-point thermocouple inserted about half-way into the gel.

The power applied to a pH gradient of 3.5 to 9.5 under 'slight condensation conditions' was the following:

For isoelectric focusing across the width of the
gel:
  Starting voltage   480 V/100 mA   48 W
  Finishing voltage   1160 V/26 mA   30.4 W
  Focusing time about
    1.5 h

 For isoelectric focusing across the length of the
gel:
  Starting voltage   1000 V/49 mA   49 W
  Finishing voltage   2500 V/12 mA   30 W
  Focusing time about
    3.5 h

The voltage is raised at intervals during the
entire experiment.

7.12   DETERMINATION OF THE pH GRADIENT

The pH gradient can be determined either by cutting
out small gel pieces and homogenising them in small
amounts of de-aerated distilled water or more
directly with a surface pH electrode (e.g. Type LOT
403-30-48, Ingold, Zürich, Switzerland). In the
latter case, which we have found very convenient,
the gel plates can be left on the cooling plate and
the pH determined directly at the end of the
experiment. However, to get absolutely correct pH
values the pH electrode should also be at the same
temperature as the gel plate.

7.13   STAINING WITH COOMASSIE BRILLIANT BLUE
         ACCORDING TO VESTERBERG[5]

Coomassie Brilliant Blue R-250 (0.75 g) is
dissolved in methanol (225 ml) by stirring for 5 to
10 min. It is necessary to check that all the stain
has dissolved. The stain is spread onto the
surface of the methanol before stirring. The
staining solution is poured into water (465 ml) and
mixed thoroughly. Finally, while stirring,
sulphosalicylic acid (22.5 g) and then
trichloroacetic acid (75.0 g) are added. This gives
a total volume of approx. 690 ml, sufficient to
stain two gels.
       The staining solution should be used the same
day. The gel is stained for 15 min at 60°C and then
destained in a solution containing: water (1950 ml),
ethanol (750 ml) and glacial acetic acid (240 ml)
($H_2O:C_2H_5OH:CH_3COOH$, 8:3:1). The staining
procedure is described in detail by Vesterberg[5]. If
it is necessary to remove the Ampholines before
staining, the gel should be washed in 10 to 15%

(w/v) trichloroacetic acid for approx. 5 to 10 h
with several changes of washing solution. During
the staining and destaining procedures, the
polyacrylamide gel usually separates from the glass
plate. The handling of the gel is made easier if a
net with large pores is used.

7.14   STORAGE AND DRYING OF THE STAINED
POLYACRYLAMIDE GEL

After destaining, the polyacrylamide gel can either
be stored in a sealed plastic bag supported by a
glass plate or thick chromatography paper, or dried
on a glass plate. In the latter case, the gel is
soaked for 30 min in destaining solution containing
5% (v/v) glycerol put on a glass plate and wrapped
in cellophane also wetted with the glycerol
solution. The gel is then allowed to dry at room
temperature.

ACKNOWLEDGEMENTS

Some of the experimental results were obtained at
the LKB Application Laboratory by Mr. Christer
Karlsson and Miss Ulla Birgitta Andersson, whom I
wish to thank for putting their results at my
disposal.

REFERENCES

1. AWDEH, Z.L., WILLIAMSON, A.R. and ASKONAS, B.A.,
    'Isoelectric Focusing in Polyacrylamide Gel and
    its Application to Immunoglobulins'. Nature,
    219, 66-67 (1968)
2. LEABACK, D.H. and RUTTER, A.C.,
    'Polyacrylamide-Isoelectric-Focusing a New
    Technique for the Electrophoresis of Proteins'.
    Biochem. Biophys. Res. Comm., 32, 447-453 (1968)
3. RADOLA, B.J., 'Thin-Layer Isoelectric Focusing of
    Proteins'. Biochim. Biophys. Acta, 194,
    335-338 (1969)
4. WRIGLEY, C., 'Gel Electrofocusing - A Technique
    for Analyzing Multiple Protein Samples by
    Isoelectric Focusing'. Science Tools, 15,
    17-23 (1968)
5. VESTERBERG, O., 'Isoelectric Focusing of Proteins
    in Polyacrylamide Gels'. Biochim. Biophys.
    Acta, 257, 11-19 (1972)
6. VESTERBERG, O., personal communication
7. FINLAYSON, R. and CHRAMBACH, A., 'Isoelectric
    Focusing in Polyacrylamide Gel and Its
    Preparative Application'. Anal. Biochem., 40,
    292-311 (1971)

8. ROBINSON, H.K., 'Comparison of Different
    Techniques for Isoelectric Focusing on
    Polyacrylamide Gel Slabs Using Bacterial
    Asparaginases'. Anal. Biochem., 219, 353-366
    (1972)

9. MILES, L.E.M., SIMMONS, J.E. and CHRAMBACH, A.,
    'Instability of pH Gradients in Isoelectric
    Focusing on Polyacrylamide Gel'. Anal.
    Biochem., 49, 109-117 (1972)

10. BATES, L.S. and DEGOE, C.W., 'Polyacrylamide Gel
    Electrofocusing and the Ampholine Shift'.
    J. Chromatogr., 73, 296-297 (1972)

11. CATSIMPOOLAS, N., 'Transient State Isoelectric
    Focusing. Digital Measurement of Zone
    Position, Zone Area, Segmental pH Gradient,
    and Isoelectric Point as a Function of Time'.
    Anal. Biochem., 54, 66-78 (1973)

8. HIGH VOLTAGE ANALYTICAL AND PREPARATIVE ISOELECTRIC FOCUSING

P.G. Righetti and A.B.B. Righetti

8.1 INTRODUCTION

Isoelectric focusing in solid support media has become a technique of widespread use. At the beginning, the method borrowed the type of gel (acrylamide) and the apparatus from commercially available disc electrophoresis equipment[1-3]. Soon, however, the technique was adapted for use in thin-layer apparatus, for example, that described by Awdeh et al.[4] and by Leaback and Rutter[5]. Other supports, such as agarose[6] and Sephadex[7], have been tried. Several two-dimensional techniques have also been successfully used. These include (a) gel isoelectric focusing in the first dimension followed by immunodiffusion[8], (b) gel isoelectric focusing followed by gel electrophoresis in a slab[9], and (c) gel isoelectric focusing followed by gradient gel electrophoresis[10].

The great advantage of isoelectric focusing is its very high resolving power. Molecules differing by as little as 0.02 pI units can be successfully separated[11]. For a routine laboratory method, however, this advantage is many times offset by the long time required to reach equilibrium conditions. While a standard analytical disc electrophoresis run is usually completed in 30 min to 1 h[12], in the common gel isoelectric focusing system at least 5 to 6 h are required to ensure true equilibrium conditions[13,14]. By using a high voltage, pulsating power supply and properly cooled rod or thin-layer gels, we are now able to reach isoelectric equilibrium in approximately 1 h.

8.2 MATERIALS AND METHODS

Ampholine (40%, w/v) with buffering capacities in
the pH range 3 to 10 were purchased from LKB
Produkter AB, Bromma 1, Sweden.
N,N,N',N'-Tetramethylethylene diamine (TEMED) was
obtained from Eastman Organic Chemicals Co.,
Rochester, N.Y. Acrylamide and N,N'-methylene
bisacrylamide (bis) were from B.D.H., Poole,
England. Acrylamide was recrystallised from
chloroform, and bis from acetone, according to
Loening[15]. In the stock solution, the ratio
acrylamide:bis was always 25:1. Riboflavin was
obtained from Sigma Chemical Co., St. Louis, Mo.;
horse spleen ferritin, twice crystallised and
cadmium-free, was from Mann Research Laboratories,
New York, N.Y.; human haemoglobin was purified from
red blood cells by the method of Drabkin[16].
Carbamylated haemoglobins were a gift from Dr. J.V.
Kilmartin, University of Cambridge, England.

8.2.1 Isoelectric Focusing in Gel Rods
The apparatus and the technique have been described
previously[13,17]. We routinely polymerise gels
containing 4% (w/v) acrylamide, 0.16% (w/v) bis,
2% (w/v) Ampholine and 5% (v/v) glycerol. However,
we prefer to avoid the use of ammonium persulphate,
and we use riboflavin as a catalyst instead. A
stock solution of riboflavin (0.004%, w/v) is made
monthly and kept at 4°C in a dark bottle. Both
riboflavin and TEMED are added to the gel mixture
to a final concentration of 0.0004% (w/v). The use
of riboflavin instead of persulphate allows higher
initial voltages to be applied, since riboflavin
does not contribute to the system conductivity.

8.2.2 Isoelectric Focusing in Thin-Layer Gels
We use the technique of Awdeh et al.[4] as modified by
Vesterberg[18]. The thin-layer apparatus was a
prototype (LKB 2117 Multiphor) kindly lent to us by
LKB Produkter, Bromma 1, Sweden. In this system
60 ml of gel mixture are used to form a thin-layer
gel 250 mm x 100 mm and 2 mm thick. Simply by
changing the electrode positions, the proteins can
be run to equilibrium either in the short (100 mm)
or in the long (250 mm) dimension. Usually the
sample is soaked in a piece of filter paper, of
size 5 mm x 10 mm, and applied to the thin-layer
gel[18]. This allows the application of a volume of
approx. 10 µl on each filter paper, and the
simultaneous running of about 20 samples. If the
sample is too dilute, or is of unknown

concentration, a long strip of paper cut in the form of an acute angle-triangle can be applied. The focused zones will appear as long, thin lines of linearly increasing concentration, allowing a quick estimate of the proper amount of sample to be loaded.

When needed, staining and destaining are performed according to Vesterberg[19].

8.3 RESULTS

8.3.1 The Bosi Constant Wattage Power Supply

The power supply used in this work (Bosi patent No. 833364) was a constant wattage apparatus which allows a wide selection of pulses having frequencies ranging from 5 to 4000 Hz. This power supply is particularly convenient in isoelectric focusing where, as the current decreases as the system approaches equilibrium, the voltage has to be increased. This has to be done manually in constant voltage or constant amperage power supplies. In our system, once the initial conditions are selected, the power supply adjusts itself automatically by maintaining a constant wattage. Also, by selecting the proper pulse frequency, one can apply high voltages with considerably reduced joule effects thus shortening the analysis time.

Figure 8.1 shows the voltage and amperage profiles with the power set at different frequencies and on:off ratios (i.e. the ratio of the total time during which power is applied to the time during which it is switched off). A frequency of 1000 Hz (on:off ratio = 1:3) has been found particularly suitable for gel isoelectric focusing since it allows high voltages (up to 3000 V) without affecting the protein samples and the gel matrix. In the thin-layer gel technique we apply initially up to 100 W to the entire gel. In the gel rod technique, we start with 5 W per gel rod. In both systems the gel is connected to a high-capacity (500 W) water bath, thermostated at 1°C.

8.3.2 Heating Effects

To measure joule effects, we have used a differential thermocouple (copper-constantane with a sensitivity of 40 μV/centigrade degree) connected to a potentiometric recorder calibrated between 0 and 60°C. The probe was inserted in the gel during polymerisation since we found that plunging the thermocouple into a pre-cast gel, thus breaking the polymer matrix, badly affected the temperature measurements.

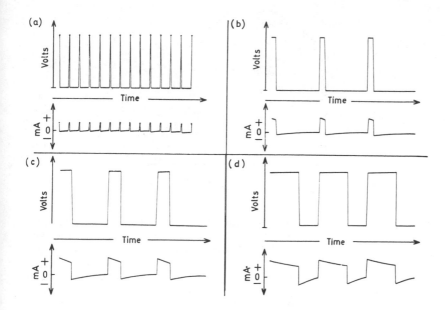

<u>Figure 8.1</u> Voltage and amperage profiles with the
pulsephor set at different frequencies. The
voltage applied was always 2000 V. (a) on:off
ratio = 1:9; frequency = 3000 Hz. (b) on:off
ratio = 1:9; frequency = 600 Hz. (c) on:off
ratio = 1:4; frequency = 600 Hz. (d) on:off
ratio = 3:2; frequency = 600 Hz. It should be noted
that during the 'off'time the current becomes
negative and approaches a value of zero
                (dipolarisation phenomenon)

      Many authors have performed gel isoelectric
focusing by trapping the protein sample within the
gel polymer. <u>Figure 8.2</u> shows the heat of
polymerisation in tubes of 4.5 mm and 3 mm inner
diameter. Depending on the gel strength and tube
diameter up to 40°C can be reached during
polymerisation and this could adversely affect
heat-labile enzymes. When using persulphate as a
catalyst, the reaction is usually terminated in
less than 5 min. With riboflavin, polymerisation
takes place in approx. 1 h. It can also be seen
from <u>Figure 8.2</u> that the rate of heat removal in
water is at least 50 times faster than the heat
dissipation in air. This is an important point to
be stressed. Many authors believe that they
effectively cool their gels simply by running the

E

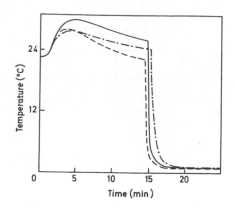

Figure 8.2 Heat of polymerisation of acrylamide
gel in: (———), quartz tube (4.5 mm inner diameter);
(—·—), 'thick wall' (1.7 mm) plastic tube (3 mm
inner diameter); (- - -), 'thin wall' (0.8 mm) plastic
tube (3 mm inner diameter). The gel contained 4%
(w/v) acrylamide gel (0.16% (w/v) bis), 2% (w/v)
Ampholine. Polymerisation was with persulphate.
The sharp drop after 15 min is due to cooling in
water in contrast to heat dissipation in air during
the first 15 min

apparatus in the cold room. Figure 8.3 shows what
happens under these conditions. A 4% (w/v)
acrylamide gel, 0.16% (w/v) bis, containing 2% (w/v)
Ampholine, pH range 6 to 8, was first run to
equilibrium and then subjected sequentially to
wattages of 2.25 W, 1 W and 0.25 W for 40 min each.
The curves shown in Figure 8.3 represent isowattage
profiles, since the gel had already reached
isoelectric equilibrium, and therefore the power
applied to the gel was constant during the time of
the experiment. It can be seen that during the
first 8 min, as long as the gel was immersed in
circulating coolant at 1°C, its temperature was
constant and barely a couple of degrees above that
of the coolant for the highest wattage applied.
However, as soon as the coolant was removed and the
gel allowed to dissipate the heat in air, it began
to warm up quite considerably; in the case of the
2.25 W applied (upper curve), the temperature
reached 40°C and then slowly declined. When the
water circulation was started again, as indicated by
the three arrows in the right side of Figure 8.3,
the gel was quickly and efficiently cooled in all
the three cases. Therefore, we feel it is more

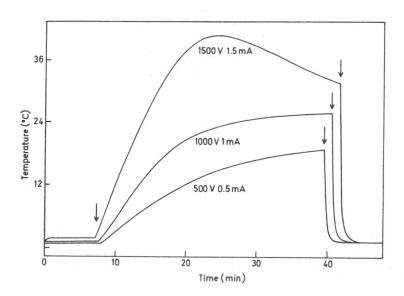

<u>Figure 8.3</u> A comparison of air cooling and water
cooling. The same gel was run sequentially at
0.25 W (lower curve), 1.0 W (middle curve) and
2.25 W (upper curve). During the first 8 min water
cooling was applied. Between 8 and 40 min the
coolant was removed (as indicated by arrows) and
the gel dissipated heat into the air. At approx.
40 min, the cooling water was allowed to circulate
again. Experiments were performed in 'thin wall'
          plastic tubes (3 mm inner diameter)

appropriate to speak of 'rate of heating in air'
instead of 'rate of cooling in air' as usually
reported in the literature.
       Some commercially available apparatus for disc
electrophoresis, and for gel isoelectric focusing,
provide indirect cooling of the gels. This is
achieved by immersing the gels in 1 to 2 litres cold
buffer in one electrode compartment fitted with an
outer cooling jacket. <u>Figure 8.4</u> shows that this
too is an ineffective method of heat control. When
the gel is immersed in non-circulating coolant, and
the power applied, the gel temperature rises
quickly from 1 to 15°C. Only when the coolant was
circulated (first arrow in <u>Figure 8.4</u>) did the gel
temperature drop to approx. 5°C. When the power
supply is turned off (second arrow in <u>Figure 8.4</u>)
the gel equilibrated with the coolant in approx.
30 sec.

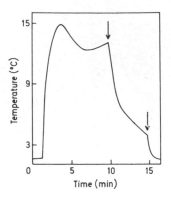

<u>Figure 8.4</u> Indirect gel cooling. A gel cast in a
'thin wall' plastic tube (3 mm inner diameter) was
immersed in non-circulating coolant at 1°C. When
500 V were applied to it, its temperature rose by
15°C. When water circulation was started (first
arrow) the gel was cooled to approx. 5°C. When the
power supply was turned off (second arrow) the gel
    equilibrated with the coolant in approx. 30 s

     We then investigated the possibility of using
quartz or plastic tubes for high voltage gel
isoelectric focusing. We chose material readily
available commercially, i.e. 4.5 mm inner diameter
quartz tubes and 3.0 mm inner diameter plastic
tubes. The latter had a wall thickness of 1.7 mm
which was machined down to a thickness of 0.8 mm.
The temperature profiles in <u>Figure 8.5</u> show that in
both quartz and thin-wall plastic tubes,
considerable heat is developed in the first 5 to 10
min. After that, the temperature declines steadily
until the gel equilibrates at a few degrees above
the coolant temperature. The experiments were
started with a potential differential of 1000 V and
ended at 2000 V. The diphasic shape of the thermal
curve was reproducible from run to run. We have no
ready explanation for this, except that perhaps the
wattage might not be constant during this period.
     Plastic tubes with a thick wall (1.7 mm) are
not suitable for high voltage gel isoelectric
focusing. When 1000 V are applied to these tubes
the temperature in the gel reaches up to 80°C, and
the polyacrylamide sometimes disintegrates (<u>Figure
8.6</u>). In comparison, the same tubes machined to
0.8 mm, subjected to the same wattage, never heat
up above 36°C.

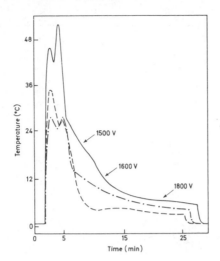

Figure 8.5   Heating effects in quartz and plastic
tubes. (———), Quartz tube (6.7 mm outer and 4.5 mm
inner diameters) with starting voltage of 1000 V;
(—•—), same tube with starting voltage of 500 V;
(- - -), plastic tube (4.7 mm outer and 3 mm inner
diameters) with starting voltage of 1000 V.   The
voltage values indicated on the upper thermal
curve represent increases in the initial voltage, at
the times indicated by the abscissa, as the system
goes to equilibrium.   The pH gradient is practically
formed in 15 min

8.3.3 Analysis of Haemoglobin by High Voltage Isoelectric Focusing in Gel Rods

Figure 8.7 shows the isoelectric spectrum of
partially oxidised human haemoglobin focused in the
pH range 6 to 8.   The total running time was 45 min,
starting at 1500 V and ending with 2500 V (on:off
ratio = 1:4).   That the system had reached
equilibrium conditions was ensured by subjecting two
control gels to a further electrofocusing time of
1 h; no change in banding patterns nor pI values was
observed.   When the bands were cut and their
respective pI values measured, they were found to be
the same as reported by Bunn and Drysdale[20].   The
brown upper band (ferrihaemoglobin, $\alpha_2^+ \beta_2^+$) had a pI
of 7.20 and the fourth one (oxyhaemoglobin, $\alpha_2 \beta_2$)
had a pI of 6.95.

The two intermediate bands are components IB_I
and IB_{II}, which have been identified[20] as $\alpha_2 \beta_2^+$ and
$\alpha_2^+ \beta_2$.   The three faint bands below oxyhaemoglobin
represent normal haemolysate components A_{IA}, A_{IB}

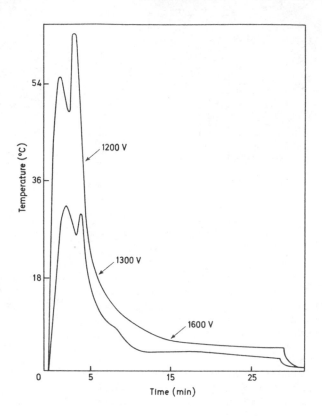

<u>Figure 8.6</u> Heating effects in thick-walled plastic
tubes (6.4 mm outer and 3 mm inner diameter) with
starting voltage of 1000 V; lower curve obtained
with starting voltage of 500 V. With the same tubes
machined to a wall thickness of 0.8 mm the
temperature never rose above 36°C with a starting
          voltage of 1000 V (see <u>Figure 8.5</u>)

and A_{IC}, as described by Drysdale <u>et al</u>.[21]. When
each of the four major focused bands was cut and
re-run in another gel, they banded in the same
position.

8.3.4 <u>Analysis of Haemoglobin by High Voltage</u>
<u>Isoelectric Focusing in Thin Layer Gels</u>
We have also tried the flat-bed technique, since
this method appears to be more useful for routine
clinical analysis when many samples have to be
analysed at once. Thin-layer gel isoelectric
focusing is usually started at 1.5 V/cm and the run

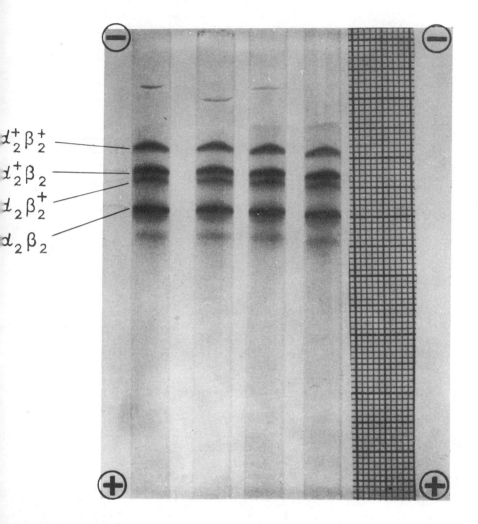

$\alpha_2^+ \beta_2^+$

$\alpha_2^+ \beta_2$

$\alpha_2 \beta_2^+$

$\alpha_2 \beta_2$

Figure 8.7 Isoelectric focusing of partially oxidised human haemoglobin in gel rods. 4% (w/v) acrylamide (0.16% (w/v) bis) gel rods, containing 2% (w/v) Ampholine pH range 6 to 8, were cast in quartz tubes. The starting voltage was 1500 V and this increased to a final voltage of 2500 V (on:off ratio = 1.4; frequency = 1000 Hz). Samples of 500 μg haemoglobin were applied to each tube after 10 min of pre-focusing. Total running time, 45 min

is made for several hours[18]. <u>Figure 8.8</u> shows the
focusing of carbamylated haemoglobins in a
thin-layer gel, in the pH range 7 to 7.5. The run
was completed in 1 h at 250 V/cm (final voltage).

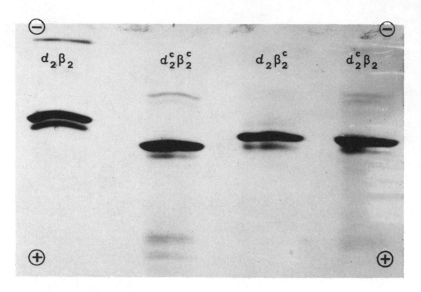

<u>Figure 8.8</u> Isoelectric focusing of carbamylated
haemoglobins in a gel slab. The slab contained 4%
(w/v) acrylamide (16% (w/v) bis) and 2% (w/v)
Ampholine pH range 7 to 7.5. $\alpha_2\beta_2$, normal human
haemoglobin; $\alpha_2^c\beta_2^c$, α- and β-chain carbamylated
human haemoglobin; $\alpha_2\beta_2^c$, β-chain carbamylated
haemoglobin; $\alpha_2^c\beta_2$, α-chain carbamylated haemoglobin.
300 μg of each sample were applied as described in
the text. Running time: 1 h at 250 V/cm (final
voltage). Pulsephor set at 1000 Hz and an on:off
ratio of 1:3

The samples were soaked in a rectangular piece of
filter paper and applied from both cathodic and
anodic ends. Equilibrium conditions were ensured
by the fact that the pattern shown in <u>Figure 8.8</u>
is the merged profile of the zones travelling from
the cathode as well as from the anode ends.
      The pI difference between $\alpha_2\beta_2$ and $\alpha_2^c\beta_2^c$ was
found to be 0.1 of a pH unit. The two partially
blocked tetramers, $\alpha_2^c\beta_2^c$ and $\alpha_2\beta_2^c$ have pI values
intermediate between the two extremes and lay 0.05
pH units apart from either $\alpha_2\beta_2$ or $\alpha_2^c\beta_2^c$. However,
$\alpha_2^c\beta_2$ and $\alpha_2\beta_2^c$ show apparently the same pI and they
focus as a single band when mixed together. This

means that, if the two partially carbamylated
species differ in their pI values at all, it must
be by less than 0.02 of a pH unit, which is the
resolution limit of this technique. In the zone of
α_2^c β_2^c some bands can be seen below the main
component: they probably represent over-reacted
species in which the cyanate has not only
carbamylated the terminal α-amino group of α and
β chains, but also some lysine ε-amino groups[22].

8.3.5 <u>High Voltage Preparative Isoelectric Focusing</u>
We have also performed high voltage preparative
isoelectric focusing using the LKB 110 ml column.
In this system, at least 24 h are usually needed to
ensure equilibrium conditions. <u>Figure 8.9</u> shows
the isoelectric profile of horse spleen ferritin
monomer run in a gradient of pH range 4 to 5
(obtained by isoelectric fractionation of pH 3 to 5
Ampholines). The run was over in 8 h at a final
voltage of 4000 V (on:off ratio = 2:3). At least
six bands could be seen to be isoelectric between
pH 4.2 and 4.6. It has been demonstrated that this
polydispersity is neither due to iron content nor
aggregate size[23]. Recently it has been suggested
that this microheterogeneity could be an artefact[24].
On the other hand, the isoferritins have been shown
to be tissue-specific and they can also be
reproduced by DEAE-Sephadex chromatography[17].
Similar results have been obtained by Urushizaki
<u>et al</u>.[25].

8.4 DISCUSSION

The present paper describes a system in which rapid
equilibrium is obtained in gel isoelectric focusing
by means of high voltage (150 to 300 V/cm)
pulsating waves in the frequency range 5 to 4000 Hz.
In most of the previous papers, conditions are
described which result in equilibrium in a minimum
of 5 h and up to between 10 and 12 h. As a
representative figure, when running the gels at
200 V at 0 to 5°C, 8 h are needed to ensure
equilibrium conditions[14].
    Gel isoelectric focusing operated at room
temperature with acrylamide concentrations ranging
from 5 to 10% (w/v), 54 V/cm and high Ampholine
concentration (1 to 2%, w/v), has been claimed to
reach equilibrium in 1.5 to 3 h[26]. Catsimpoolas[3]
has obtained equilibrium in 1 h at 23 V/cm in 5%
(w/v) acrylamide and 2% (w/v) Ampholine at room
temperature. Grossbach[27], using capillary columns
(50 to 300 μ internal diameter) has claimed

E*

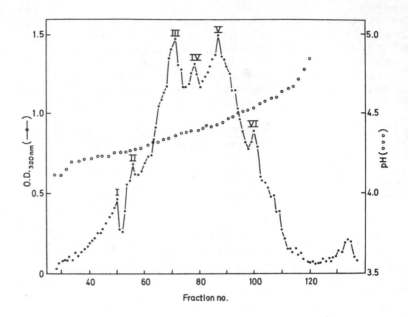

<u>Figure 8.9</u> Preparative isoelectric focusing in an
LKB 110 ml column. 10 mg ferritin monomer were
focused in 1% (w/v) Ampholine pH range 4 to 5, in a
20 to 50% (w/v) sucrose density gradient. The
cathode was uppermost. Focusing time: 8 h at 4000 V
(final voltage). Pulsephor set at on:off ratio =
2:3 and a frequency of 2000 Hz. Fractions of 0.5 ml
were collected. (——•——), $A_{320\ nm}$; open circles, pH
  gradient; I–VI denote multiple forms of ferritin

isoelectric focusing times from 10 to 120 min, in
gels containing 7% (w/v) acrylamide and 2% (w/v)
Ampholine, run at room temperature at 17 V/cm.
    None of the reported conditions seems to be
satisfactory nor could they be applied generally.
In the Grossbach[27] technique equilibrium is never
quite reached, since the high electro-endosmotic
flow in the quartz capillaries continuously washes
away the pH gradient and protein patterns. Besides,
the protein sample is mixed with the monomer
solution and polymerised within the gel matrix in
the presence of ammonium persulphate. This is a
very dangerous technique since enzymes could be
denatured either by foaming during the degassing
step or by persulphate treatment.
    With few exceptions[7,13,17,18] the systems

reported up to 1972 provided no heat control and so are not acceptable as routine gel isoelectric focusing methods. We must stress also that adequate cooling is not provided by simply performing gel isoelectric focusing in the cold room as reported by some authors. This might perhaps affect the buffer viscosity but will provide little, if any, cooling of the gels during isoelectric focusing. In order to prevent accidental electrocution of the operator, this type of apparatus is also enclosed in plastic boxes in which there is practically no air circulation. This, in addition to the fact that the heat exchange in air is much lower than in liquid, means that the operator works more closely to an adiabatic rather than a thermally equilibrated system.

At present, we feel that only three properly cooled systems have been described which are suitable for gel isoelectric focusing: the gel rod apparatus of Righetti and Drysdale[13,17] and the thin-layer gels of Vesterberg[18] and Radola[7]. These systems allow a rapid thermal exchange because the gels are directly immersed in, or are in close contact with, the coolant. The advantages of a gel slab for isoelectric focusing have already been described[18,28]. However, the gel rod technique too offers a few interesting features, namely:

(i)   The possibility of simultaneously running different samples in different pH gradients or replicate samples under different analytical procedures.
(ii)   The possibility of analysing oxygen-sensitive enzymes or proteins under completely anaerobic conditions.
(iii) The very small amount of Ampholine required (50 µl of concentrated solution) to analyse each sample.
(iv)   The better heat control obtained in the gel rod, completely surrounded by the coolant, than in the thin-layer gel which is cooled on one side only. In terms of W/cm^2 of gel surface, a 3 mm diameter gel rod can stand 60 times the wattage applied to a thin-layer gel.

The advantage of the present technique lies in the fact that, with short equilibration times, gel isoelectric focusing becomes as convenient for routine analysis as present disc gel electrophoresis. The advantage of using constant power for gel isoelectric focusing was predicted by Finlayson and Chrambach[14] and by Righetti and Drysdale[17]. A good and yet very simple experimental

approach to this problem[29] employs an appropriate
resistance in series with the gel isoelectric
focusing apparatus to achieve a minimum power
variation.   Very short equilibration times (40 min)
have also been obtained by running the thin layer at
constant wattage (50 W) and with a high field
strength (130 V/cm)[28].

In our system, of course, the average power is
constant while the instantaneous power is not.
Schaffer and Johnson[30] have ruled out any advantage
of a pulsed power supply in comparison to a constant
DC power supply.   Since Söderholm et al.[28] obtain
results very similar to ours it cannot be excluded
that the main contribution to the short
equilibration times in gel isoelectric focusing is
primarily due to the high field strength and to the
constant wattage applied rather than to the wave
pulses.

We feel that the present method is amenable to
use in routine clinical analysis.   A good example is
the application to haemoglobin screening.
Isoelectric focusing patterns of haemolysates from
adults homozygous for haemoglobin C or S, for
instance, are distinguishable at a glance from
normal adult patterns[21].   Since each thin-layer gel
can accommodate up to 20 samples, provided a
laboratory has a supply of polymerised slabs, a
single technician can handle more than one hundred
samples a day.   If the slabs are run in parallel,
several hundred samples can be tested each day.
Such a system has the advantage of giving error-free
results: in fact the patterns are so typical and
reproducible that there is almost no possibility of
errors.   Moreover, in case of doubts one can further
characterise the abnormal haemoglobin by measuring
its pI.   This can be easily done by pressing an
antimony microelectrode into the band of interest[31].

8.5 SUMMARY

A new technique of high voltage analytical and
preparative isoelectric focusing is described.   By
using a constant wattage power supply, generating
waves ranging in frequencies from 5 to 4000 Hz, and
by applying to the gels voltage gradients ranging
from 150 to 300 V/cm, equilibrium can be reached in
approx. 45 min.   In the LKB 110 ml sucrose density
gradient apparatus equilibrium can be reached in 8 h
by applying up to 4000 V to the column.   The
technique has been successfully applied to gel rods
as well as to thin-layer systems.   In this method
proper gel cooling is essential: the heat has to be

dissipated by contact with a cooled liquid (a
Peltier element might be an alternative). Air
cooling, such as placing the gels in the cold room,
was found to be totally unsatisfactory.

Proteins with low and high molecular weights as
well as enzymes have been successfully analysed. It
is anticipated that this technique, especially the
thin-layer version, might become an important tool
in routine clinical analysis. An example for
routine analysis of normal and abnormal haemoglobins
is given.

ACKNOWLEDGEMENTS

This work was supported in part by a grant from
Consiglio Nazionale delle Ricerche (C.N.R.). We
thank Dr. H. Davies, LKB Produkter, Sweden, for help
and advice with the thin-layer technique and Drs. I.
Bosi and R. Dal Pero Bertini for assistance in using
the high voltage, pulsed power supply.

REFERENCES

1. WRIGLEY, C.W., 'Analytical Fractionation of
   Plant and Animal Proteins by Gel
   Electrofocusing'. J. Chromatog., 36, 362-365
   (1968)
2. RILEY, R.F. and COLEMAN, M.K., 'Isoelectric
   Fractionation of Proteins on a Microscale in
   Polyacrylamide and Agarose Matrices'.
   J. Lab. Clin. Med., 72, 714-720 (1968)
3. CATSIMPOOLAS, N., 'Micro Isoelectric Focusing
   in Polyacrylamide Gel Columns'. Anal. Biochem.,
   26, 480-482 (1969)
4. AWDEH, Z.L., WILLIAMSON, A.R. and ASKONAS, B.A.,
   'Isoelectric Focusing in Polyacrylamide Gel and
   its Applications to Immunoglobulins'. Nature,
   219, 66-67 (1968)
5. LEABACK, D.H. and RUTTER, A.C., 'Polyacrylamide
   Isoelectric Focusing. A new Technique for the
   Electrophoresis of Proteins'. Biochem.
   Biophys. Res. Commun., 32, 447-453 (1968)
6. CATSIMPOOLAS, N., 'Immunoelectrofocusing in
   agarose Gels'. Clin. Chim. Acta, 23, 237-238
   (1969)
7. RADOLA, B.J., 'Thin-Layer Isoelectric Focusing
   of Proteins'. Biochim. Biophys. Acta, 194,
   335-338 (1969)
8. CATSIMPOOLAS, N., 'Sectional
   Immunoelectrofocusing'. Biochim. Biophys.
   Acta, 175, 214-216 (1969)

9. DALE, G., LATNER, A.L., 'Isoelectric Focusing
    of Serum Proteins in Acrylamide Gels Followed
    by Electrophoresis'. Clin. Chim. Acta, 24,
    61-68 (1969)
10. KENRICK, K.G. and MARGOLIS, J., 'Isoelectric
    Focusing and Gradient Gel Electrophoresis. A
    Two-Dimensional Technique'. Anal. Biochem.,
    33, 204-207 (1970)
11. VESTERBERG, O. and SVENSSON, H., 'Isoelectric
    Fractionation, Analysis, and Characterization
    of Ampholytes in Natural pH Gradients. IV.
    Further Studies on the Resolving Power in
    Connection with Separation of Myoglobins'.
    Acta Chem. Scand., 20, 820-834 (1966)
12. DAVIS, B.J., 'Disc Electrophoresis. II. Method
    and Application to Human Serum Proteins'.
    Annals. N.Y. Acad. Sci., 121, 404-427 (1964)
13. RIGHETTI, P.G. and DRYSDALE, J.W.,
    'Isoelectric Focusing in Polyacrylamide Gels'.
    Biochim. Biophys. Acta, 236, 17-28 (1971)
14. FINLAYSON, G.R. and CHRAMBACH, A.,
    'Isoelectric Focusing in Polyacrylamide Gel
    and its Preparative Application'. Anal.
    Biochem., 40, 292-311 (1971)
15. LOENING, U.E., 'The Fractionation of
    High-Molecular-Weight Ribonucleic Acid by
    Polyacrylamide-Gel Electrophoresis'.
    Biochem. J., 102, 251-257 (1967)
16. DRABKIN, D.J., 'The Crystallographic and Optical
    Properties of the Hemoglobin of Man in
    Comparison with those of Other Species'.
    J. Biol. Chem., 164, 703-723 (1946)
17. RIGHETTI, P.G. and DRYSDALE, J.W., 'Small Scale
    Fractionation of Proteins and Nucleic Acids by
    Isoelectric Focusing in Polyacrylamide Gels'.
    Annals N.Y. Acad. Sci., 209, 163-186 (1973)
18. VESTERBERG, O., 'Isoelectric Focusing of
    Proteins in Polyacrylamide Gels'. Biochim.
    Biophys. Acta, 257, 11-19 (1972)
19. VESTERBERG, O., 'Staining of Protein Zones after
    Isoelectric Focusing in Polyacrylamide Gels'.
    Biochim. Biophys. Acta, 243, 345-348 (1971)
20. BUNN, H.F. and DRYSDALE, J.W., 'The Separation
    of Partially Oxidized Hemoglobins'. Biochim.
    Biophys. Acta, 229, 51-57 (1971)
21. DRYSDALE, J.W., RIGHETTI, P.G. and BUNN, H.F.,
    'The Separation of Human and Animal
    Hemoglobins by Isoelectric Focusing in
    Polyacrylamide Gel'. Biochim. Biophys. Acta,
    229, 42-50 (1971)

22. STARK, G.R. 'Modification of Proteins with Cyanate'. In: Methods in Enzymology, Vol. 11, Eds. S.P. Colowick and N.O. Kaplan, Academic Press, New York, 590-594 (1967)

23. DRYSDALE, J.W., 'Microheterogeneity in Ferritin Molecules'. Biochim. Biophys. Acta, 207, 256-258 (1970)

24. BRYCE, C.F.A. and CRICHTON, R.E., 'Microheterogeneity in Apoferritin Molecules - an Artifact'. Hoppe-Seyler's Zeit. Physiol. Chem., 354, 344-346 (1973)

25. URUSHIZAKI, I., NIITZU, Y., ISHITANI, K., MATSUDA, M. and FUKUDA, M., 'Microheterogeneity of Horse Spleen Ferritin and Apoferritin'. Biochim. Biophys. Acta, 243, 187-192 (1971)

26. WRIGLEY, C., 'Gel Electrofocusing - A Technique for Analyzing Multiple Protein Samples by Isoelectric Focusing'. Science Tools, 15, 17-23 (1968)

27. GROSSBACH, U., 'Microelectrofocusing of Proteins in Capillary Gels'. Biochem. Biophys. Res. Commun., 49, 667-672 (1972)

28. SÖDERHOLM, J., ALLESTAM, P. and WADSTRÖM, T., 'A Rapid Method for Isoelectric Focusing in Polyacrylamide Gels'. FEBS Lett., 24, 89-92 (1972)

29. AWDEH, Z.L., 'Minimum Power Variation in Isoelectric Focusing'. Science Tools, 19, 27-28 (1972)

30. SCHAFFER, H.E. and JOHNSON, F.M. 'Constant (optimum) Power Electrophoresis'. Anal. Biochem., 51, 577-583 (1973)

31. BEELEY, J.A., STEVENSON, S.M. and BEELEY, J.G., 'Polyacrylamide Gel Isoelectric Focusing of Proteins. Determination of Isoelectric Points Using an Antimony Electrode'. Biochim. Biophys. Acta, 285, 293-300 (1972)

9. HIGH VOLTAGE THIN-LAYER ISOELECTRIC FOCUSING IN POLYACRYLAMIDE GEL WITH AUTOMATIC CONSTANT WATTAGE

J. Söderholm and T. Wadström

9.1 TECHNIQUES FOR ISOELECTRIC FOCUSING IN POLYACRYLAMIDE GEL

Techniques for isoelectric focusing in polyacrylamide gel have been developed for gel rods and thin-layer gels[1,2]. Provided that there is efficient cooling of the gel, when high voltage and constant wattage are used with the thin-layer technique, focusing of proteins is complete in 40 to 50 min[3]. By contrast, many investigators reported focusing times of between 4 and 12 h with more conventional apparatus[1,2]. Söderholm et al.[3] maintained constant wattage by manually adjusting a constant voltage power supply so that the product of voltage and current was kept constant during isoelectric focusing at values between 2.1 and 2.6 mW/mm^3 in the gel and between 3.2 and 3.8 mW/mm^2 on the cooling surface. The field strength was 12.5 V/mm after 40 min.

Studies on the formation and deformation of pH gradients during isoelectric focusing in gels have been described previously[4-11]. It was shown that after formation of the pH gradient, deformation and drift were aggravated by increasing the time of isoelectric focusing and increasing the field strength.

For optimal resolution of proteins carrier ampholyte concentration, gel properties, field strength and focusing time can be varied. The aim of this investigation was to study the formation and deformation of pH gradients using high voltage with automatic constant wattage.

9.2 MATERIALS

Carrier ampholyte solutions (Ampholine, LKB) pH
3-10, batch 17, 40% (w/v); pH 4-6, batch 49, 40%
(w/v); pH 5-7, batch 47, 40% (w/v) and pH 9-11,
batch 1, 20% (w/v), were obtained from
LKB-Produkter AB, Bromma, Sweden. Acrylamide,
N,N'-methylenebisacrylamide and riboflavin were
from B.D.H. Chemicals Ltd., Poole, England.
Sorbitol was from E. Merck AG, Darmstadt, Germany;
Coomassie Brilliant Blue R-250 (CI 42660) was from
I.C.I., Manchester, England. All other chemicals
used were of reagent grade.
    Human haemoglobin (2 x cryst.) was obtained
from Nutritional Biochemicals Corp., Cleveland,
Ohio, U.S.A.; bovine serum albumin from Pentex
Biochemicals, Miles Laboratories Inc., Kankakee,
Illinois, U.S.A.; sperm whale myoglobin (cryst.,
salt-free) from Schwarz-Mann Bioresearch Inc.,
Orangeburg, New York, U.S.A.; bovine thyroglobulin,
type I, from Sigma Chemical Co.,   St. Louis, Mo.,
U.S.A.; ovalbumin (5 x cryst.) Miles-Seravac Ltd.,
Maidenhead, Berkshire, England. Three preparations
of diphtheria toxin - crude, highly purified, and
formaldehyde-inactivated purified (toxoid), were
obtained from SBL, Stockholm, Sweden.

9.3 METHODS

For the pH 3 to 10 gradients the mixture of
Ampholines given in Table 9.1 was used.

Table 9.1   Mixture of Ampholines used to give a
pH gradient of 3 to 10

pH Range	Volume (ml)	% of total (w/v)	Weight (g)
3-10	4.25	85	1.70
4-6	0.25	5	0.10
5-7	0.25	5	0.10
9-11	0.50	5	0.10
Total	5.25	100	2.00

(The total concentration of carrier ampholytes in
this mixture was 38.1% (w/v).)

To prepare 100 ml of gel mixture the following
were mixed:

riboflavin 50 µg/ml	1.0 ml
ampholyte mixture 38.1% (w/v)	5.25 ml
bisacrylamide 1.0% (w/v)	15.0 ml
acrylamide 30.0% (w/v)	16.17 ml
sorbitol	10.0 g
distilled water to	100 ml

The concentration of carrier ampholytes in the
gel mixture was 2.0% (w/v), acrylamide 4.85% (w/v),
bisacrylamide 0.15% (w/v), sorbitol 10.0% (w/v),
riboflavin 500 ng/ml, and the T and C values were
5 and 3 respectively[12]. The volume of gel mixture
needed to prepare one gel plate was 30 ml.
      Gels (100 x 195 x 1.5 mm) with a volume of
29.3 ml were photopolymerised on a glass plate
(110 x 205 x 0.8 mm), and sandwiched between two
3 mm thick glass plates of the same size, as
recently described[3]. For photopolymerisation of
the gel four 20 W daylight fluorescent tubes
(Philips TL 20W/29) were used, with two tubes on
each side at about 100 mm from the gel mould.
      The glass cooling plate, made by AB Wicklunds
Glasinstrument, Stockholm, Sweden, was a
modification of the design of Vesterberg[13]. It had
an effective cooling surface 120 x 250 mm, and a
thickness of 1.4 mm with a cooling channel depth of
0.8 to 0.9 mm. The plate was cooled by circulating
water from a refrigerated thermostat bath (Lauda
K 4 RD, Lauda MGW, Tauber, Germany) at +4°C. The
outlet and inlet of the circulation pump in the
thermostat bath were connected to the cooling plate
via tubing and T-tubes in such a way that the flow
was in the direction of the long dimension of the
plate. A flow-meter (VEB Prüfgerätewerk, Dresden,
DDR.) was connected between the outlet of the pump
and the plate. The waterflow in the system was
48 ml/s. The cooling capacity of the system was
about 400 W.
      To ensure good thermal contact it was
essential to have a water layer free from air
bubbles between the thin glass plate carrying the
gel and the cooling plate. Sufficient distilled
water was spread on the cooling plate and the thin
glass plate was slowly applied in such a way that a
straight progressing water front was seen to move
between the plates without trapping any air. Excess
water had to be carefully removed to prevent acid or
base from coming into contact with the water layer
between the glass plates because of the risk of
electrical discharges.

The carbon electrodes were soaked and stored in 1 M H_3PO_4 or 1 M NaOH for several hours, and then applied to the long edges of the gel on filter paper strips (Whatman 3MM 10 x 195 mm), moistened with the same electrode solutions, care being taken to avoid excess acid or base. After application of the electrodes, the size of the gel available for separation was 80 x 195 x 1.5 mm with a volume of 2.34×10^4 mm^3 and an area of 1.56×10^4 mm^2.

All proteins were dissolved in the carrier ampholyte mixture (2%, w/v) used in the gel to give a protein concentration of 2.5 µg/µl. The proteins were applied to the gel in duplicate on filter papers (Whatman 3MM 10 x 10 mm) 5 mm from the cathode and with 5 mm between each sample. In each case 20 µl samples, containing 50 µg protein, were applied to each filter paper. The adsorptive effect of this paper was about 10 µg per 100 mm^2 (Chapter 12).

The power supply and constant wattage regulator are described elsewhere (see Chapter 10). Experiments were carried out at 60 W and 110 W, with 2.6 or 4.7 mW/mm^3 in the gel and 3.8 or 7.0 mW/mm^2 on the cooling surface. Voltage and current were recorded with a six-channel recorder (6520-H, LKB-Produkter AB) used in a two-channel mode.

A Radiometer pH meter PHM 26 (Radiometer A/S, Copenhagen, Denmark) was used with the built-in temperature compensator set at $+4^{\circ}C$. A flat membrane combined microelectrode, Ingold LoT 403-30 (W. Ingold AG, Zürich, Switzerland) was used for measuring pH directly on the gel surface[14]. The electrode was stored in 3 M KCl at $+4^{\circ}C$ in the thermostat bath between measurements. For measurements of pH with 'increased accuracy' (using the electrode sensitivity control included) the pH meter was calibrated with two standard buffers of pH values 3.16 and 6.62 at $+4^{\circ}C$ (P.-H. Thamm, Altuna, Sweden).

The pH measurements were performed in such a way that the power was applied for a certain period of time, then switched off immediately before measurements were made; thereafter the power was applied for a further period. Measurements of pH were made at 5 mm intervals starting from the anode and were completed within 5 min of switching off the current.

The gels were fixed and stained in a freshly prepared solution of 0.1% (w/v) Coomassie Brilliant Blue R-250 dissolved in 3% (w/v) sulphosalicylic acid, 10% (w/v) trichloroacetic acid, and 35% (v/v) ethanol in distilled water. They were destained in 8.5% (v/v) acetic acid and 25% (v/v) ethanol in

distilled water and before drying the gels were
equilibrated with 5% (v/v) glycerol in the same
solution.

9.4   RESULTS

The formation of the pH gradient against time is
shown in Figure 9.1 for gels run at 2.6 mW/mm^3, and
in Figure 9.2 for gels run at 4.7 mW/mm^3 in the gel.
An almost linear gradient is formed in 15 and 10
min, respectively. Figures 9.3 and 9.4 show the
deformation of the pH gradient against time at 2.6
and 4.7 mW/mm^3, respectively. Deformation
('plateau phenomenon') was not very pronounced
during the 20 to 50 min of the experiments.

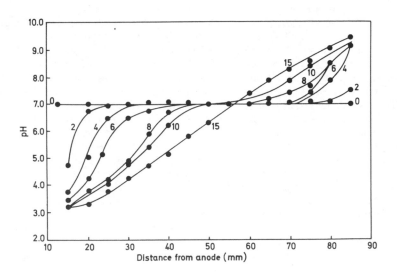

Figure 9.1   Formation of the pH gradient in gels run
at 2.6 mW/mm^3. The numbers on the curves indicate
the cumulative time in minutes from the start of the
experiment, during which power was applied.

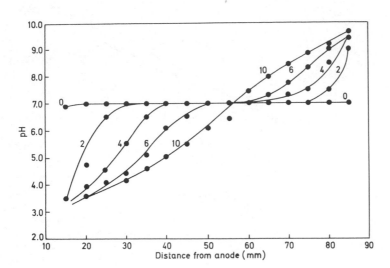

Figure 9.2   Formation of the pH gradient in gels run at 4.7 mW/mm^3.   The numbers on the curves indicate the cumulative time in minutes from the start of the experiment, during which power was applied

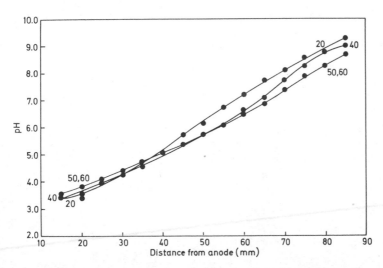

Figure 9.3   Deformation of the pH gradient at 2.6 mW/mm^3.   The numbers on the curves indicate the cumulative time in minutes from the start of the experiment, during which power was applied

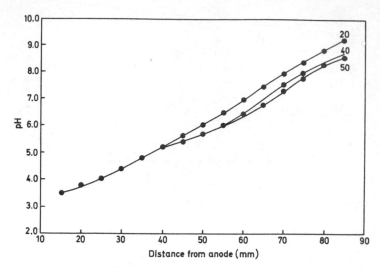

Figure 9.4 Deformation of the pH gradient at 4.7 mW/mm^3. The numbers on the curves indicate the cumulative time in minutes from the start of the experiment, during which power was applied

The recordings of current and voltage during the experiments are shown in **Figures 9.5** and **9.6.**

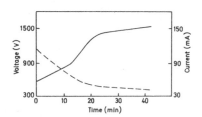

Figure 9.5 Recording of current and voltage during experiments at 2.6 mW/mm^3. (———), Voltage; (- - -), current

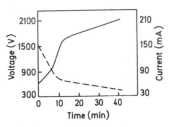

Figure 9.6 Recording of current and voltage during experiments at 4.7 mW/mm^3. (———), Voltage; (- - -), current

The points of inflection occur at 18 and 12 min
respectively. These times coincide approximately
with the time for the formation of the linear pH
gradient (Figures 9.1 and 9.2). The field strength
during the experiments is varying from 7 to 20 V/mm
for 2.6 mW/mm^3 and 9 to 27 V/mm for 4.7 mW/mm^3.
From the curves shown in Figures 9.5 and 9.6 values
for the resistance and wattage were calculated.
The variation of the total resistance in the gel
with time is shown in Figure 9.7. Each resistance
curve is composed of a sigmoid and a linear part,
the latter starting at 38 min for 2.6 mW/mm^3 and at
28 min for 4.7 mW/mm^3. The variation in the wattage
values calculated from the curves in Figure 9.5 is
between 5 and 6%. In Figure 9.6 the variation is
between 5 and 8%.

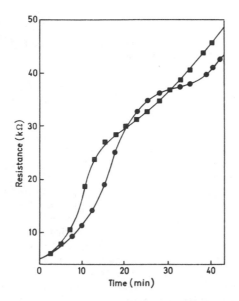

Figure 9.7 Values of resistance in kiloohms
calculated from the curves in Figures 9.5 and 9.6
at various times during the experiments. (——●——),
2.6 mW/mm^3; (——■——), 4.7 mW/mm^3

    A series of ripples on the surface of the gel,
parallel to the electrodes, was observed during and
after high voltage isoelectric focusing in
thin-layer gels. The ripples were not uniformly
distributed on the gel; in certain areas they
formed groups, in others they were sparse. There
was a direct correlation between distortions in the
parallelism of the ripples towards the electrodes

and distorted protein zones after staining.
      Viewed from the side after experiments, the
gels were thinner in the middle, increasing in
thickness towards both the electrodes with local
variations caused by the ripples. Both the ripples
and the variation in thickness increased with
increasing wattage. After fixing and staining,
human haemoglobin was resolved into 5 to 8 major
bands, bovine serum albumin into 4 to 9, sperm
whale myoglobin into 2 to 3 major and 2 to 5 minor
components, bovine thyroglobulin into 8 to 14 thin
bands and ovalbumin into 2 to 4 major bands and 2 to
8 minor bands. Crude diphtheria toxin was resolved
into 15 to 20 bands and highly purified toxin into
5 to 7 bands; toxoid prepared from the latter gave
a single band.

9.5   DISCUSSION

Linear pH gradients can be established in 10 to 15
min at 2.5 to 5.0 mW/mm^3 at high voltage and
constant wattage. The gradients seem to be fairly
stable for up to at least one hour, in which time
the proteins studied, with the exception of
thyroglobulin, had focused. Molecular sieving
depending upon the pore size of the gel and the
molecular size of the proteins will increase the
focusing times. With large pore gels it will be
possible to focus even high molecular weight
proteins in very short times.
      By recording the voltage and current during
experiments valuable information is obtained, and
from the curves it seems possible to judge when
linear pH gradients are established. The variation
of total resistance with time may be due to
variations in temperature and dimensions of the gel,
but further studies are needed.
      The dissipation of heat generated during
experiments is a major problem. Work is in progress
to measure the temperature with thermistors at
various points on the gel surface during
experiments. A hot zone was formed near the anode
in the first 10 min of an experiment after which
time it disappeared. At 2.6 mW/mm^3 the temperature
rose to 30°C and at 4.7 mW/mm^3 to 60°C in the hot
zone. After the disappearance of the hot zone the
temperature near the electrodes varied between 15
and 12°C, and in the middle of the gel between 25
and 20°C at 2.6 mW/mm^3. The corresponding values
for 4.7 mW/mm^3 were 20 to 30°C and 35 to 30°C
respectively.

It is important both to know and control the temperature at all points on the gel surface throughout experiments. No protein must at any time be exposed to adverse temperatures because of the risk of thermal denaturation. This was fortuitously avoided in this study as the samples were applied towards the cathode. The temperature of the gradient during the experiments must be known to enable pH measurements to be made at the same temperature after the runs. This has not been possible in the present report, but in principle it is important to follow the steps suggested in Methods (section 9.3) for pH measurements.

Because of the variation in the concentration of the carrier ampholytes in the gel and the resulting variations in the resistance, the total resistance values measured are mean values, and hence the effect per volume and per area, as well as field strength, are mean values.

High voltage isoelectric focusing in polyacrylamide gels at constant wattage was applied to the study of highly purified diphtheria toxin, which showed microheterogeneity. After formaldehyde inactivation of the purified toxin, the toxoid appeared as one band indicating the suitability of the method for the study of toxoiding processes.

The technique described allows high resolution of protein components combined with a convenient short separation time favourable for unstable proteins. Further studies on the control and measurement of temperatures during experiments will be needed before it can be used as a routine method.

The method is a sensitive tool for studies on natural and induced heterogeneities of proteins, the latter caused by different purification procedures, storage conditions, and chemical modifications.

ACKNOWLEDGEMENT

We thank P.-A. Lidström, H. Rilbe, C.J. Smyth and G. Walldén for assistance, advice and valuable criticism.

REFERENCES

1. CATSIMPOOLAS, N., 'Isoelectric Focusing of Proteins in Gel Media'. Separ. Sci., 5, 524-544 (1970)
2. CATSIMPOOLAS, N., 'Isoelectric Focusing and Isotachoforesis of Proteins'. Separ. Sci., 8, 71-121 (1973)

3. SÖDERHOLM, J., ALLESTAM, P. and WADSTRÖM, T.,
    'A Rapid Method for Isoelectric Focusing in
    Polyacrylamide Gel'. FEBS Letters, 24,
    89-92 (1972)
4. FINLAYSON, G. and CHRAMBACH, A., 'Isoelectric
    Focusing in Polyacrylamide Gel and its
    Preparative Application'. Anal. Biochem. 40,
    292-311 (1971)
5. RIGHETTI, P. and DRYSDALE, J.W., 'Isoelectric
    Focusing in Polyacrylamide Gels'. Biochim.
    Biophys. Acta, 236, 17-28 (1971)
6. MILES, L.E.M., SIMMONS, J.E. and CHRAMBACH, A.,
    'Instability of pH Gradients in Isoelectric
    Focusing on Polyacrylamide Gel'. Anal.
    Biochem., 49, 109-117 (1972)
7. ROBINSON, H.K., 'Comparison of Different
    Techniques for Isoelectric Focusing on
    Polyacrylamide Gel Slabs Using Bacterial
    Asparaginases'. Anal. Biochem. 49, 353-366
    (1972)
8. CHRAMBACH, A., DOERR, P., FINLAYSON, G.R.,
    MILES, L.E.M., SHERINS, R. and RODBARD, D.,
    'Instability of pH Gradients Formed by
    Isoelectric Focusing in Polyacrylamide Gel'.
    Ann. N.Y. Acad. Sci., 209, 44-64 (1973)
9. RIGHETTI, P.G. and DRYSDALE, J.W., 'Small-Scale
    Fractionation of Proteins and Nucleic Acids by
    Isoelectric Focusing in Polyacrylamide Gels'.
    Ann. N.Y. Acad. Sci., 209, 163-186 (1973)
10. BATES, L.S. and DEYOE, C.W., 'Polyacrylamide
    Gel Electrofocusing and the Ampholyte Shift'.
    J. Chromatog., 73, 296-297 (1972)
11. RADOLA, B.J., 'Isoelectric Focusing in Layers
    of Granulated Gels. I. Thin-Layer Isoelectric
    Focusing of Proteins'. Biochim. Biophys.
    Acta, 295, 412-428 (1973)
12. HJERTÉN, S., 'The "Molecular Sieve"
    Chromatography on Polyacrylamide Gels,
    Prepared According to a Simplified Method'.
    Arch. Biochem. Biophys. Suppl., 1, 147-151
    (1962)
13. VESTERBERG, O., 'Isoelectric Focusing of
    Proteins in Polyacrylamide Gels'. Biochim.
    Biophys. Acta, 257, 11-19 (1972)
14. RADOLA, B.J., 'Thin-Layer Isoelectric Focusing
    of Proteins'. Biochim. Biophys. Acta, 194,
    335-338 (1969)

10. A REGULATOR MAINTAINING CONSTANT WATTAGE WITH CONSTANT VOLTAGE OR CONSTANT CURRENT POWER SUPPLIES

J. Söderholm and P.-A. Lidström

To reduce the separation time when using isoelectric focusing in polyacrylamide gel, Söderholm, Allestam and Wadström[1] manually adjusted a constant voltage power supply so that the product of voltage and current was kept constant during the runs. This was tedious and a simple device was constructed to automate the process.

A constant wattage regulator was constructed according to the principles shown in Figure 10.1. A photograph of the equipment is shown in Figure 10.2. The output voltage and current from a constant voltage or constant current power supply are monitored and fed via protection circuits into a voltage and current sense amplifier. An analogue multiplier multiplies the voltage and current signals from the amplifiers. The product signal from the multiplier passes to a wattmeter and a comparator where the output signal is compared with the selected wattage of the output level control of the constant wattage regulator. If there is a difference between the signals, the servo amplifier actuates the servo motor coupled to the output voltage or current control of the power supply, so that the two signals are equalised. A reversible 5 rev/min synchronous motor actuated from the servo amplifier by a relay, has been successfully used as a servo motor. In isoelectric focusing in thin-layer gels the resistance of the gel will vary considerably during runs (see Chapter 9) but the constant wattage regulator will keep the product of output voltage and current constant. With the maximum voltage control, a maximum permissible voltage can be set so that regulation

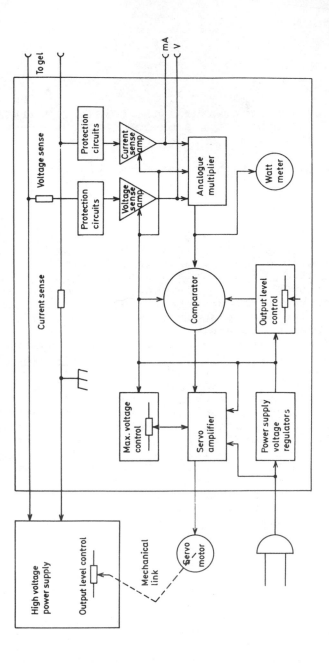

Figure 10.1   Block diagram of the constant wattage regulator

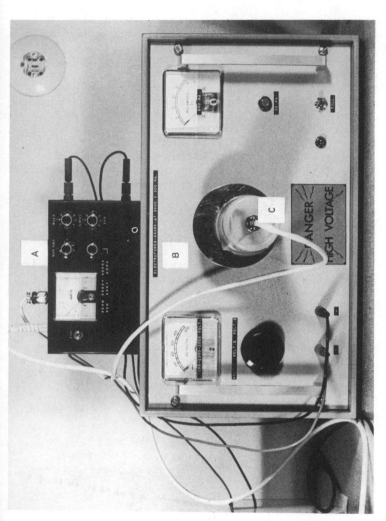

Figure 10.2 The constant wattage regulator used with a constant voltage power supply. A, constant wattage regulator with two ranges: (i) maximum of 30 W, 300 V, 60 mA, and (ii) maximum of 300 W, 3000 V, 300 mA; B, constant voltage power supply with a maximum of 3000 V, 300 mA; C, reversible 5 rev/min synchronous motor

is switched from constant wattage to constant voltage or current when the maximum voltage is reached. The signals from the voltage and current sense amplifiers can be recorded with a two-channel recorder.

The constant wattage regulator described has been used for more than one year in our laboratory for high voltage thin-layer gel isoelectric focusing. Recently, a similar device was described[2] which incorporated electronic control of output voltage and current. We believe that regulation via a servo motor offers several important advantages:

(i)   Any constant voltage or constant current power supply can be used with this type of wattage regulator with only minor modifications. The servo motor is easily attached to the axis of the output level of the power supply by means of a friction coupling.

(ii)   Very simple power supplies can be used, e.g. a power supply comprising a variable transformer, or a high voltage transformer, a rectifier and suitable filters.

(iii) It is an inexpensive solution to the problem of regulating high voltages and currents. The system at present allows regulation up to 300 W with a maximum of 3000 V and 300 mA. This maximum wattage exceeds the optimum for the present design of cooling plates with the gel systems currently in use. Regulators allowing much higher wattages, voltages and currents could easily be built on the same principles at a reasonable cost.

REFERENCES

1. SÖDERHOLM, J., ALLESTAM, P. and WADSTRÖM, T., 'A Rapid Method for Isoelectric Focusing in Polyacrylamide Gel'. FEBS Letters, 24, 89-92 (1972)
2. SCHAFFER, H.E. and JOHNSON, F.M., 'Constant (Optimum) Power Electrophoresis'. Anal. Biochem., 51, 577-583 (1973)

11. DETERMINATION OF pH GRADIENTS IN ISOELECTRIC FOCUSING GELS

J.A. Beeley, S.M. Stevenson and J.G. Beeley

Isoelectric focusing in polyacrylamide gels has become established as a valuable method for the separation of proteins[1]. In addition to its use as a fractionation technique, gel isoelectric focusing may be used to determine the isoelectric points of particular proteins or of individual species of proteins occurring in multiple forms. Provided that some characteristic property of the protein, such as enzymatic or immunological activity can be detected, it is possible to determine isoelectric points even in impure preparations. This can be a valuable aid to the selection of an appropriate purification method. For purified proteins, determination of pI is a useful means of characterisation; it may also be valuable in the examination of charge heterogeneity of proteins[2]. Determination of the pI values of proteins by gel isoelectric focusing requires the measurement of pH or of pH gradients in gels.

Among the methods which have been applied to the determination of pH gradients in isoelectric focusing gels are the elution of gel samples with water[3,4], the use of marker pH indicators[5] and direct measurements made with an electrode on the gel surface[6,7]. The most widely used of these methods has been the elution of gel samples with distilled water followed by measurement of the pH value of the supernatant solution. While this method requires only simple apparatus and can give reproducible results, it is liable to interference from atmospheric carbon dioxide. In addition, the dilution of gel samples occurring on extraction with water may result in appreciable pH variation,

147

particularly at the extremities of the gel[7]. These problems can be avoided by the direct determination of pH gradients in gels using a microelectrode.

A method which we have found to be simple and which gives reproducible results is to make pH measurements on gel surfaces using an antimony microelectrode with a calomel reference microelectrode (Figure 11.1). The antimony electrode, originally designed by Kleinberg[8], for making pH measurements in dental plaque, has the advantages of rapid response and small size (diameter 1 mm). Because of the small dimensions of the electrode, it is possible to make pH measurements at precisely defined points on the surface of a gel rather than measuring an average pH over a wider area as is the case with gel elution methods. The precise measurement of pH gradients in flat-bed isoelectric focusing gels revealed that the pH gradients were non-linear when Ampholine of pH range 3 to 10 was used. This has been confirmed by other workers and it has been reported that linearity of the pH gradient can be improved by making mixtures of ampholytes covering different pH ranges[9].

Figure 11.1 Measurement of the pH in a thin-layer polyacrylamide gel using an antimony microelectrode and calomel reference electrode. The antimony electrode is on the left of the picture

The direct measurement of pH with a microelectrode allows the rapid determination of gradients without disturbing the surface of the thin-layer gels on which the measurements are made. Thus it is possible to determine how the pH gradient changes with time. This is an important preliminary to the determination of isoelectric points as it is desirable that a stable pH gradient should be established before the gradient is measured and the position of the protein located. Measurements with the antimony electrode are easier to carry out on the surface of a thin-layer gel, but the electrode may also be used with cylindrical gels.

For the determination of isoelectric points it is necessary to relate the pH gradient to the position of the focused bands of protein. When the protein is visible without staining, the pI value can be obtained by direct measurement of pH on the protein band. However, when the gel has to be stained, it is important to make allowance for swelling or shrinking. This can be done simply by cutting notches into the edge of the gel with a scalpel blade at measured intervals parallel to the direction of the pH gradient, prior to fixation.

The temperature at which measurements are made has an appreciable effect on the pH gradient which is obtained. It was observed by Vesterberg and Svensson[10] that for two species of myoglobin the pI values pertaining to 25°C could be obtained by making pH measurements at this temperature regardless of the temperature at which isoelectric focusing was performed. However, as it is not yet clear how far this is generally true, it would appear desirable to make measurements of pH at the same temperature as that at which the gels were focused. In any case it is important that both the temperature of focusing and of pH measurement should be stated. Focused bands diffuse rapidly when an electrical potential is no longer applied and for this reason, too, it seems preferable to make pH measurements rapidly and at the temperature of focusing.

The pI values of the major components of a number of proteins with isoelectric points ranging from 4.5 to 9.0 have been determined using thin-layer gel isoelectric focusing where measurements of the pH gradient were made with an antimony electrode[7]. Using a broad gradient (pH 3 to 10) it was found that all determinations were reproducible within ± 0.13 pH units. The accuracy of the method may be considerably refined by the use of narrower pH gradients.

It may be anticipated that improvements in ampholyte mixtures and in cooling of gels may lead to greater consistency and accuracy in pI values determined by this method. It would be of considerable interest to employ the antimony electrode in conjunction with high voltage thin-layer gel isoelectric focusing (Chapters 8 & 9). Development of the technique has been limited by the slight distortions which may occur in thin-layer gels rather than by the sensitivity of pH measurements. Final comment on the accuracy of the pI values obtained from isoelectric focusing gels must await the accumulation of more reliable data on the pI values of proteins determined by density gradient column isoelectric focusing and other methods.

REFERENCES

1. HAGLUND, H., 'Isoelectric Focusing in pH Gradients - A Technique for Fractionation and Characterization of Ampholytes'. In: Methods of Biochemical Analysis, 19, 1-104 (1971)
2. BEELEY, J.G., 'Ovomucoid Heterogeneity Examined by Flat Bed Isoelectric Focusing'. Biochim. Biophys. Acta, 230, 595-598 (1971)
3. FRATER, R., 'Artifacts in Isoelectric Focusing'. J. Chromatog., 50, 469-474 (1970)
4. SALAMAN, M.R. and WILLIAMSON, A.R., 'Isoelectric Focusing of Proteins in the Native and Denatured States'. Biochem. J. 122, 93-99 (1971)
5. CONWAY-JACOBS, A. and LEWIN, M., 'Isoelectric Focusing in Acrylamide Gels: Use of Amphoteric Dyes as Internal Markers for Determination of Isoelectric Points'. Anal. Biochem., 43, 394-400 (1971)
6. RADOLA, B.J., 'Thin Layer Isoelectric Focusing of Proteins'. Biochim. Biophys. Acta, 194, 335-338 (1969)
7. BEELEY, J.A., STEVENSON, S.M. and BEELEY, J.G., 'Polyacrylamide Gel Isoelectric Focusing of Proteins: Determination of Isoelectric Points Using an Antimony Electrode'. Biochim. Biophys. Acta, 285, 293-300 (1972)
8. KLEINBERG, I., 'The Construction and Evaluation of Modified Types of Antimony Microelectrodes for Intra-Oral Use'. Brit. Dent. J., 104, 197-204 (1958)
9. KARLSSON, C., DAVIES, H., ÖHMAN, J. and ANDERSSON, V. 'LKB 2117 Multiphor. 1.

Analytical Thin Layer Gel Electrofocusing in
Polyacrylamide Gel'. LKB Application Note
No. 75, 1-14 (1973)
10. VESTERBERG, O. and SVENSSON, H., 'Isoelectric
Fractionation, Analysis and Characterization
of Ampholytes in Natural pH Gradients'.
Acta Chem. Scand., 20, 820-834 (1966)

12.   SOME APPLICATIONS OF A ZYMOGRAM METHOD IN
       COMBINATION WITH ISOELECTRIC FOCUSING IN
       POLYACRYLAMIDE GELS

T. Wadström and C.J. Smyth

12.1   INTRODUCTION AND DEFINITIONS

A number of procedures for the detection of enzymic
reactions in gels after electrophoretic
separations have been described during the past
decade. Naturally occurring high molecular weight
substrates, such as DNA, RNA, starch and proteins,
and synthetic chromogenic and non-chromogenic
substrates can be used for the detection of enzyme
activities. Much of this work has been recently
reviewed[1-6]. The methods are based mainly on one of
the two following principles:
  (i)   inclusion of the substrate in the gel either
        prior to the electrophoretic separation of
        the enzymes or by soaking the gel in a
        solution of substrate after the separation;
  (ii) detection of enzymic activity in a gel
        overlayer, i.e. by overlaying the
        polyacrylamide gel, on completion of
        isoelectric focusing, with another gel
        containing substrate.
A modification of the latter is the 'contact print'
method, where the activity is detected in a film of
substrate which can be removed after an appropriate
incubation time.
     Zymogram methods have been applied mainly to
studies of multiple molecular forms of enzymes in
animals, plants and micro-organisms[7] after the
pioneer work by Hunter and Makert[8] and Makert and
Möller[9], who studied the heterogeneity of esterases
and lactate dehydrogenase (LDH). Wróblewski and
Gregory[10] were the first to use the term 'isoenzyme'
when they described the different forms of LDH.
     Paper, agar gel and starch gel electrophoresis
were the techniques mainly used for the separation

of multiple forms until a few years ago. More
recently, the development of electrophoresis and
isoelectric focusing in polyacrylamide gels has
supplied us with analytical separation methods of
much greater resolving power[4].

12.2 DEVELOPMENT OF GEL ELECTROFOCUSING AND ZYMOGRAM METHODS

Two of the first publications on isoelectric
focusing in polyacrylamide gel described the
detection of LDH[11] and alkaline phosphatase[12] by
histochemical staining after isoelectric focusing.
Radola and his collaborators[13-15] showed how enzyme
activities could be detected by a 'contact print'
method after isoelectric focusing in Sephadex or
Biogel supporting media. These and some more recent
papers on such methods are summarised in Tables 12.1
and 12.2.
     Development of thin-layer methods for
isoelectric focusing in gels in several laboratories
(for reviews see Catsimpoolas[16] and Vesterberg[17])
and the LKB Multiphor equipment[18] has greatly
facilitated work on isoelectric focusing in
polyacrylamide gels in combination with zymogram
methods. The application of high voltage
techniques in our laboratory[19,20] is of great
practical interest in the study of enzymes since a
short separation time makes it possible to complete
several experiments within one day. This will make
the methods applicable in routine work, e.g. studies
of isoenzymes in clinical biochemistry. The aim of
this report is to describe the development of rapid
and simple methods for the study of some enzymes
such as phospholipase C, protease, α-amylase,
penicillinase and, in addition, haemolytic
bacterial toxins, by such techniques. The emphasis
will be put on the development of the methodology,
as such data are of more general interest and will,
we hope, be of some help in the study of other
enzyme systems and for the further development of
zymogram methods.

12.3 GENERAL PROCEDURE

A general outline of the zymogram procedure is shown
in Table 12.3. This procedure should also be
applicable to other enzymes not included in this
study.
     Gels were prepared between two glass plates
according to Vesterberg[17]. In some experiments gels
were polymerised without Ampholine as described by

Table 12.1 Zymogram methods used with isoelectric focusing and employing low molecular weight substrates

Gel rod technique - Histochemical staining

Enzyme	Substrate*	Authors
Lactate dehydrogenase	Lactate/PMS/tetrazolium MTT	Dale and Latner[11] Chamoles and Karcher[69]
β-Glucuronidase	8-Oxy-chinolin-D-glucuronide/ Fast black K salt	Coutelle[70]
L- and D-amino acid oxidase	L-Leu or D-Phe/PMS/ triphenyltetrazolium	Hayes and Wellner[46]
Esterase	α-Naphthyl acetate/ Fast red TR salt	Bianchi and Stefanelli[36]
Procarboxypeptidase A	n-Carbo-β-naphthoxy-L-Phe/ Diazo blue B/trypsin	Kim and White[71]
Alkaline phosphatase	α-Naphthyl phosphate/ 4-aminodiphenylamine diazonium sulphate	Righetti and Drysdale[40]
Alkaline phosphatase	β-Naphthyl phosphate/ Fast blue BB salt <u>or</u> 4-methyl umbelliferone phosphate	Smith, Lightstone and Perry[35]

Table 12.1 (contd.)

Enzyme	Substrate*	Authors
Thin-layer gel technique – Histochemical staining or paper print method		
Acid phosphatase	4-Methyl-umbelliferyl phosphate.	Leaback and Rutter[12]
NAD/NADP dehydrogenase	Substrate/NAD-NADP/PMS/ tetrazolium salt MTT	Humphryes[72]
Peroxidase†	Urea peroxide/guaiacol or o-toluidine and mesidine	Delincée and Radola[13,14] Rücker and Radola[15]

* Abbreviations: PMS, phenazine methosulphate; Leu, leucine; Phe, phenylalanine; MTT, 3-(4,5)- dimethyl – thiazolyl – 2,5 diphenyl tetrazolium bromide.
† Print technique with Whatman No. 1 chromatography paper impregnated with buffered substrate.

Table 12.2 Zymogram methods used with isoelectric focusing and employing high molecular weight substrates

Enzyme	Substrate	Zymogram technique	Authors
Thin-layer gel technique			
Staphylokinase*	Fibrin clot containing plasminogen	'Substrate' gel	Vesterberg and Eriksson[38]
Cellulase	Carboxymethyl cellulose	Paper print	Eriksson and Pettersson[73]
α-Amylase	Starch—iodine	Starch—film print	Beeley, Stevenson and Beeley[74]
Pepsin	Albumin/ Coomassie Blue	Immersion	Vesterberg[39]
Subtilopeptidase, trypsin, δ-chymotrypsin, crude bacterial proteases	Vitamin—free casein	Agarose overlayer	Arvidson and Wadström[37]

* Plasminogen activator produced by Staphylococcus aureus.

Table 12.3   Suggested procedure for an isoelectric
focusing-zymogram method

_____

1. Isoelectric focusing is performed at constant
   wattage (approx. 60 W) for 1 h at 4°C up to
   2000 V. (Starting voltage: broad pH range 500 to
   600 V; narrow pH range 800 to 1000 V. The
   following are important technical points:
   (i)   Good contact is made between gel and
           electrodes by means of filter paper
           electrode wicks soaked in electrode
           solutions.
   (ii)   Good contact between cooling plate and
           glass plate carrying gel (without
           trapped air bubbles) is essential; the
           glass plate carrying gel should be not
           more than 0.8 mm thick.
   (iii)   Samples (20 µl) should be applied on
           filter paper squares or directly onto the
           gel, towards the anode and cathode.
   (iv)   If filter paper, or other sample
           applicator, is used, it should be removed
           after 20 min.
2. pH measurements are made with a surface
   electrode every 5 mm on a line from anode to
   cathode 30 to 40 mm in from the edge of the gel.
3. Gel is soaked in 0.4 M buffer of appropriate pH
   (containing activating ions) for 5 to 8 min
   while still attached to plate; gel is drained and
   surplus buffer removed from edges with absorbant
   tissue or filter paper.
4. Surface of gel is 'dried' in a stream of cool air
   from a fan for 1 to 2 min (per-evaporation).
5. Gel is placed in closely fitting plexiglass mould,
   4 mm in depth, and overlayered with 1% (w/v)
   buffered agarose containing substrate (and
   activating ions).
6. The system is incubated at 37°C, and photographed
   at intervals or the results drawn by placing
   graph paper below the glass plate as a reference
   grid.

_____

F*

Bours and van Doorenmaalen[21] and then soaked
overnight to remove unpolymerised monomer and excess
catalyst. The gel was per-evaporated to remove 10%
of the weight and then soaked in 3% (w/v) Ampholine
solution overnight (16 to 18 h). The final
concentration of Ampholine in all gels was
calculated to be 2% (w/v) and the composition of the
gel was as follows: T = 5% (w/v) and C = 5% (w/w)[22].
Most of the experiments were performed on a cooled
glass plate[17] with carbon electrodes applied to the
gel surface. More recently the work was repeated in
an LKB Multiphor apparatus with platinum wire
electrodes on filter paper as recommended by the
manufacturer.

Samples of enzyme solutions (10 or 20 µl) were
applied to the gel by one of the following
procedures:

(i)   on filter paper squares (Table 12.4);
(ii)   directly onto the gel surface in the form of
        rectangular drops or streaks using
        micropipettes (Oxford Sampler, Oxford
        Laboratories International Corp., Dublin,
        Eire) or capillary pipettes (Wiretrol,
        Drummond Sci. Co., Broomall, Pa., U.S.A.);
(iii)   in glass basins on the gel surface[20];
(iv)   in basins made of plastic strips in 15 mm x
        15 mm pieces with 8 mm x 8 mm wells kindly
        supplied by Dr. C. Karlsson, LKB Produkter;
(v)   on polyacrylamide squares dried down to 80%
        of the initial weight by per-evaporation
        with or without Ampholine (2% w/v);
(vi)   cellulose acetate squares (Table 12.4).

The compositions of the substrate overlayers
used are summarised in Table 12.5. The results
described below (Section 12.4) will be reported in
detail elsewhere in a series of papers (Smyth and
Wadström; Arvidson and Wadström; Wadström,
Kjellgren and Nord; Wretlind, Nord and Wadström,
manuscripts in preparation).

After incubation, the gels were photographed on
Kodak photo-micrography colour film (PCF 135 - 36
2483) which seems to give a higher contrast than
several black and white films tested.

12.4 ZYMOGRAM METHODS

12.4.1 Proteases

Trypsin, chymotrypsin, subtilopeptidase and crude
preparations of protease from Staphylococcus aureus
and Pseudomonas aeruginosa have been studied.
Inclusion of $CaCl_2$ in the overlayer was found to
stabilise trypsin and to activate at least one of

Table 12.4 **Absorbent papers and cellulose acetate membranes employed as sample applicators**

Absorbent paper (type)	Grade	Weight* (g/m^2)	Thickness (mm)
Whatman	1	87	0.16
	3	185	0.38
	3MM	180	0.32
Schleicher and Schüll	2043 B	120	0.23
Munktells	OO	80	0.25
	OB	90	0.20
	3	90	0.25
	5	130	0.35
	2OR	70	0.20
	1300	90	0.10
LKB electrofocusing strip		520	1.20
Beckman	Blotter	230	0.50
Gelman	Absorbent	310	0.80
Millipore	AP10042OR	290	0.90

Cellulose acetate	Type
Millipore	Filter membrane (0.45 μ)
Beckman	Electrophoresis membrane
Gelman	Sepraphore III

* Data from Morris and Morris[27] or determined by the authors.

the Pseudomonas enzymes; the requirement for calcium
was confirmed using a casein overlayer containing
1 mM EDTA instead of $CaCl_2$. The Pseudomonas enzyme
with an isoelectric point (pI) of 4.0 then
disappeared, while a second enzyme species (pI 7.0)
was not affected. Similar experiments have also
been performed with the staphylococcal proteases of
strain V8 (S. Arvidson, unpublished data). Enzymes
with similar substrate specificities, in crude
mixtures, can therefore be differentiated on the
basis of differing ion requirements or differing
degrees of activation by reducing agents. The
subtilopeptidase was found to have a pI of 7.0
which is considerably lower than the previously
reported value of 9.4(ref. 23). Samples of 1.0 µg
applied between the middle of the gel and the anode
focused around pH 7.0, while samples applied closer
to the cathode focused around pH 9.0 (Figure 12.1).
However, isoelectric focusing in glycerol density
gradients with samples applied at different
positions in a pre-run gradient gave a pI value of
8.3. There is no simple explanation for these
confusing results, but it is known that
subtilopeptidase is unstable in alkaline solutions
and might auto-digest in such an environment.

These observations indicated that more
detailed studies on different procedures of sample
application are required. They also emphasise
the need for careful control experiments in the
analysis of complex protein mixtures, such as serum
proteins and crude extracellular bacterial proteins
by isoelectric focusing in gels.

12.4.2 Phospholipase C

The casein-precipitating capacity of proteases and
the ability of phospholipase C, from different
sources, to cause opacification in egg yolk and
lecithin media make both overlayers very sensitive
methods of detection[24,25], e.g. with less than 1 µg
of enzyme applied on the gel.

Furthermore, studies on both enzymes have
revealed similar phenomena of general interest,
e.g. at least 10 types of filter papers with
different absorbing capacities, adsorbed enzyme
which was not released during the experiments.
Removal of the filter papers during the run was
necessary to prevent the appearance of an enzyme
activity spot in the substrate overlayer at the
points of sample application. The adsorption of
enzyme to filter paper was pH-dependent, being more
pronounced at pH values below the pI values of these
proteins (Figure 12.2). Similar effects were

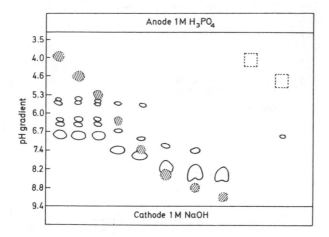

Figure 12.1 Subtilopeptidase zymogram.
Diagrammatic representation of cumulative findings
from several experiments in pH 3 to 10 gradients.
Gels were run for 40 to 45 min at 56 W at 4°C to a
final voltage between 1400 and 1600 V. Samples
applied as 10 µl (1 µg) drops (cross-hached circles)
or on Whatman 3MM filter paper applicators (dotted
squares). pH of gel equilibrated with 0.4 M Tris-HCl
buffer, pH 7.4. Overlayer of agarose containing
vitamin-free casein. Approximate development time
1 to 2 h at 37°C. Zones of precipitated paracasein
are indicated as open areas. Note the doublet
satellite bands when samples were applied near the
anode, and the shift in pI value of the major
zymogram band as the application site became
cathodic. It can also be seen that filter paper at
                the anode adsorbed enzyme

described previously on cellulose chromatography
and paper electrophoresis[26,27].

Different procedures for sample application
Commercial preparations of Clostridium perfringens
phospholipase C and crude and purified enzyme
preparations prepared in our laboratory have been
studied in great detail by the gel isoelectric
focusing zymogram method[28]. Samples have been
applied to the gel by all six methods described
above (Section 12.3), with special reference to
different filter papers. Figures 12.3 and 12.4

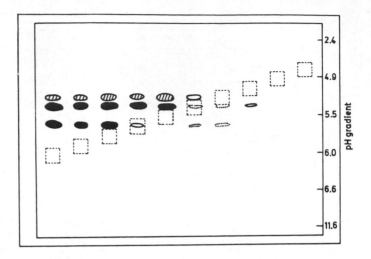

Figure 12.2 Phospholipase C zymogram showing loss
of zymogram bands by selective adsorption on filter
paper of individual components below their pI
values。 Phospholipase (10 µg) was applied on
Whatman 3MM filter paper applicators placed on a
pre-run gel with a pre-formed pH 5 to 8 gradient
(1 h at 56 W to 2000 V at 4°C)。 Sample
application sites are indicated by dotted squares。
The pH gradient did not shift with isoelectric
focusing for a further hour, i.e。 the duration of
the experiment. pH of the gel was equilibrated
with 0.4 M Tris-HCl buffer, pH 7.2, containing 1 mM
$CaCl_2$ and 1 mM $ZnCl_2$. Overlayer of agarose
containing lecithin. Appearance of opacity zones in
the gel overlayer due to the release of diglyceride
is indicated by: shaded, intense zone; hached,
strong opacity; open, weak opacity; dotted, faint
or indistinct zone。 Incubation for 5.5 h at 37°C。
Note the disappearance of bands in a definite order
as the filter papers were applied nearer to the
anode

show the effect of sample application site on the
detection of enzyme activity。
    In conclusion, no filter paper was found to
combine good absorptive capacity suitable for large
sample loading with low adsorptive properties。
For instance, Whatman 3MM and Whatman No. 1 papers
adsorb about 1 µg of protein per 10 mm^2; these
adsorptive effects have been confirmed by protein
staining[19]. Application of samples directly onto

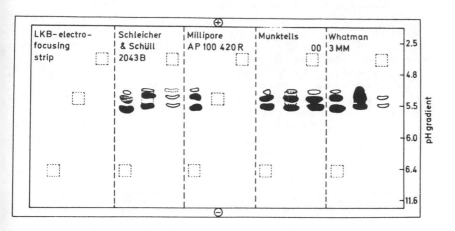

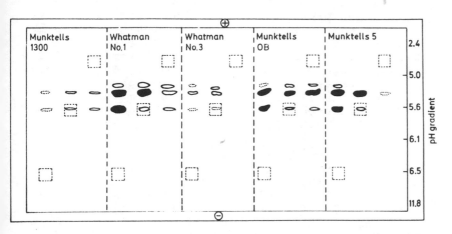

Figure 12.3 (upper diagram) and Figure 12.4 (lower diagram) Phospholipase C zymogram. Diagram illustrating the different adsorptive properties of 10 different grades of filter paper and the effect of sample application site in each case. pH 5 to 8 gradient. Experiments performed using LKB Multiphor apparatus. Isoelectric focusing performed at 60 W for 1 h at 4°C to a final voltage of 2000 V. 10 µg of phospholipase C were applied in 20 µl to each filter paper applicator. Overlayer of agarose containing lecithin. Incubation at 37°C for 2 h. Zones of opacity recorded as stated in legend to
Figure 12.2

the gel surface at different positions showed that
pH inactivation was probably not the reason for
these anomalous results, as it was in the case of
subtilopeptidase。 Cellulose acetate offers no real
advantage over direct sample application as it must
be applied to a dry gel surface and does not have a
very high capacity to absorb enzyme samples。
Polyacrylamide gel pieces, dried down to increase
their absorptive capacity, were also ⌐ied。 Pieces,
with or without Ampholine solution, gave identical
results。 However, since the pH gradient is set up
in the polyacrylamide applicator, this should not be
applied too close to the pI value of the protein(s)
being studied, in order to permit migration into the
separating gel。

Specificity and sensitivity of substrate overlayer
Since so-called 'egg yolk reactions' can be caused
by phospholipases as well as by lipases and
proteases, a more specific substrate for studies of
crude enzyme preparations is advantageous. However,
10% (v/v) egg yolk suspension was found to be 8 to
16 times more sensitive for the detection of
phospholipase activity than an overlayer containing
1。5% (w/v) egg or soya bean lecithin. In both cases,
lower substrate concentrations gave less distinct
zymogram spots although very low enzyme activities
could be detected after 18 h incubation, with
equally clear zone definitions。

12。4。3 Amylase Zymograms
Starch gel overlayers have been employed as the
conventional method for the detection of amylase
activity after electrophoresis. A new chromogenic
substrate for the Phadebas[R] amylase test
(Table 12。5), which permits the detection of enzyme
activity without the addition of any reagent, was
employed in studies of α-amylase in human saliva。
The development of zymogram spots can be followed
easily for up to 24 h. Four bands of enzyme
activity developed in the pH range 5.4 to 7.2
(Figure 12。5); the two most basic enzyme bands
developed faster and to a greater intensity。
Samples applied closer to the anode (i。e。 below pH
4。1) gave only three bands upon incubation. These
results show, once again, the importance of the
sample application site and that zymograms should
always be interpreted with great caution。
        These observations on human salivary α-amylase
by isoelectric focusing in gel are similar to those
obtained by electrophoresis of human saliva on paper
and in agar and polyacrylamide gels which resolved

Table 12.5 Enzymes studied by the use of buffered agarose overlayers containing appropriate substrates

Enzyme	Substrate*	Buffer/ions*
α-Amylase	Phadebas^R amylase test (Pharmacia) 1 tablet/10 ml	0.05 M Tris–HCl, pH 7.4
Deoxyribonuclease	Salmon sperm (Koch–Light) or Calf thymus DNA (Koch–Light) 1% (w/v)	0.05 M Tris–HCl, pH 7.4, 12.5 mM CaCl$_2$ and 12.5 mM MgCl$_2$
Penicillinase	0.2% Soluble starch (Merck) Benzylpenicillin (AB Kabi) 20 mM Lugol's solution:dist. H$_2$O = 1:1 (v:v)	0.1 M KH$_2$PO$_4$, pH 5.9
Phospholipase C	Soya bean lecithin (Sigma) 1.5% (w/v) emulsified	0.15 M NaCl in 0.02 M Tris–HCl, pH 7.4, 1 mM CaCl$_2$ and 1 mM ZnCl$_2$
Protease	Vitamin–free casein (NBC) 1% (w/v), pH 7.4, containing 2 mM KH$_2$PO$_4$	1 mM CaCl$_2$
Staphylococcal haemolysin	Rabbit, human or sheep erythrocytes (3%, v/v)	0.15 M NaCl in 0.02 M Tris–HCl, pH 7.4
Elastase	Elastin (Worthington) 0.5% (w/v)	0.01 M Tris–HCl, pH 8.8

* Final concentrations of substrate and buffer ions in 1.0 or 1.5% (w/v) agarose overlayers.

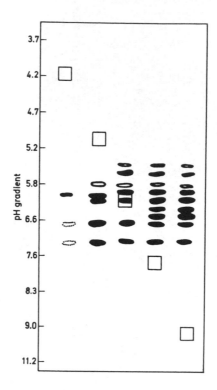

<u>Figure 12.5</u> Amylase zymogram. Composite
diagrammatic representation of various zymogram
bands detected depending on the sites of sample
application onto the gel on filter paper
applicators of Gelman AP 10042OR filter paper
(solid squares). Gels were run for 45 min at 4°C
to a final voltage of 1400 to 1600 V. pH gradients
were 3 to 10. Gels were equilibrated with 0.4 M
phosphate buffer, pH 7.4. Approximate times of
development of zymograms 1 to 2 h at 37°C.
Overlayer of agarose containing Phadebas[R] amylase
test substrate. Note the reduction in the number of
bands when samples were applied near the anode,
compared with the complex heterogeneity when samples
were applied close to the cathode

up to six different components, with three or four
in most reports[29].

12.4.4 <u>Penicillinase Zymograms</u>
Cells of 15 strains of <u>Bacteroides fragilis</u>,
suspended in buffer, after growth in a complex

liquid medium, were washed and subjected to
ultrasonic treatment. Samples of the supernatants
after this treatment were applied in duplicate, one
sample on each side of the middle of the gel, and
treated by the standard procedure (Table 12.3).
An overlayer of agarose containing either
benzylpenicillin or cephalothin (Eli Lilly and Co.,
Indianapolis, U.S.A.) was applied and the gel
incubated at 37°C (Nord, Wretlind and Wadström,
manuscript in preparation). Penicillinase activity
was detected after the addition of Lugol's
solution. All 15 strains gave a single band of
penicillinase activity with a pI of 5.9 ± 0.2. No
cephalosporinase activity was detected when a starch
overlayer containing cephalothin was applied. A
control with commercial penicillinase from Bacillus
cereus (2000 U Neutrapen[R], Riker Laboratories,
Loughborough, England), was resolved into three
enzymatically active components between pH 3 and 5.
We believe that this method for analytical
separation of bacterial penicillinases offers a
great advantage over the standard starch gel
electrophoresis method used for grouping bacterial
penicillinases[30], since the resolving power of gel
isoelectric focusing is much higher, (Chapter 18).
This application is being studied further.

12.4.5 Staphylococcal Haemolysins

Staphylococcus aureus produces at least four
different haemolysins[31], termed α, β, γ and δ.
Only β-lysin has been shown to be an enzyme, namely,
sphingomyelinase C. Since these toxins exhibit
different specific activities on erythrocytes from
different animal species they can be studied by a
'toxinogram' method[32] according to the outline in
Table 12.3. Such studies are of great interest in
relation to the search for new cytolytic agents
which might be virulence factors[33]. In addition
the heterogeneity of α-toxin previously studied in
density gradient isoelectric focusing (Chapter 16)
has also been confirmed by the 'toxinogram' method.
Application of agarose overlayers containing
monolayers of tissue culture cells is a possible
further development of 'toxinogram' methods for
studies of bacterial and snake toxins.

12.5 GENERAL COMMENTS ON PROBLEMS AND ARTEFACTS

The thin-layer technique used in this study offers
several advantages and advances over gel rod methods
used by other authors (Table 12.1):

(i)   several samples can be easily applied and run
        in parallel;
(ii)   thinner gels permit more rapid and efficient
        cooling which is of particular importance for
        high voltage techniques; furthermore, the
        focusing time is shorter;
(iii)   the thin-layer gel is more easily
        equilibrated with substrate solutions;
(iv)   the enzymes can migrate more easily into
        substrate overlayers;
(v)   the technique permits investigation of
        enzymes hydrolysing high molecular weight
        substrates.

However, the rod technique would appear to be more
advantageous in the study of oxygen-sensitive
enzymes[34].

12.5.1 pH Equilibration of Gels, Ampholine Inhibition, and Addition of Ions

To our knowledge, only three groups of authors[35-37]
have emphasised the importance of equilibrating the
gel with buffer before substrate is applied either
as an overlayer or soaked into the separating gel.
By contrast, in studies of staphylokinase and
pepsin respectively[38,39], it was found that the pI
values of these factors were very close to their pH
optima and activity would be detected in substrates
of suitable pH without prior pH equilibration of the
gel. Furthermore, equilibration of gels before
histochemical staining for alkaline phosphatase
activity has been described[40] but there was no
evidence of inhibitory effects due to Ampholine.
On the other hand, in a separate study[35], the same
enzyme was found to be inhibited by Ampholine and a
rather complicated dialysis technique was developed
for pH equilibration and Ampholine removal.

Removal of ions during isoelectric focusing and
the chelating properties of Ampholine can decrease
the yield of metal ion requiring enzymes such as
human liver alkaline phosphatase[41], and
phospholipase C[42,43]. However, addition of Zn^{2+}
ions can reactivate both enzymes. Appropriate ions
should be included in the equilibration buffer and
the substrate solution in zymogram methods when
necessary for enzyme activity. Removal of
Ampholine by the equilibration step must facilitate
such reactivation. Studies with ^{14}C-labelled
Ampholine would be necessary to quantitate the
removal of Ampholine during the brief soaking
procedure employed since it is likely that the
buffer ions migrate faster into the gel than the
Ampholine diffuses out because of differences in
molecular size. The 5 min immersion in buffer

recommended in Table 12.3 is not sufficient to
equilibrate the area of the gel close to the anode
and a 10 mm wide slice at the anode must always be
cut away before or after the overlayering to prevent
non-specific hydrolysis of substrates or lysis of
erythrocytes as in the 'toxinogram'. However, it is
conceded that with certain substrate-enzyme
combinations, such as albumin and pepsin[39], this may
not be necessary.

Thus, equilibration of gels with buffer can be
recommended as a general rule, obviating pH and
ion-chelating effects of Ampholine.

12.5.2 Artefacts and Problems of Sample Application

As is the case with any technique, users are loathe
to admit that artefacts can, or do, occur. Those
summarised below should not, however, dissuade
potential users from applying gel isoelectric
focusing to their studies, but rather serve as an
index of caution and a guide.

It has been noted that the application of
proteins with pI values below 4.5 near the anode
resulted in denaturation and artefacts, whilst
cathodic reduction of proteins with alkaline pI
values could produce similar effects[44]. The
formation of artefact bands on gels when different
sample positions were used has also been
described[45]. This was attributed to the formation
of protein-Ampholine complexes (see also Hayes and
Wellner[46]). The author also observed that these
effects could occur with basic, as well as with
acidic proteins. Robinson[47] reported that in narrow
pH gradients, asparaginases did not focus with the
same pI and attributed this in part to the
possibility that, at certain application sites,
longer times might be required for proteins to reach
equilibrium.

Polymerisation of gels in the absence of
Ampholine has been used by some authors to permit
removal of the riboflavin and persulphate and
unpolymerised acrylamide monomer catalysts by
washing, all of which have been found to cause
anomalous results (for references see Maurer[4]).
Such gels, reconstituted with Ampholine by the
procedures outlined by several authors[12,21,47],
have been reported to possess lower endo-osmotic
flow, which may be caused by Ampholine binding to
the gel matrix with in situ polymerisation[17].
Ovalbumin and sperm whale myoglobin have been found
to adsorb to Whatman 3MM filter paper[19].

Clearly some of these observations are in
accordance with the findings reported here.

However, none of the enzymes studied by us gave
differing results between experiments on gels
containing Ampholine polymerised in situ or
subsequently added. Lewin[48,49] has advocated the
pre-running of gels to form the pH gradient before
sample application of pH-sensitive proteins, and
Frater[45] concluded that application of samples to
a pre-run gel avoided the formation of
Ampholine-protein complexes. However, from the
studies reported here, the method of application
would seem to be of paramount importance.

12.6   FUTURE DEVELOPMENTS OF ZYMOGRAM
PROCEDURES

Isoelectric focusing in gels requires a medium with
very low electro-endosmosis. Agarose gels have been
used for electrophoresis, with or without
subsequent detection of separated components by
specific zymogram techniques. However, agarose
exhibiting low electro-endosmotic flow is not yet
commercially available, although a few recent
publications have described methods for preparing
highly purified agarose with low pyruvate and
sulphate contents[50,51]. Although agarose was one of
the first support media tried for gel isoelectric
focusing both alone and in combination with
polyacrylamide[52], other authors have discussed the
problems of its usage[53].
     Such a separating medium would facilitate a
combination of gel isoelectric focusing with other
analytical techniques, for the analysis of complex
enzyme-antigen mixtures, e.g. classical
immunodiffusion followed by zymogram staining of
specific immuno-precipitates, a combination with
methods of electro-immunoassay, such as crossed
immunoelectrophoresis[54,55]. Zymogram techniques
in combination with crossed immunoelectrophoresis
have been employed in studies of mammalian
glycosidases[56] and the enzymes of normal liver cells
and hepatoma cells[57,58].
     Two recent publications[59,60] present the first
attempts at combining crossed immunoelectrophoresis
with isoelectric focusing. Further possibilities
for immuno-isoelectric focusing have been reviewed
by Catsimpoolas[61]. Two-dimensional procedures
combining isoelectric focusing in disc gels and
electrophoresis in flat-bed gels were an early
development[62]. These could be further developed by
the use of pore-limit or gradient-gel
electrophoresis in the second direction[63].

Finally, apart from its application to clinical chemistry[64], gel isoelectric focusing should prove useful in combination with zymogram procedures in bacterial taxonomy, extending the pioneering work of Norris[65] and the larger studies of others[66-68]. It is our opinion that further developments will make isoelectric focusing zymogram techniques very valuable tools in the analysis of enzymes in complex protein mixtures.

ACKNOWLEDGEMENTS

The skilful technical assistance of Marianne Kjellgren and P. Allestam is gratefully acknowledged. We wish to thank S. Arvidson, N. Axelsen, F. Blomberg, R. Eriksson, R. Möllby, C.-E. Nord, O. Vesterberg and B. Wretlind for their collaboration, stimulating discussions and criticisms. We are also grateful to C. Karlsson and H. Davies of LKB Produkter for the use of an LKB Multiphor apparatus before it became commercially available.

REFERENCES

1. URIEL, J., 'Characterisation of Precipitates in Gels'. In: Immunology and Immunochemistry, Vol. 3, Ed. C.A. Williams and M.W. Chase, Academic Press, New York and London, p294 (1971)
2. CAWLEY, L.P., Electrophoresis and Immunoelectrophoresis, Little, Brown and Company, Boston, p227 (1969)
3. SMITH, I., Chromatographic and Electrophoretic Techniques, Vol. 2: Zone Electrophoresis, 2nd edn., Heinemann, London (1960)
4. MAURER, H.R., Disc Electrophoresis and Related Techniques of Polyacrylamide Gel Electrophoresis, 2nd edn., Walter de Gruyter, Berlin and New York, pp. 59, 102, 132 (1971)
5. LATNER, A.L. and SKILLEN, A.W., Isoenzymes in Biology and Medicine, Academic Press, London and New York (1968)
6. CLAUSEN, J., 'Immunochemical Techniques for the Identification and Estimation of Macromolecules'. In: Laboratory Techniques in Biochemistry and Molecular Biology, Vol. 1, Ed. T.S. Work and E. Work, North-Holland Publishing Company, Amsterdam and London, p. 397 (1969)
7. VESELL, E.S. (Editor), 'Multiple Molecular Forms of Enzymes'. Ann. N.Y. Acad. Sci., 151, 1-689 (1968)

8. HUNTER, R.L. and MAKERT, C.L. 'Histochemical
    Demonstration of Enzymes Separated by Zone
    Electrophoresis in Starch Gels'. Science, 125,
    1294-1295 (1957)
9. MAKERT, C.L. and MÖLLER, F., 'Multiple Forms of
    Enzymes: Tissue, Ontogenetic and Species
    Specific Patterns'. Proc. Nat. Acad. Sci.
    (U.S.A.), 45, 753-763 (1959)
10. WRÖBLEWSKI, F. and GREGORY, K., 'Lactic
    Dehydrogenase Isozymes and their Distribution
    in Normal Tissues and Plasma and in Disease
    States'. Ann. N.Y. Acad. Sci., 94, 912-932
    (1961)
11. DALE, G. and LATNER, A.L., 'Isoelectric Focusing
    in Polyacrylamide Gels'. The Lancet, i,
    847-848 (1968)
12. LEABACK, D.H. and RUTTER, A.C.,
    'Polyacrylamide-Isoelectric-Focusing: A New
    Technique for the Electrophoresis of Proteins'.
    Biochem. Biophys. Res. Comm., 32, 447-453
    (1968)
13. DELINCÉE, H. and RADOLA, B.J., 'Thin-Layer
    Isoelectric Focusing on Sephadex Layers of
    Horseradish Peroxidase'. Biochim. Biophys.
    Acta, 200, 404-407 (1970)
14. DELINCÉE, H. and RADOLA, B.J., 'Isoelectric
    Fractionation of Horseradish Peroxidase'.
    In: Protides of the Biological Fluids, 18th
    Colloquium of Bruges, Ed. H. Peeters,
    Pergamon Press, New York and London, 493-497
    (1971)
15. RÜCKER, W. and RADOLA, B.J., 'Isoelectric
    Patterns of Peroxidase Isoenzymes from Tobacco
    Tissue Cultures'. Planta (Berlin), 99,
    192-198 (1971)
16. CATSIMPOOLAS, N., 'Isoelectric Focusing and
    Isotachophoresis of Proteins'. Separ. Sci., 8,
    71-121 (1973)
17. VESTERBERG, O., 'Isoelectric Focusing of
    Proteins in Polyacrylamide Gels'. Biochim.
    Biophys. Acta, 257, 11-19 (1972)
18. KARLSSON, C., DAVIES, H., ÖHMAN, J. and
    ANDERSSON, U.-B., 'LKB 2117 Multiphor - I.
    Analytical Thin Layer Gel Electrofocusing in
    Polyacrylamide Gel'. LKB Application Note
    (March 29), LKB-Produkter AB, Stockholm, Sweden
    (1973)
19. SÖDERHOLM, J., ALLESTAM, P. and WADSTRÖM, T.,
    'A Rapid Method for Isoelectric Focusing in
    Polyacrylamide Gel'. FEBS Letters, 24, 89-92
    (1972)

20. WADSTRÖM, T., 'Separation of Australia Antigen
    and Some Bacterial Proteins by Isoelectric
    Focusing in Polyacrylamide Gels'. Ann. N.Y.
    Acad. Sci., 209, 405-414 (1973)
21. BOURS, J. and van DOORENMAALEN, W.J., 'Gel
    Isoelectric Focusing of Lens Crystallins'.
    Science Tools, 17, 36-38 (1970)
22. HJERTÉN, S., 'Molecular Sieve Chromatography on
    Polyacrylamide Gels, prepared according to a
    Simplified Method'. Arch. Biochem. Biophys.,
    Suppl. 1, 147-151 (1962)
23. GÜNTELBERG, A.V. and OTTESEN, M., 'Purification
    of the Proteolytic Enzyme from Bacillus
    subtilis'. Compt. Rend. Trav. Lab. Carls., 29,
    36-48 (1954)
24. HABERMANN, E. and HARDT, K.L., 'A Sensitive and
    Specific Plate Test for the Quantitation of
    Phospholipases'. Anal. Biochem., 50, 163-173
    (1972)
25. SCHUMACHER, G.F.B. and SCHILL, W-B., 'Radial
    Diffusion in Gel for Micro Determination of
    Enzymes. II. Plasminogen Activator, Elastase
    and Non-Specific Proteases'. Anal. Biochem.,
    48, 9-26 (1972)
26. CORBERT, W.M., HESTRIN, S., GREEN, J.W.,
    WHISTLER, R.L., BEMILLER, J.N. and RAPSON,
    W.H., 'Preparation of Cellulose'. In: Methods
    in Carbohydrate Chemistry, Vol. 3, Ed. R.L.
    Whistler, Academic Press, New York and London,
    3-22 (1963)
27. MORRIS, C.J.O.R. and MORRIS, P., 'Separation
    Methods in Biochemistry, Pitman and Sons Ltd.,
    London, pp. 55, 687 (1964)
28. MÖLLBY, R. and WADSTRÖM, T., 'Purification of
    Phospholipase C (Alpha-Toxin) from Clostridium
    perfringens'. Biochim. Biophys. Acta, 321,
    569-584 (1973)
29. MEITES, S. and ROFOLS, S., 'Amylase and
    Isoenzymes'. CRC Critical Reviews in Clinical
    Laboratory Science, 2, 103-138 (1971)
30. RICHMOND, M.H. and SYKES, R.B., 'The
    β-lactamases of Gram-negative Bacteria and
    their Possible Physiological Role'. Advan.
    Microb. Physiol., 9, 31-88 (1972)
31. WADSTRÖM, T. and MÖLLBY, R., 'Some Biological
    Properties of Purified Staphylococcal
    Haemolysins'. Toxicon, 10, 511-519 (1972)
32. WADSTRÖM, T., THELESTAM, M. and MÖLLBY, R.,
    'Biological Properties of Extracellular
    Proteins of Staphylococcus aureus'. Ann. N.Y.
    Acad. Sci., in press (1974)

33. ALI, M.I. and HAQUE, R-U., 'Identification of
    Staphylococcal Epsilon Hemolysin'. Canad.
    J. Microbiol., 18, 535-536 (1972)
34. REPASTKE, A., 'A Method for Anaerobic Column
    Chromatography'. In: Methods in Enzymology,
    Vol. 22, Ed. W.B. Jacoby, Academic Press,
    New York and London, p. 322 (1971)
35. SMITH, I., LIGHTSTONE, P.J. and PERRY, J.D.,
    'Isoelectric Focusing of Alkaline Phosphatases.
    A Focusing-Disc Electrophoresis Transfer
    Technique'. Clin. Chim. Acta, 35, 59-66 (1971)
36. BIANCHI, U. and STEFANELLI, A., 'Zimogrammi di
    esterasi attenuti su poliacrilamide ed in
    gradienti di pH da omogenati di Anopheles
    atroparvus'. Atti Accad. Nat. Lincei Rend.,
    Serie VIII, 93, 539-542 (1970)
37. ARVIDSON, S. and WADSTRÖM, T., 'Detection of
    Proteolytic Activity after Isoelectric
    Focusing in Polyacrylamide Gel'. Biochim.
    Biophys. Acta, 310, 418-420 (1973)
38. VESTERBERG, O. and ERIKSSON, R., 'Detection of
    Fibrinolytic Activity by a Zymogram Technique
    after Isoelectric Focusing'. Biochim. Biophys.
    Acta, 285, 393-397 (1972)
39. VESTERBERG, O., 'Isoelectric Focusing of
    Acidic Proteins: Studies on Pepsin'. Acta
    Chem. Scand., 27, 2415-2420 (1973)
40. RIGHETTI, P. and DRYSDALE, J.W., 'Isoelectric
    Focusing in Polyacrylamide Gels'. Biochim.
    Biophys. Acta, 236, 17-28 (1971)
41. LATNER, A.L., PARSONS, M.E. and SKILLEN, A.W.,
    'Isoelectric Focusing of Human Liver Alkaline
    Phosphatase'. Biochem. J., 118, 299-302
    (1970)
42. SMYTH, C.J. and ARBUTHNOTT, J.P., 'Isoelectric
    Focusing of Clostridium perfringens α- and
    θ-Toxins'. J. Gen. Microbiol., 59, v
    (Abstract) (1969)
43. MÖLLBY, R., NORD, C.-E. and WADSTRÖM, T.,
    'Biological Activities Contaminating
    Preparations of Phospholipase C (α-Toxin) from
    Clostridium perfringens'. Toxicon, 11, 139-147
    (1973)
44. GRAESSLIN, D., TRAUTWEIN, A. and BETTENDORF, G.,
    'Gel Isoelectric Focusing of Glycoprotein
    Hormones'. J. Chromatog., 63, 475-477 (1971)
45. FRATER, R., 'Artifacts in Isoelectric Focusing'.
    J. Chromatog., 50, 469-474 (1970)
46. HAYES, M.B. and WELLNER, D., 'Microheterogeneity
    of L-Amino Acid Oxidase: Separation of Multiple
    Components by Polyacrylamide Gel
    Electrofocusing'. J. Biol. Chem., 244, 6636-6644
    (1969)

47. ROBINSON, H.K., 'Comparison of Different
    Techniques for Isoelectric Focusing on
    Polyacrylamide Gel Slabs Using Bacterial
    Asparaginases'. Anal. Biochem., 49, 353-366
    (1972)
48. LEWIN, S., 'Use of Electrofocusing for the
    Detection of Carrier Proteins and their
    Differentiation from Antibodies'. Biochem. J.,
    118, 37P (1970)
49. LEWIN, S., 'The Effect of pH Placing of Sample
    in Isoelectric Focussing of Proteins'.
    Biochem. J., 117, 41P (1970)
50. HJERTÉN, S., 'Some New Methods for the
    Preparation of Agarose'. J. Chromatog., 61,
    73-80 (1971)
51. DUCKSWORTH, M. and YAPHE, W., 'Preparations of
    Agarose by Fractionation from the Spectrum of
    Polysaccharides in Agar'. Anal. Biochem., 44,
    636-641 (1971)
52. RILEY, R.F. and COLEMAN, M.K., 'Isoelectric
    Fractionation of Proteins on a Microscale in
    Polyacrylamide and Agarose Matrices'. J. Lab.
    Clin. Med., 72, 714-720 (1968)
53. QUAST, R., 'The Electroosmotic Flow in Agarose
    Gels and the Value of Agarose as Stabilising
    Agent in Gel Electrofocusing'. J. Chromatog.,
    54, 405-412 (1971)
54. AXELSEN, N.H., KRØLL, J. and WEEKE, B.,
    (Editors), A Manual of Quantitative
    Immuno-electrophoresis: Methods and
    Applications, Universitetsforlaget, Oslo (1973)
    also available as Scand. J. Immunol., 2,
    Suppl. 1, 1-169 (1973)
55. LAURELL, C.-B., (Editor), 'Electrophoretic and
    Electro-Immunochemical Analysis of Proteins'.
    Scand. J. Clin. Lab. Invest., 29, Suppl. 124,
    1-136 (1972)
56. RAUNIO, V., 'Characterisation of Glycosidases by
    Immunoelectrophoresis'. Acta Pathol. et
    Microbiol. Scand., Suppl. 195, 1-48 (1968)
57. GREENE, E.L., HALBERT, S.P. and JEQUIER, S.,
    'Analysis of the Tissue Constituents and
    Enzymes of Human Liver by Crossed
    Immunoelectrophoresis - Comparison of Normal
    and Cystic Fibrosis Liver'. Internat. Arch.
    Allergy, 42, 751-763 (1972)
58. RAFTELL, M. and BLOMBERG, F., 'Membrane
    Fractions from Rat Hepatoma. III.
    Immunochemical Characterisation of Detergent
    Soluble Membrane Phosphatases, Electron
    Transport Chains and Catalase'. Biochim.
    Biophys. Acta, 291, 442-453 (1973)

59. SKUDE, G. and JEPPSON, J.O., 'Thin Layer
    Electrofocusing Followed by Electrophoresis in
    Antibody Containing Gel'. Scand. J. Clin. Lab.
    Invest., 29, Suppl. 124, 55-58 (1972)
60. ALPERT, E., DRYSDALE, J.W. and ISSELBACHER,
    K.J., 'Isoelectric Focusing of Human
    α-Fetoprotein: An Aid in Purification and
    Characterisation of Microheterogeneity'.
    Ann. N.Y. Acad. Sci., 209, 387-396 (1973)
61. CATSIMPOOLAS, N., 'Immuno-Isoelectric Focusing'.
    Ann. N.Y. Acad. Sci., 209, 144-146 (1973)
62. DALE, G. and LATNER, A.L., 'Isoelectric Focusing
    of Serum Proteins in Acrylamide Gels Followed
    by Electrophoresis'. Clin. Chim. Acta, 24,
    61-68 (1969)
63. MARGOLIS, J. and KENRICK, K.G.,
    'Two-dimensional Resolution of Plasma Proteins
    by Combination of Polyacrylamide Disc and
    Gradient Gel Electrophoresis'. Nature (Lond.),
    221, 1056-1057 (1969)
64. LATNER, A.L., 'Some Clinical Biochemical Aspects
    of Isoelectric Focusing'. Ann. N.Y. Acad.
    Sci., 209, 281-298 (1973)
65. NORRIS, J.R., 'The Classification of Bacillus
    thuringiensis'. J. Appl. Bacteriol., 27,
    439-447 (1964)
66. GREEN, S.S., GOLDBERG, H.S. and BLENDEN, D.C.,
    'Enzyme Patterns in the Study of Leptospira'.
    Appl. Microbiol., 15, 1104-1113 (1967)
67. TODD, E., The Classification of the
    Micrococcaceae. Ph.D. Thesis, University of
    Glasgow, (1968)
68. BAPTIST, J.N., SHAW, C.R. and MANDEL, M.,
    'Zone Electrophoresis of Enzymes in Bacterial
    Taxonomy'. J. Bacteriol., 99, 180-188 (1969)
69. CHAMOLES, N. and KARCHER, D., 'Isoelectric
    Focusing in Acrylamide Gel of Human Tissue
    Lactate Dehydrogenase'. Clin. Chim. Acta, 30,
    359-364 (1970)
70. COUTELLE, R., 'Resolution of beta-Glucuronidase
    from Ehrlich Ascites Carcinoma Cells and Mouse
    Brain by Isoelectrofocusing in Polyacrylamide'.
    Acta Biol. Med. Germ., 27, 681-691 (1971)
71. KIM, W.J. and WHITE, T.T., 'Four Forms of Human
    Pancreatic Procarboxypeptidase A Demonstrated
    by Isoelectric Focusing'. Biochim. Biophys.
    Acta, 242, 441-445 (1971)
72. HUMPHRYES, K.C., 'Isoelectric Focusing of
    Trypanosoma brucei Subgroup Antigens in
    Polyacrylamide Gel Thin Layers: A Method for
    Resolving and Characterising
    Protein-Carbohydrate Complexes of an Enzymic

and Immunological Nature'. J. Chromatog., 49,
503-510 (1970)
73. ERIKSSON, K.-E. and PETTERSSON, B., 'A Zymogram
Technique for the Detection of Carbohydrases'.
Anal. Biochem., 56, 618-620 (1973)
74. BEELEY, J.A., STEVENSON, S.M. and BEELEY, J.G.,
'Polyacrylamide Gel Isoelectric Focusing of
Proteins: Determination of Isoelectric Points
Using an Antimony Electrode'. Biochim.
Biophys. Acta, 285, 293-300 (1972)

13. ^{14}C-LABELLED CARRIER AMPHOLYTES DESIGNED FOR
     PREPARATIVE PEPTIDE SEPARATIONS

V. Gasparić and Å. Rosengren

13.1 INTRODUCTION

The successful applications of isoelectric focusing
to peptide separations have so far been restricted
to analytical problems because of difficulties in
removing the carrier ampholytes from the peptides.
Separation of carrier ampholytes from peptides by
gel filtration would be the method of choice
provided that satisfactory resolution could be
obtained. Use of carrier ampholytes having a low
apparent molecular weight should improve the
possibility of using gel filtration for the
separation of Ampholine from peptides. However,
reduction of the molecular weight represents a major
problem, as it is necessary to keep the number of
carrier ampholyte species as high as possible in
order to retain the high resolution.
     In order to investigate the distribution of
carrier ampholytes on different gel filtration
materials we have synthesised ^{14}C-labelled carrier
ampholytes with limited apparent molecular weights
and ^{14}C-labelled conventional carrier ampholytes
corresponding to the commercially available
Ampholine.

13.2 EXPERIMENTAL

The carrier ampholytes used were of pH range 3.5 to
10.0. They were ^{14}C-labelled and the specific
activity was 5 μCi/g dry weight. The distribution
of the different ampholytes on Sephadex G25 was
studied on an LKB-4220 chromatography column
(25 x 1000 mm). The column was equilibrated with
1 M NaCl, and calibrated with polyethylene glycols
of molecular weights: 4000, 1000, 600 and 300, and

monoethyleneglycol.   160 µl ^{14}C-labelled carrier
ampholytes (40%, w/v) in 10 ml 1 M NaCl were used in
each experiment.   The eluate was passed through a
Waters differential refractometer R 403 (Karlsson
Instrument AB, S-126 22 Hägersten, Sweden) and 5 ml
fractions were collected.   The radioactivity of each
fraction was measured by liquid scintillation
counting (LKB Wallac 8100 Automatic Liquid
Scintillation Counter) using 200 µl aliquots and
Aquasol (New England Nuclear Chem. GmbH, Per
Hansson, Pomonavägen 12, S-170 10 Ekerö, Sweden) as
scintillant.

13.3   RESULTS

The distribution of conventional carrier
ampholytes on a Sephadex G25 column is shown in
Figure 13.1.   The ^{14}C-radioactivity curve shows
that the highest apparent molecular weight is in
the vicinity of 5000 daltons.   From the calibration
data it has been estimated that 0.0312% (w/w) of
carrier ampholytes had an apparent molecular weight
above 4000 daltons, 0.728% had a molecular weight
above 1000 daltons and 6.22% had a molecular weight
above 600 daltons.   Data obtained using a
differential refractometer showed a similar
distribution.

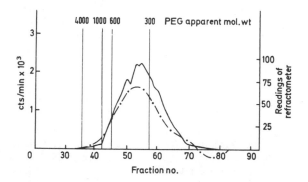

Figure 13.1   Gel filtration of ^{14}C-labelled
conventional Ampholine on a column of Sephadex G25.
(———), ^{14}C-radioactivity; (——●——), differential
refractometer signal.   The figures at the top
indicate the positions of elution of polyethylene
      glycols (PEG) of known molecular weights

   The results of the experiment with limited
apparent molecular weight carrier ampholytes are
shown in Figure 13.2. In this case no material had
an apparent molecular weight greater than 1900
daltons. The ^{14}C-radioactivity above 1000 daltons
accounted for 0.215% and above 600 daltons for 1.47%
of the total activity. Again the refractometer data
demonstrate a similar trend. The distribution of
radioactivity from the two experiments is compared
in Table 13.1.

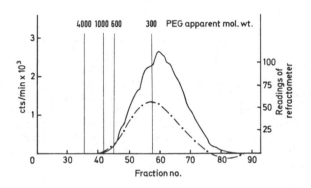

Figure 13.2 Gel filtration of ^{14}C-labelled carrier
ampholytes with limited apparent molecular weight.
(———), ^{14}C-radioactivity; (—•—), differential
refractometer signal. The figures at the top
indicate the positions of elution of polyethylene
     glycols (PEG) of known molecular weights

13.4 DISCUSSION

Since the possibility of separating peptides from
carrier ampholytes by gel filtration is dependent
upon their actual behaviour on the gel, and not
strictly on their molecular weight, in this paper
we have used the expression 'apparent molecular
weight' to emphasise that the results are not in
fact indicative of the real molecular weight of the
carrier ampholytes concerned. We have determined
the apparent molecular weight of the carrier
ampholytes by calibrating the column with
polyethylene glycols of known molecular weights in
the same buffer system. The possibility of
performing a successful separation is, of course,
also dependent on the apparent molecular weight of
the peptides in the same system.

Table 13.1

Apparent molecular weight	Conventional carrier ampholytes	Limited apparent molecular weight carrier ampholytes
	% of total radioactivity	
> 4 000	0.031	0
> 1 900	0.108	0
> 1 000	0.728	0.215
> 600	6.22	1.47

The results show that in the buffer system used, gel filtration on Sephadex G25 is not suitable for the separation of peptides from conventional Ampholine. However, it should be possible to use gel filtration to separate ^{14}C-labelled limited molecular weight carrier ampholytes from peptides having an apparent molecular weight greater than 2000 daltons. The distribution of the carrier ampholytes on Sephadex G25, as shown in Figures 13.1 and 13.2, indicates that this system is not optimal; Sephadex G50, for example, should give better resolution. It therefore appears possible to separate peptides, with an apparent molecular weight greater than 5000 daltons, from ordinary Ampholine and to separate peptides, having an apparent molecular weight of 2000 daltons, from limited apparent molecular weight ampholytes. Work on separations using Sephadex G50 is now in progress.

ACKNOWLEDGEMENT

The authors are indebted to Alice Fri, Application laboratory, LKB-Produkter AB, Stockholm, Sweden, for valuable help in the liquid scintillation work.

G

14.   SOME ASPECTS OF PREPARATIVE ISOELECTRIC
       FOCUSING IN LAYERS OF GRANULATED GELS

B.J. Radola

14.1   INTRODUCTION

A number of approaches have been suggested for
preparative isoelectric focusing including vertical
columns with density gradient stabilisation[1],
continuously polymerised polyacrylamide gels in the
form of either thin-layer gels[2] or gel rods[3], layers
of granulated gels[4,5], continuous flow systems with
gel or density gradient stabilisation[6]
multi-membrane devices[1], and zone convection[7].
Comparison of these techniques is difficult because
sufficient data are not available.
    The two main methods of anti-convective
stabilisation in preparative isoelectric focusing
used at present are density gradients and
polyacrylamide gels. The use of a density gradient
for preparative separations in vertical columns has
several limitations[1]:
  (i)   low load capacity
  (ii)   sensitivity to local temperature
         fluctuations
  (iii) difficulties in ensuring efficient cooling
         which impose finite limits on the column
         design
  (iv)   loss of resolution due to re-mixing on
         elution of proteins from the column
  (v)   precipitation of proteins at their
         isoelectric points.
Some of these drawbacks can be overcome by
continuous flow density gradient systems[6] or by
short vertical columns (see Chapter 3).
    The main application of continuously
polymerised polyacrylamide gels is in analytical
separations, either as gel rods or flat-bed gels.
A high load capacity, in terms of weight of

protein/mm^3 for a single zone, has been demonstrated
for gel rods[3] but due to the unfavourable geometry
such gels cannot be used for the separation of
larger amounts of protein on a preparative scale.

Granulated gels, such as Sephadex or Bio-Gel,
when employed in layers of variable length and
thickness, offer a promising alternative to the
anti-convective systems discussed previously[5].
This paper describes some of the advantages of
preparative isoelectric focusing in layers of
granulated gels. Emphasis will be placed on the
following aspects: load capacity, scaling up of
preparative focusing for the separation of 0.1 to
10 g protein loads, and an evaluation of
isoelectric focusing used as a fractionation step in
combination with other methods.

14.2   MATERIALS AND METHODS

Carrier ampholytes, Ampholines, were from LKB
Produkter AB, Bromma, Sweden and Sephadex gels from
Pharmacia, Uppsala, Sweden. Pronase P and E were
obtained from Serva, Heidelberg, or Merck,
Darmstadt, W. Germany, respectively. The
horseradish peroxidase was from Boehringer,
Mannheim, W. Germany. Proteins with known
isoelectric points and other reagents were obtained
as described previously[8].

The 'Double Chamber' apparatus from Desaga,
Heidelberg was used both for preparative and
analytical isoelectric focusing. Cooling water at
2 to 10°C was circulated through the apparatus from a
Lauda K2/RD refrigerated constant temperature
circulator (Dr. Wobser, Lauda, W. Germany). A type
641 digital pH meter from Knick, Berlin, W. Germany
and a micro glass electrode of approx. 1.5 mm
diameter, combined with a reference electrode
(Desaga, Heidelberg), was used for the pH
measurements[8].

Thin-layer isoelectric focusing was performed
as described previously[8]. After focusing,
proteolytic activity was detected with a buffered
paper (0.3 M Tris, pH 7.2) impregnated with
haemoglobin. The dried print was washed with
trichloroacetic acid (10%, w/v) to remove the
degraded haemoglobin and then stained with
Coomassie Violet R-150 (B.J. Radola, unpublished
method). Protease activity in the eluates was
determined by the dimethyl casein method[9].

Small-scale preparative isoelectric focusing
was performed using glass plates of several sizes
(200 x 100 mm, 200 x 200 mm or 400 x 200 mm).

These were coated with a thick suspension of
Sephadex G-75 (Superfine) containing 1% (w/v) of
carrier ampholytes. The amount of gel suspension
used for coating the plate was selected so as to
give a layer 1 to 2 mm thick (Figure 14.1). The
total volume of gel required to give this thickness
for plates of the sizes indicated above, ranged
from 25 to 250 ml.

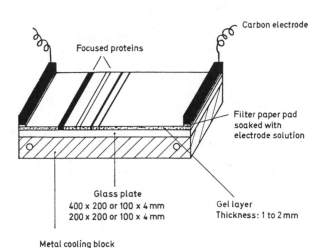

Figure 14.1   Schematic representation of small-scale
preparative isoelectric focusing in layers of
granulated gels

     For large-scale preparative isoelectric
focusing, a trough consisting of a glass plate at
the bottom and a lucite frame (the sides of which
had a cross-sectional area of 10 mm x 10 mm) were
used with gel layers up to a thickness of 10 mm.
Again, the area of the trough was variable
(Figure 14.2). The total gel volume in the trough
ranged from 300 to 800 ml.
     Gels formed on plates or in the troughs were
dried in air until a layer was obtained which did
not move when the plate was inclined at an angle
of 45°. The sample was applied as a streak either
directly on the surface of the gel layer or into a

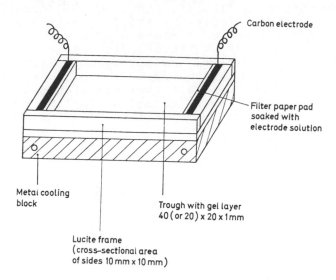

Figure 14.2 Schematic representation of preparative isoelectric focusing in a trough of granulated gels

groove made at any site on the layer, usually in the middle or at the anodic side. The plate was then placed on the pre-cooled cooling block of the 'Double Chamber' apparatus. An electrical field was applied through flat carbon electrodes which made contact with the gel layer through pads of a thick paper (MN 866 with a surface weight of 650 g/m^2, Macherey, Nagel and Co., Duren, W. Germany) soaked with the corresponding electrode solutions; 1 M sulphuric acid at the anode and 2 M ethylene diamine at the cathode. pH measurements were made at 25°C as described for thin-layer isoelectric focusing, either directly in the gel layer or in 20-30 µl gel samples liquified by addition of an equal volume of CO_2-free water[8]. Proteins were located after focusing by the print technique with a thick paper (MN 827, surface weight 270 g/m^2, Macherey, Nagel and Co.). The prints were stained with Light Green SF. A detailed description of the method will appear elsewhere.

14.3 RESULTS AND DISCUSSION

14.3.1 Thin-layer Isoelectric Focusing of Pronase
Pronase, a proteolytic enzyme obtained from <u>Streptomyces griseus</u>, was chosen as material for

preparative isoelectric focusing. A variety of
different fractionation methods have shown that
Pronase consists of a mixture of endo- and
exopeptidases[10-16]. Thin-layer isoelectric focusing
has shown Pronase to consist of about 30 stainable
protein zones distributed over a broad range from
pH 4 to 9 with some distinct major components
(Figure 14.3). Small quantitative differences were
observed between the patterns of the two types of

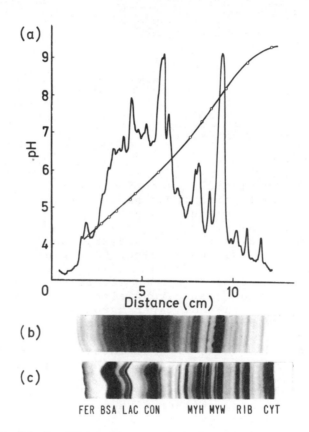

FER BSA LAC CON   MYH MYW RIB CYT

Figure 14.3 Thin-layer isoelectric focusing of
Pronase E in pH 3 to 10 ampholytes. (a) (———),
Densitometer tracing of a print stained with
Coomassie Blue G-250; (o———o), pH gradient.
(b) Stained print of Pronase (upper strip) and a
mixture of proteins with known isoelectric points
(lower strip) focused on the same plate. FER,
ferritin; BSA, bovine serum albumin; LAC,
β-lactoglobulin; CON, conalbumin; MYH, horse
myoglobin; MYW, sperm whale myoglobin; RIB,
              ribonuclease; CYT, cytochrome C

the enzyme (P and E) of differing purity, as well as
between the patterns of different batches of a
single preparation。 However, the overall pattern of
Pronase on thin-layer isoelectric focusing was
highly reproducible。

Detection of enzyme activity by means of a
buffered paper impregnated with haemoglobin or
casein as a substrate revealed about 20 proteolytic
zones, again distributed over a broad pH range, with
3 to 5 major components isoelectric between pH 5。7
and 8。0 (Figure 14。4)。 The heterogeneity of this
enzyme viewed in relation to its frequent
application in studies of proteolytic digestion of
proteins emphasised the importance of these
findings。 Further purification and characterisation
of the components of Pronase might provide important
new tools for the selective hydrolysis of certain
peptide bonds。

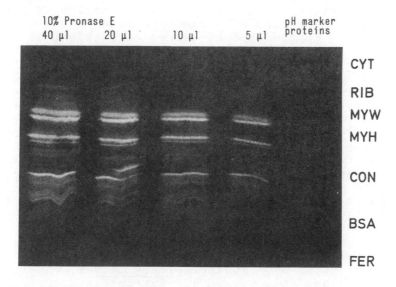

Figure 14。4 Detection of proteolytic activity in
decreasing volumes of a 10% (w/v) solution of
Pronase E after thin-layer isoelectric focusing in
pH 3 to 10 ampholytes。 An enzyme print was made
with buffered paper (pH 7。2) impregnated with 0。3%
haemoglobin。 The background was stained with
Coomassie Violet R-150 which stained the pH marker
proteins。 CYT, cytochrome C; RIB, ribonuclease;
MYW, sperm whale myoglobin; MYH, horse myoglobin;
CON, conalbumin; BSA, bovine serum albumin;
                FER, ferritin

14.3.2 <u>Load Capacity</u>

Two approaches have been chosen to determine the
maximum load capacity, a factor of paramount
importance in preparative isoelectric focusing.
These were analytical experiments, in which
increasing amounts of protein were applied, and
small-scale preparative experiments. Load capacity
is defined as the weight (mg) of protein per ml gel
suspension used for preparing the gel layers. The
load capacity of a system is obtained by dividing
the total load by the volume of a focusing system
in which the pH gradient is established. Defining
load capacity in this way facilitates comparison
with focusing systems which employ a different
geometry and/or other forms of anti-convective
stabilisation. The appearance of a regular pattern
of zones was used as the criterion in determining
the highest permissible protein load capacity.
Overloading resulted first in the formation of
irregular zones and a further increase in the amount
of protein applied led to marked aberrations in the
pattern of zones and the formation of droplets.

    <u>Figures 14.3</u> and <u>14.5</u> show thin-layer
isoelectric focusing of Pronase E when applied at
increasing amounts on 200 mm plates. When the load
capacity optimal for staining (0.75 mg protein per
ml gel suspension) was doubled (<u>Figure 14.3</u>) no
change in the pattern was observed. Also at a load
capacity of 5 mg protein per ml basically the same
pattern was obtained (<u>Figure 14.5a</u>); the small
differences were due probably to the use of a
different, less sensitive dye for staining (Light
Green SF instead of Coomassie Blue G-250) and to a
modification of the pH gradient resulting from the
high concentration of protein in some regions of
the pH gradient. At the highest load capacity (10
mg protein per ml gel suspension), there are obvious
indications of overloading (<u>Figure 14.5b</u>). The
protein zones show marked aberrations in the region
pH 5 to 6. Also, in other regions of the pH
gradient a pattern different from that obtained at
lower load capacities is observed. In spite of
signs of overloading in parts of the pH gradient,
some of the minor components have still been well
focused. The limit of load capacity appeared to be
between 5 and 10 mg protein per ml. The validity
of this finding was checked in small-scale
preparative experiments with total loads of 100 mg
and 400 mg Pronase E focused in a gel volume of
50 ml on 200 x 100 mm plates having a thickness of
2 mm. This corresponded to load capacities of 2 and

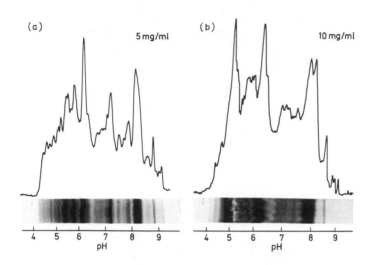

Figure 14.5 Determination of load capacity by
thin-layer isoelectric focusing in pH 3 to 10
ampholytes. Staining was with Light Green SF. Load
capacity: (a) 5 mg and (b) 10 mg protein per ml gel
       suspension used for coating the plates

and 8 mg protein per ml respectively. Such
experiments have shown that the results obtained in
both analytical and in preparative scale experiments
are comparable. Moreover, it became evident that a
higher load capacity was better tolerated by gels
of 2 mm thickness than in the analytical
experiments.

14.3.3 Focusing of Gramme Quantities of Proteins
Based on the preceding experiments it seemed
feasible to focus gramme quantities of Pronase by
increasing the total gel volume. Advantage was
taken of the fact that better resolution can be
achieved when a longer focusing distance is used
and plates or troughs 400 mm long were therefore
employed. In an experiment with 1.2 g Pronase E, a
400 x 200 mm plate coated with a gel volume of
250 ml was used (Figure 14.6). The load capacity of
approx. 5 mg protein per ml in this experiment
corresponded to that of the analytical experiments.
Comparison of the patterns reveals that the
excellent resolution of the analytical separation
is achieved also in preparative runs at high total

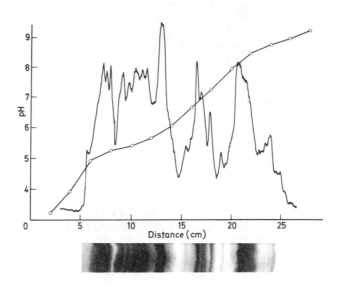

Figure 14.6   Preparative isoelectric focusing of
1.2 g Pronase E in a 400 x 200 x 2 mm gel layer.
Load Capacity: 5 mg protein per ml gel suspension.
A dialysed sample containing 1.2 g protein in 6 ml,
with 1% (w/v) carrier ampholytes was applied 100 mm
from the anode. Focusing was carried out in pH 3 to
10 ampholytes at 400 V for 20 h followed by 800 V
for 8 h. (———), Densitometer tracing of a paper
print stained with Light Green SF; (o———o), pH
gradient (25°C). The paper print is shown in the
lower part of the figure

protein loads. Furthermore, in the preparative run,
Pronase is resolved into more than 25 stainable
protein zones which focused between pH 4 and 9.
     Total protein recovery based on A_{280}
measurements was over 80%. To determine protein
recovery, a 350 x 20 mm gel strip was removed
lengthways from the layer. The proteins were
eluted from the gel with water, using a water:gel
ratio of 1.5 - 2.0:1 (v/v). This approach, in which
all proteins were eluted simultaneously from a
continuous strip of gel permits a more reliable
estimate of recovery than the usual procedure in
which protein recovery is calculated by summation of
the protein content of individual isolated

fractions. The latter method involves loss of the
protein between the zones and the inevitable loss of
some protein resulting from manipulation of many
small fractions. The recovery of proteolytic
activity was determined in a similar way. The
recovery was in the range of 40 to 80%, depending
on the experimental conditions. Small-scale
preparative experiments at load capacities ranging
from 0.5 to 10 mg Pronase per ml gel suspension
have shown that the recovery of proteolytic activity
increased with increasing load capacity from 14 to
80%. The highest recovery was repeatedly found at
load capacities of 5 to 10 mg Pronase per ml. Since
the caseinolytic activity of Pronase is inhibited by
EDTA[10], inactivation of Pronase following
isoelectric focusing could be due to the chelating
properties of the carrier ampholytes[17]. The
dependence of enzyme recovery on load capacity and
therefore also on the ratio of enzyme to the carrier
ampholytes is compatible with this explanation.
However, addition of calcium[11] after focusing did
not improve the recovery of enzyme activity.

For preparative focusing of still higher
quantities of Pronase, a 400 x 200 mm trough with a
10 mm gel layer and a total gel volume of 800 ml was
used (Figure 14.2). The pattern after focusing of
10 g Pronase E (Figure 14.7) again demonstrates the
excellent resolution obtainable at a load capacity
of approx. 12 mg protein per ml of gel. Some
difficulty was experienced in obtaining adequate
destaining of the print shown in the lower part of
Figure 14.7. As in the preceding experiments, many
clearly separated translucent zones could be seen
directly in the gel layer. Also at this very high
protein load and high load capacity the pattern
closely resembles that of analytical separations.
After refocusing in analytical gels, many of the
Pronase fractions were homogeneous, even when large
amounts of protein were applied. However, some
fractions did prove still to be heterogeneous on
refocusing, with additional components appearing in
a part of the pH gradient rather distant from the
original position of the refocused fraction.
Autolytic degradation of the proteolytically active
fractions could account for this finding.

The heterogeneity of Pronase found on detection
of proteolytic activity (Figure 14.4) could be due
to the presence of proteases with different
specificities. This was tested in preliminary
experiments in which fractions obtained by
preparative isoelectric focusing were used to digest
crystalline ovalbumin at different enzyme/protein

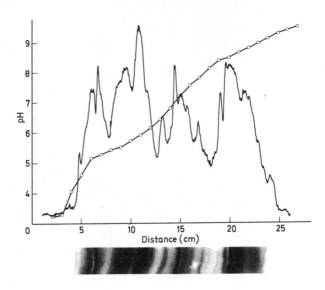

Figure 14.7 Preparative focusing of 10 g Pronase E
in a 400 x 200 mm trough with a 10 mm gel layer.
Load capacity: 12 mg protein per ml gel suspension.
40 ml of a 25% (w/v) dialysed sample with 1% (w/v)
carrier ampholytes were applied 100 mm from the
anode. Focusing was carried out in pH 3 to 10
ampholytes at 300 V for 20 h followed by 600 to 800
V for 6 h. (———), Densitometer tracing of a paper
print stained with Light Green SF; (o———o), pH
gradient (25°C). The stained paper print is shown
in the lower part of the diagram

ratios. After incubation with different Pronase
fractions, the patterns of the degraded, but still
macromolecular ovalbumin were found to differ when
analysed by thin-layer isoelectric focusing. Also,
high voltage paper electrophoresis disclosed
differences in the patterns of the
ninhydrin-staining low molecular weight products of
the digested ovalbumin.

14.3.4 <u>Use of Preparative Isoelectric Focusing in
Combination with Other Fractionation Methods</u>
Although isoelectric focusing has excellent

Table 14.1   Fractionation of horseradish peroxidase
by different techniques

Fractionation method	Number of steps	Purity $\dfrac{A_{403\ nm}}{A_{275\ nm}}$	Comments
Starting material	0	0.6	>20 Isoenzymes
Gel filtration	1	1.5	>20 Isoenzymes
Preparative isoelectric focusing, pH 3 to 10	1	1.7	Major isoenzymes homogeneous
Preparative isoelectric focusing, pH 6 to 8	1	2.3	Major isoenzymes homogeneous
CM-Cellulose	1	2.6	Mixture of isoenzymes
{1. CM-Cellulose {2. Preparative isoelectric focusing, pH 6 to 8	2	2.8	Major isoenzymes homogeneous
{1. Gel filtration {2. CM-Cellulose	2	3.0	Mixture of isoenzymes
{1. Gel filtration {2. CM-Cellulose {3. Preparative isoelectric focusing, pH 6 to 8	3	3.1 - 3.3	Isoenzymes isoelectrically homogeneous

resolving power and isoelectrically homogeneous
components can be isolated in a single step in high
quantity, extensive purification of proteins usually
requires the combined use of fractionation methods
based on different properties. The question then is
raised: at which step should preparative
isoelectric focusing be used? In Table 14.1 the
effect of different fractionation methods on the
purity and homogeneity of horseradish peroxidase
isoenzymes is shown (H. Delincée and B.J. Radola,
manuscript in preparation).

The horseradish peroxidase used as starting
material consists of more than 20 isoenzymes with pI
values distributed over a wide range from pH 3.5 to
9.0 ref. 18. When preparative isoelectric focusing
in pH 3 to 10 ampholytes is employed as a single
fractionation step, the major isoenzymes are
isolated in an isoelectrically homogeneous form.
However, the purity of the isolated isoenzymes is
low because contaminating proteins are also focused
in the corresponding region. Purity improves when
focusing is performed in pH 6 to 8 ampholytes but in
this case the isoenzymes isoelectric outside of this
range are lost. Combination of two fractionation
methods further improves the purity. Gel filtration
combined with anion-exchange chromatography is more
effective in raising the purity than other two-step
procedures, but again isoelectrically homogeneous
isoenzymes are only obtained when preparative
isoelectric focusing is included as one of the
fractionation steps.

Only by a sequence of three fractionation steps
can isoelectrically homogeneous isoenzymes of high
purity be isolated. Since both gel filtration and
ion-exchange chromatography can easily be scaled up
to process large quantities of proteins, it seems
advantageous to apply these methods first and to use
preparative isoelectric focusing as the final step.
In some applications in which high purity of all the
components, rather than separation of only some
components is desired, preparative isoelectric
focusing applied as a single step could prove to be
the method of choice.

14.4   CONCLUSIONS

Granulated gels offer a number of advantages when
used in layers for the anti-convective stabilisation
of the pH gradient in preparative isoelectric
focusing. As shown in the experiments with Pronase,
these gels have high load capacities ranging from 5
to 10 mg protein per ml gel suspension with pH 3 to

10 carrier ampholytes. For individual proteins,
load capacities in the order of 0.25 to 1 mg per ml
gel suspension have been estimated for this system.
Similar figures have also been found in experiments
with a number of other proteins thus confirming the
validity of the results with Pronase. The
experiments with Pronase were performed with pH 3 to
10 carrier ampholytes. For narrow pH-range
ampholytes, much higher loads have been found for
individual proteins (B.J. Radola, manuscript in
preparation).

It is not only the high load capacity but also
the excellent resolution obtainable with layers of
granulated gels which is appealing. High load
capacities can be employed in preparative
isoelectric focusing using the density gradient
column but only at the expense of resolution[19].
The facility to employ high load capacities presents
three advantages:

  (i)   It might allow isoelectric focusing to be
         used economically.
  (ii)   The resulting high ratio of protein to
         carrier ampholytes could lead to improved
         recovery of enzyme activity where
         inactivation occurs due to the chelating
         properties of carrier ampholytes.
  (iii) It facilitates the isolation of focused
         proteins in that even uncoloured proteins
         can be detected in the gel layer as
         refractile zones.

Recovery of proteins after focusing in layers
of granulated gels is high and elution simple. The
focused proteins are usually obtained in a small
volume and at relatively high concentrations. The
absence of sucrose is a definite advantage on
subsequent removal of the carrier ampholytes from
the focused proteins by most of the techniques
currently employed[20].

The geometry of a gel layer is favourable for
heat dissipation thus permitting the use of high
electrical potentials, a factor important for good
resolution. Also, the free accessibility of the gel
layer during the separation is of practical value.

The scaling up of preparative isoelectric
focusing could be achieved simply by variation of
the length, width and thickness of the gel layer.
With only minor modification of the basic procedure
of focusing in layers of granulated gels, it was
possible to proceed from analytical to preparative
separations without loss of resolution. The
flexibility of the system permits the dimensions of
the gel layer to be optimally adapted to the amount

of protein to be focused. An upper total load of
10 g protein has been described in this paper but it
seems feasible to scale up the method for even
higher protein loads.

REFERENCES

1. RILBE, H., 'Trends in Instrumental and
    Methodical Development of Isoelectric
    Focusing'. In: Protides of the Biological
    Fluids, Vol. 17, Ed. H. Peeters, Pergamon Press,
    Oxford, 369-382 (1970)
2. LEABACK, D.H. and RUTTER, A.C.,
    'Polyacrylamide-Isoelectric Focusing. A New
    Technique for the Electrophoresis of Proteins'.
    Biochem. Biophys. Res. Commun., 32, 447-453
    (1968)
3. FINLAYSON, G.R. and CRAMBACH, A., 'Isoelectric
    Focusing in Polyacrylamide Gel and its
    Preparative Application'. Anal. Biochem., 40,
    292-311 (1971)
4. RADOLA, B.J., 'Analytical and Preparative
    Isoelectric Focusing of Proteins in Sephadex
    and Bio-Gel Layers'. In: Protides of the
    Biological Fluids, Vol. 18, Ed. H. Peeters,
    Pergamon Press, Oxford, 487-491 (1971)
5. RADOLA, B.J., 'Analytical and Preparative
    Isoelectric Focusing in Gel-Stabilized Layers'.
    Ann. N.Y. Acad. Sci., 209, 127-143 (1973)
6. FAWCETT, J.S., 'Continuous Flow Isoelectric
    Focusing and Isotachophoresis'. Ann. N.Y.
    Acad. Sci., 209, 112-125 (1973)
7. VALMET, E., 'Zone Convection Electrofocusing -
    A New Technique for Fractionating Ampholytes
    in Free Solution'. Sci. Tools, 16, 8-13 (1969)
8. RADOLA, B.J., 'Isoelectric Focusing in Layers
    of Granulated Gels. I. Thin-Layer Isoelectric
    Focusing of Proteins'. Biochim. Biophys. Acta,
    295, 412-428 (1973)
9. LIN, Y., MEANS, G.E. and FEENEY, R.E., 'The
    Action of Proteolytic Enzymes on N, N-Dimethyl
    Proteins'. J. Biol. Chem., 244, 789-793 (1969)
10. NARAHASHI, Y. and YANAGITA, M., 'Studies on
    Proteolytic Enzymes (Pronase) of Streptomyces
    griseus K-1. I. Nature and Properties of the
    Proteolytic Enzyme System'. J. Biochem.
    (Tokyo), 62, 633-641 (1967)
11. NARAHASHI, Y., SHIBUYA, K. and YANAGITA, M.,
    'Studies on Proteolytic Enzymes (Pronase) of
    Streptomyces griseus K-1. II. Separation of
    Exo- and Endopeptidases of Pronase'.
    J. Biochem. (Tokyo), 64, 427-437 (1968)

12. HIRAMATSU, A. and OUCHI, T., 'On the Proteolytic Enzymes from the Commercial Protease Preparation of Streptomyces griseus (Pronase P)'. J. Biochem. (Tokyo), 54, 462-464 (1963)

13. WÅHLBY, S., 'Studies on Streptomyces griseus Protease. I. Separation of DFP-Reacting Enzymes and Purification of one of the Enzymes'. Biochim. Biophys. Acta, 151, 394-401 (1968)

14. JURÁSEK, L., JOHNSON, P., OLAFSON, R.W. and SMILLIE, L.B., 'An Improved Fractionation System for Pronase on CM-Sephadex'. Canad. J. Biochem., 49, 1195-1201 (1971)

15. LÖFQVIST, B. and SJÖBERG, L.B., 'Studies on the Heterogeneity of Streptomyces griseus Protease. I. Polyacrylamide Gel Electrophoresis of Commercial Pronase P, Derived from Streptomyces griseus K-1'. Acta Chem. Scand., 25, 1663-1678 (1971)

16. AWAD, W.M., SOTO, A.R., SIEGEL, S., SKIBA, W.E., BERNSTROM, G.G. and OCHOA, M.S., 'The Proteolytic Enzymes of the K-1 Strain of Streptomyces griseus Obtained from a Commercial Preparation (Pronase). I. Purification of four Serine Endopeptidases'. J. Biol. Chem., 247, 4144-4154 (1972)

17. DAVIES, H., 'Some Physical and Chemical Properties of the Ampholine Chemicals'. In: Protides of the Biological Fluids, Vol. 17, Ed. H. Peeters, Pergamon Press, Oxford, 389-396 (1970)

18. DELINCÉE, H. and RADOLA, B.J. 'Thin-Layer Isoelectric Focusing on Sephadex Layers of Horseradish Peroxidase'. Biochim. Biophys. Acta, 200, 404-407 (1970)

19. VESTERBERG, O., 'Isoelectric Focusing of Proteins'. Inaugural dissertation, Stockholm (1968)

20. VESTERBERG, O., 'Isoelectric Focusing of Proteins'. In: Methods in Enzymology, Vol. 22, Ed. W.B. Jacoby, Academic Press, New York and London, 389-412 (1971)

SECTION II

Applications in Protein Structure Studies

15. ISOELECTRIC FOCUSING AS AN AID TO OTHER TECHNIQUES FOR THE SEPARATION AND CHARACTERISATION OF PROTEINS

D.H. Leaback

15.1 INTRODUCTION

Density gradient column and polyacrylamide gel techniques have been developed which now enable near-ideal results to be obtained for many proteins after separation by isoelectric focusing. Such techniques have been employed mainly for relatively small-scale preparative purposes or for high-resolution analytical studies on protein mixtures. This paper shows that information from analytical isoelectric focusing of proteins can be extremely valuable as an aid to other methods used for the separation and characterisation of proteins.

15.2 THE IMPORTANCE OF ISOELECTRIC POINTS IN RELATION TO GRADIENT PORE ELECTROPHORESIS

In 1968, Margolis and Kendrick[1] described the preparation of gels in which the concentration of polyacrylamide increased progressively along the length of the gel slab. Although there is some difference of opinion as to the nature of the 'pores' in such gel matrices[2], globular proteins forced to migrate through the gels meet increasing resistance and often become practically stationary. Proteins are then said to have reached their 'pore-limits' and reports have appeared[3,4] indicating that various protein species assume positions in the gels which can be related quantitatively to the sizes of the respective protein molecules. As their pore-limits are approached, protein bands sharpen, so that the technique is capable of very high resolving power[1,5]. There are consequently some close parallels between gradient pore electrophoresis and

201

gel isoelectric focusing but with the results
apparently dependent upon molecular size rather
than electric charge characteristics. The
attraction of two such methods used in conjunction
for the determination of these important molecular
properties of proteins in crude mixtures needs no
further elaboration.

The results of thin-layer gel isoelectric
focusing of ten human IgG myeloma sera (samples
A-K) and one representative IgA myeloma serum (L)
are shown in Figure 15.1a. The monoclonal IgG
immunoglobulins gave the characteristic patterns
reported earlier[6],[7]. These consisted of sharp,
close, regularly spaced bands which focused in the
pH range 6 to 8. These bands probably arise by
sequential loss of amide ammonia from antibody
molecules which were initially secreted as proteins.
The one example of a serum (L) containing a
monoclonal IgA protein, shows an immunoglobulin
pattern isoelectric in the pH range 5 to 6; the
complexity and relative acidity of these components
is probably due at least in part to the presence of
bound carbohydrate[6]. Estimates of the average
isoelectric points for the monoclonal proteins in
Figure 15.1a were A, 5.6; B, 6.5; C, 6.4; D, 6.5;
E, 7.1; F, 7.2; G, 7.4; H, 7.5; J, 7.6; K, 8.0; and
L, 5.2 - 5.8.

Gradient pore gel electrophoresis of the same
serum samples (A-K) together with an IgM myeloma
serum (M) gave the patterns shown in Figures
15.2a-d. The monoclonal IgG immunoglobulins, after
23 h at pH 8.3, had penetrated up to approx. 46 mm
into the gel (Figure 15.2a) whereas after 92 h at
the same pH (Figure 15.2b) migration had increased
to 51 mm. A similar degree of penetration (51 mm)
was obtained after 24 h at pH 9.3 (Figure 15.2c).
The pattern observed depended on the isoelectric
point of the IgG immunoglobulins. For instance,
there was a pronounced tendency for the protein
bands to streak when the isoelectric points were
within one pH unit of the operating pH (see samples
F, G and H in Figures 15.2a and 2b). It should also
be noted however, that even with protein zones which
had sharpened, and whose isoelectric points were 2
to 4 pH units from the running pH (e.g. samples A
and C in Figures 15.2b and 2c) the effect of
different isoelectric points was not eliminated.

This effect was still not eliminated after
electrophoresis for even 92 h at pH 9.3 (i.e. under
what are probably reasonable extremes of operating
conditions). These findings suggest that the higher
the net electric charge on a protein the further it

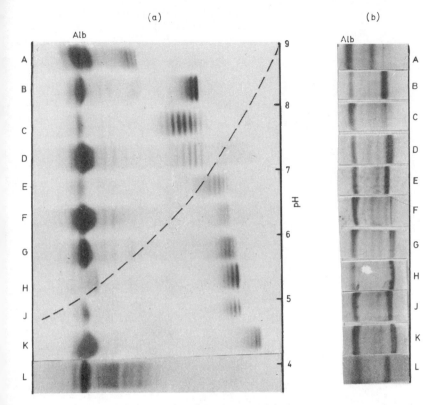

Figure 15.1 (a) Results of gel isoelectric focusing of ten human IgG (A–K) and one (L) IgA myeloma sera after 20 h at room temperature using 1.5% (w/v) pH 3 to 10 Ampholine run at 20 V/cm. The gel was then fixed in trichloroacetic acid (5%, w/v), stained for 1 h in Fast Green (0.2%, w/v) in ethanol:water: glycerol:acetic acid (50:50:20:1, v/v/v/v) before destaining in ethanol:water:acetic acid (25:70:5, v/v/v). Conditions were otherwise as described by Robinson[11]. The pH gradient (– – –) was determined by direct measurement on the surface of the gel with a combination electrode. The final position for the serum albumin is indicated (Alb).
(b) Results for the same 11 sera (A–L) after electrophoresis on 25 × 100 mm cellulose acetate strips (Oxoid) for 90 min using sodium barbitone buffer, pH 8.6 (Oxoid) and staining for 10 min in Ponceau S (0.2%, w/v) in aqueous trichloroacetic acid (3%, w/v) and destaining with acetic acid (7%, v/v). In each case the intense band to the right of each membrane represents the position of the monoclonal immunoglobulin. Alb, albumin

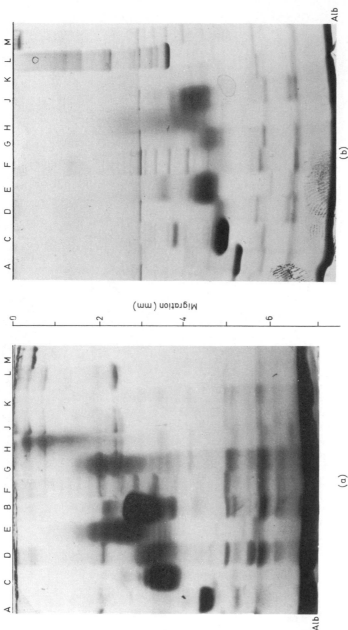

(a)

(b)

Figure 15.2 Results of the electrophoresis into 4 – 28% 'Gradipore' polyacrylamide gels (Universal Scientific Ltd., London, E.13) of the same ten human IgG (A-K) and one IgA (L) sera used in Figure 15.1, together with a human IgM serum (M). The gels were stained for 5 h, in Amido Black (0.3%, w/v) in acetic acid:methanol:water (1:3:6, v/v/v) solution and were destained according to the 'Gradipore' manufacturers' instructions. In each case the gel concentration increased from top to bottom and the extent of the penetration of the protein zones is indicated approximately by the scale (mm). (a) Results after migration towards the anode for 24 h at 5oC at about 70 V, and 20 mA in Tris (1.08%, w/v), boric acid (0.5%, w/v), sodium EDTA (0.01%, w/v), pH 8.3. (b) As for (a) except that the running time was 92 h

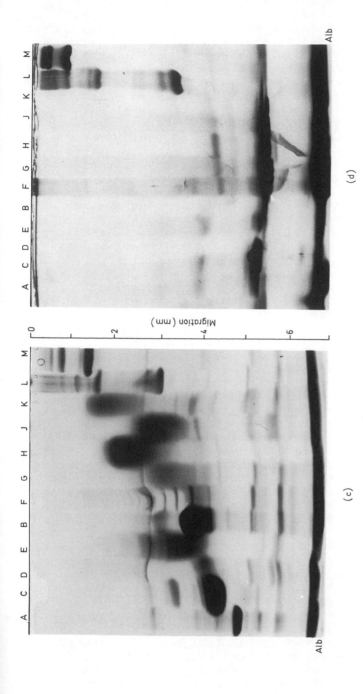

Figure 15.2 (c) As for (a) using the Tris-boric acid buffer at pH 9.3. (d) As for (a) but with migration towards cathode using 0.06 M sodium acetate buffer pH 4.0. The final position for the serum albumin is indicated (Alb) in each case

will migrate in this system. It is important, therefore, to determine the isoelectric points of proteins before attempting to assess their relative molecular sizes by gradient pore electrophoresis. However, where the isoelectric points of different samples are comparable, conclusions can be made about molecular size. This is illustrated by the behaviour of the monoclonal IgG immunoglobulin in serum sample A and the IgA proteins in serum L in gradient pore gels (Figures 15.2a-c). In this case the isoelectric points are comparable (Figure 15.1a), and the fact that the IgG protein penetrates the gradient pore gels further in each system suggests that the IgA protein shows greater resistance to migration and thus is probably larger. This is in accord with the known greater propensity of IgA proteins to polymerise or to bear larger amounts of carbohydrate. Indeed, the immunoglobulin bands of samples L and M (Figures 15.2a-d) indicate that the IgA and IgM proteins are probably highly polymerised. Gradient pore electrophoresis should therefore prove a useful tool for following such polymerisations, provided that allowance can be made for any variations in isoelectric points.

The question then arises as to how other workers[3],[4] obtained results from gradient pore gels which could be related quantitatively to the molecular weights of proteins. The determination by isoelectric focusing of the isoelectric points of four of the five proteins used as standards by Kopperschlager et al.[3] (yeast hexokinase, lactic dehydrogenase, catalase and leucine aminopeptidase, all purchased from Sigma, London) gave values of 4.8, 5.2, 5.6 - 6.0 and 4.5, respectively (author's unpublished observations). It seems possible that the apparently ideal behaviour of the proteins used for calibrating gradient pore gels[3],[4] fortuitously had a fairly narrow range of isoelectric points and consequently had rather similar electric charge densities.

Rather surprisingly, when the proteins in sera A-K are electrophoresed through a gradient pore gel towards the cathode at pH 4.0 (Figure 15.2d) the monoclonal IgG immunoglobulins with a wide range of isoelectric points (5.6 - 8.0) migrated to a similar extent in the gel (approx. 53 mm). Indications have been obtained (Leaback and Robinson, unpublished observations) that this might be a feature of the behaviour of other series of homologous proteins having different isoelectric points. There are two possible explanations of this effect.
(i)   The charge densities of the proteins may be

similar at pH 4.0 due to suppression of the
ionisation of weakly acidic groups on the
proteins; this implies that differences in
the isoelectric points of the proteins used
in this study are due mainly to variation
in the numbers of component acidic groups.
It would be interesting if this could be
validated.
(ii) The other possibility is that any endosmotic
water flow would help drive weakly charged
proteins to their pore-limits at acid pH,
but would oppose the migration of such
proteins towards the anode at alkaline pH.
 Whatever the explanation, the results in
Figures 15.2a-c are not due to molecular size
differences.

15.3 ISOELECTRIC POINTS AND CELLULOSE ACETATE
      ELECTROPHORESIS

Results of the electrophoresis of sera A-L on
cellulose acetate at pH 8.6 are shown in Figure
15.1b. The intense band towards the right of each
membrane represents the position of the monoclonal
immunoglobulin; the mean distances between the
albumin and immunoglobulin bands (on the original
membranes) were A, 22 mm; B, 32 mm; C, 30 mm; D,
31 mm; E, 34 mm; F, 35 mm; G, 36 mm; H, 37 mm; and
K, 38 mm. There seems to be a strong correlation
between the position of the immunoglobulin and its
isoelectric point (Figure 15.3). The fact that the
IgA protein in serum L has a comparable mean
isoelectric point to that of the IgG immunoglobulin
in serum A but has not migrated so far (distance
between albumin and immunoglobulin is 29 mm)
suggests that the IgA protein has greater
resistance to movement due to size. This agrees
with the results obtained with gradient pore
electrophoresis.
 It seems possible, therefore, that the zones
for the IgG and IgA immunoglobulins on cellulose
acetate electrophoretograms are likely to overlap
only with (fast moving) IgG proteins of
exceptionally low isoelectric point (as in serum A)
or with particularly slow moving (high molecular
weight) IgA immunoglobulins.

15.4 ISOELECTRIC POINTS AND ION-EXCHANGE
      CHROMATOGRAPHY

In addition to gaining insight into the behaviour of
proteins in electrophoretic techniques, a knowledge

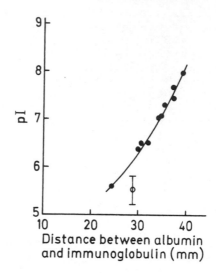

Figure 15.3   Relation between isoelectric point (pI)
of monoclonal IgG (●——●) and IgA (⦶)
immunoglobulins and the distance between the
albumin and immunoglobulin bands (mm) after
cellulose acetate electrophoresis as described in
Figure 15.1b

of the isoelectric point might be of assistance in
planning ion-exchange chromatography of protein
mixtures.
     Robinson and Leaback[8] have obtained some
preliminary results which suggest that isoelectric
points determined by isoelectric focusing can give
valuable information on the behaviour of proteins on
ion-exchange celluloses. For example, human carbon
monoxy-haemoglobin A is almost completely unadsorbed
by CM-cellulose at the isoelectric point of the
protein as indicated by isoelectric focusing, and
remains almost completely adsorbed at a pH one unit
below the isoelectric point (Figure 15.4). This
observation agrees broadly with the findings of
Lampson and Tytell[9] who employed isoelectric points
determined by other means.
     Analogous results have been obtained for the
behaviour of the B form of pig epididymal
β-N-acetyl-hexosaminidase[10] (isoelectric at approx.
pH 8.3) on CM- and DEAE-celluloses and this has
greatly facilitated the choice of experimental
conditions for the fractionation of the enzyme by
ion-exchange chromatography, and forms an essential
part of a new systematic strategy devised for the
purification of proteins from crude mixtures[8].

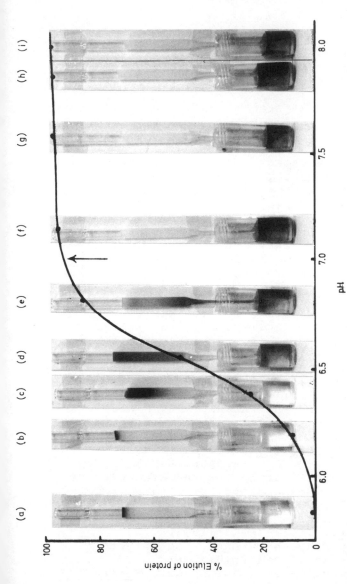

Figure 15.4   The behaviour of human carbon monoxy-haemoglobin A on CM-cellulose.
Samples (1 ml) of freshly prepared carbon monoxy-haemoglobin A in sodium phosphate
buffers (0.02 M) of pH 5.82, 6.19, 6.40, 6.55, 6.82, 7.14, 7.58, 7.88, and 8.00 were
added at 5°C to 4 x 45 mm columns (a) to (j) respectively of CM-52 cellulose (Whatman
Biochemicals, Maidstone, U.K.) equilibrated with the same buffers. The protein samples
were each washed with two further aliquots (1 ml) of the corresponding buffers and the
combined eluates collected in vials prior to spectrophotometric estimation of the
eluted haemoglobin at 550 nm to give the contour (●——●). The estimated isoelectric
point[3] of human haemoglobin A is indicated by the arrow

ACKNOWLEDGEMENT

The author is indebted to Mrs. G.M. Grant for very
skilled technical assistance in this work.

REFERENCES

1. MARGOLIS, J. and KENDRICK, K.G., 'Polyacrylamide
   Gel Electrophoresis in a Continuous Molecular
   Sieve Gradient'. Anal. Biochem., 25, 347-362
   (1968)
2. SLATER, G.G., 'Stable Position Formation and
   Determination of Molecular Size by Pore Limit
   Electrophoresis'. Anal. Chem., 41, 1039-1041
   (1969)
3. KOPPERSCHLAGER, G., DIEZEL, W., BIERWAGEN, B.
   and HOFMANN, E., 'Molekulargewichtsbestimmungen
   durch Polyacrylamid Gelelektrophorese unter
   Verwendung Eines Linearen Gelgradienten'.
   FEBS Lett., 5, 221-224 (1969)
4. ANDERSON, L.O., BOURG, H. and MICHELSON, M.,
   'Molecular Weight Estimations of Proteins by
   Electrophoresis in Polyacrylamide Gels of
   Graded Porosity'. FEBS Lett., 20, 199-202
   (1972)
5. MARGOLIS, J., 'Gradient Pore Electrophoresis'.
   Lab. Practice, 22, 107-109 (1973)
6. LEABACK, D.H., RUTTER, A.C. and WALKER, P.G.,
   'Some Applications of Gel Electrofocusing to
   the Separation and Characterization of
   Proteins'. Protides of the Biological Fluids,
   Ed. H. Peeters, Pergamon Press, Oxford,
   423-426 (1970)
7. LEABACK, D.H. and WALKER, P.G., 'Some
   Applications of Gel Isoelectric Focusing to the
   Examination of Human Serum Proteins'. Proc.
   Roy. Soc. Med., 64, 645-646 (1971)
8. ROBINSON, H.K. and LEABACK, D.H., 'A New
   Systematic Strategy for the Isolation of
   Proteins' (manuscript in preparation)
9. LAMPSON, G.P. and TYTELL, A.A., 'A Simple Method
   for Estimating Isoelectric Points'. Anal.
   Biochem., 11, 374-377 (1965)
10. LEABACK, D.H. and WALKER, P.G., 'Some
    Properties of Pig Epididymal
    β-N-acetyl-D-glucosaminidase'. Biochem. J.,
    104, 70-71P (1957)
11. ROBINSON, H.K., 'Comparison of Different
    Techniques for Isoelectric Focusing on
    Polyacrylamide Gel Slabs using Bacterial
    Asparaginases'. Anal. Biochem., 49, 353-366
    (1972)

12. WEISS, J.B., 'Chromatographic and
    Electrophoretic Techniques' Vol. 2, Ed. I.
    Smith, Heinemann Medical Books Ltd., p. 43
    (1968)

13. DRYSDALE, J.W., RIGHETTI, P. and BUNN, H.F.,
    'The Separation of Human and Animal
    Haemoglobins by Isoelectric Focusing in
    Polyacrylamide Gel'. Biochim. Biophys. Acta,
    229, 42-50 (1971)

16. MULTIPLE FORMS OF BACTERIAL TOXINS
IN PREPARATIVE ISOELECTRIC FOCUSING

J.P. Arbuthnott, A.C. McNiven and C.J. Smyth

16.1 GENERAL INTRODUCTION

The isolation of extracellular enzymes and toxins in
a highly purified form from culture filtrates of
organisms which release numerous proteins of similar
charge and molecular weight has presented
considerable difficulty. Preparative isoelectric
focusing has proved particularly useful since it
combines the following advantages:
  (i)   it has high resolving power,
  (ii)   it avoids the necessity for complex
         purification procedures,
  (iii) it is intrinsically a gentle method,
  (iv)   it results in concentration as well as
         purification,
  (v)   it allows the processing of relatively large
         amounts of protein.
    For these reasons the technique has been widely
used. Against these advantages must be set some
limitations, such as:
  (i)   the high cost of Ampholine,
  (ii)   difficulties due to isoelectric precipitation
  (iii) limitations of the geometry of currently
         available columns,
  (iv)   the possible importance of artefacts.
    It was soon realised that preparations of
bacterial toxins, apparently homogeneous by several
criteria, exhibited the presence of multiple forms
when examined by isoelectric focusing. Numerous
toxin preparations have been shown to contain
several components which have similar
physico-chemical and biological properties but which
have different isoelectric points (pIs). This
chapter is intended to summarise the application of
preparative isoelectric focusing to the study of

bacterial toxins and to assess the significance of
multiple forms. Possible reasons for such
heterogeneity will be discussed. The principal
causes of multiple forms of enzymes have been
outlined by many authors[1-4] and are summarised in
Table 16.1.

Table 16.1 Possible causes of multiple forms of
    enzymes as revealed by isoelectric focusing

_____

1. Genetically determined differences in primary
   protein structure

2. Protein-protein interactions
   (i)   involving unrelated proteins
   (ii)   involving identical subunits
   (iii) involving non-identical subunits

3. Differences in covalent structure
   (i)   deamidation of asparagine and glutamine
          residues
   (ii)   cleavage of the peptide chain due to the
          action of proteases
   (iii) attachment of carbohydrate, e.g. sialic
          acid
   (iv)   oxidation of sulphydryl groups
   (v)   oxidation of prosthetic groups
   (vi)   phosphorylation
   (vii) carbamylation due to reaction with
          cyanate ions present in high molarity
          urea solutions

4. Ligand binding

5. Protein-Ampholine interactions

6. Differences in conformation due to exposure of
   charged groups or molecular folding resulting
   in burial of previously exposed charged groups

_____

    By examining each component for immunological
identity or non-identity and where possible by
comparing amino acid compositions it is possible to
establish or exclude cause 1. Similarly, molecular
weight determinations allow an evaluation of cause
2. However, where multiple forms are
immunologically identical and have the same or
closely similar molecular weights there is
generally insufficient information available to
establish whether causes 3, 4, 5 or 6 are

H

responsible for heterogeneity. This is because the
amounts of individual components obtained by
preparative isoelectric focusing are generally
insufficient to allow detailed chemical analysis or
studies of protein conformation. It is perhaps
worth pointing out that systematic analysis of
conformational changes in proteins has been
restricted to a relatively small number of well
characterised proteins. Nevertheless, the presence
of 'conformers' is suggested where multiple forms
can be shown to be interconvertible. Also the work
of Ui[5,6] suggests that useful information can be
obtained from isoelectric focusing experiments
carried out in the presence of 6 M urea.

16.2   BACTERIAL TOXINS EXAMINED BY PREPARATIVE
         ISOELECTRIC FOCUSING

16.2.1 The Toxins of Staphylococcus aureus

Staphylococcus aureus produces many extracellular
toxins and enzymes and these were among the first
bacterial proteins to be studied by the technique
of preparative isoelectric focusing. For instance,
staphylococcal hyaluronate lyase and lipase were
investigated by Vesterberg et al.[7], and
staphylococcal deoxyribonuclease by Wadström[8].
Since then, most work has been concerned with the
resolution of the haemolytic toxins (α-, β-, γ-,
and δ-toxins), the enterotoxins and the recently
discovered epidermolytic toxin. Table 16.2 lists
the staphylococcal toxins which have been examined
by isoelectric focusing and gives a brief summary
of their properties. The isoelectric points
determined by isoelectric focusing are summarised
in Table 16.3. Since multiple forms have been
reported most often for staphylococcal α-toxin and
the enterotoxins, these will be discussed in detail.

Staphylococcal α-toxin   In 1962 Madoff and
Weinstein[26] observed two bands of α-toxin which
migrated slowly towards the cathode on starch gel
electrophoresis. Also, two components of the toxin
were found on moving boundary electrophoresis[27].
However, the first detailed study[28] of the
electrophoretic heterogeneity was made by density
gradient electrophoresis of partially purified
α-toxin; this revealed the presence of four distinct
peaks which were antigenically identical and
exhibited only minor differences in their biological
activities. Further evidence for the existence of
multiple forms came from the isoelectric focusing
study of Wadström[9]. Using culture filtrates from

Table 16.2   Properties of staphylococcal toxins

Toxin	Main properties
α-Toxin	Haemolytic, mainly for rabbit RBC (2×10^4 H.U./mg), lethal and dermonecrotic. Surface-active protein acting on cell membranes. $S_{20w} = 3.0$, Aggregation induced by certain lipids
β-Toxin	Hot-cold haemolysin acting on sheep and bovine RBC. Phospholipase C which hydrolyses only sphingomyelin. Requires Mg^{2+} ions
γ-Toxin	Poorly characterised. Haemolytic but antigenically distinct from α- and β-toxins
δ-Toxin	Haemolytic for RBC of many species. Surface-active. Widely differing molecular weights reported
Enterotoxins	Six serologically distinct toxins (A, B, C_1, C_2, D, E). Responsible for symptoms of staphylococcal food poisoning. Amino acid sequence of toxin B unknown
Epidermolytic toxin	Responsible for the symptoms of toxic epidermal necrolysis (scalded skin syndrome)

three strains of S. aureus he found four α-toxin components which he termed αIa, αIb, αII and αIII; these had pI values of 8.5, 9.1 to 9.2, 6.5 to 7.5 and 4.5 to 5.5, respectively. It was Wadström who first showed the value of preparative isoelectric focusing as a method of purifying staphylococcal α-toxin; he observed that up to 80% of the toxic activity could be recovered as the αIa form with a 40-fold increase in specific activity.

In a review of bacterial cytolytic toxins[10], Bernheimer commented briefly that his previously unpublished results also indicated the presence of multiple forms of staphylococcal α-toxin in isoelectric focusing experiments. The five forms reported by Bernheimer (pI values: 6.8, 7.1, 8.1, 8.3 and 8.7) did not agree with Wadström's values.

Table 16.3   Isoelectric points of staphylococcal toxins

Toxin	Reported pIs				References
α-Toxin	4.5——5.5	6.5——7.5	8.0———8.7* 9.1-9.2		Wadström[9] Bernheimer[10]
		6.8 7.1	8.1 8.3 8.7 9.15		McNiven, Owen and Arbuthnott[11]
		6.3 7.4	8.55		Six and Harshman[12]
		7.2	8.4		
β-Toxin	3.0			9.4	Wadström and Möllby[13]
				9.5	Maheswaran and Lindorfer[14]
				9.0	Bernheimer, Avigad and Kim[15]
γ-Toxin				9.5	Möllby and Wadström[16]
δ-Toxin	3.3 3.75	5.0	8.45	9.5	Kreger et al.[17] Maheswaran and Lindorfer[18]
				9.6	Möllby and Wadström[19]

Table 16.3 (contd.)

Toxin	Reported pIs								References
Enterotoxin A	6.6	_7.3_	7.7	8.1					Schantz et al.[20]
Enterotoxin B	7.8	8.0	_8.25_	8.55					Chang and Dickie[21]
		8.5	9.05	9.4	9.56				Metzger, Johnson and Collins[22]
Enterotoxin C$_2$	5.5	5.9	6.65						Chang et al.[23]
	5.5	5.7	5.95						_Dickie et al.[24]_
	6.2	6.55	7.35						
	6.75	6.95							
Epidermolytic Toxin	_7.0_								Melish, Glasgow and Turner[25]
	6.2	_7.0_							Arbuthnott et al. (unpublished observations)

* Underlined values indicate the pIs of the main forms.

Although no information was given to indicate
whether or not narrow pH gradients were used, it
seems possible that the 8.1, 8.3 and 8.7 components
reflect microheterogeneity not detected by
Wadström[9].

A detailed investigation was undertaken by
McNiven, Owen and Arbuthnott[11] in order

(i)   to reassess the behaviour of the multiple
        haemolytic components of S. aureus (strain
        Wood 46) in preparative isoelectric
        focusing,

(ii)   to identify the components by biological and
        immunological tests, and

(iii)   to examine individual components in
        refocusing experiments.

Some aspects of this study will be presented in
detail since it is one of the most complete yet
reported and illustrates the problems associated
with the investigation of multiple forms of
bacterial toxins.

As can be seen from Figure 16.1, up to six
haemolytic components were detected although not all
of the components were found in all experiments.
Table 16.4 summarises the mean pI values of the
haemolytic components determined in several
experiments. The distribution of haemolytic
activity expressed as a percentage of the total
recovered activity for six large-scale preparative
experiments is shown in Table 16.5.

A main component accounting for 87 to 99% of
the recovered haemolytic activity having a pI value
of 8.55 ± 0.12 was detected consistently. Apart
from components 2 (pI value 6.26 ± 0.11) and 4 (pI
value 8.55 ± 0.12), the appearance of haemolytic
components in individual experiments was
inconsistent. At the present time, it is not
possible to explain this variation in terms of the
batch of toxin used, the treatment prior to
isoelectric focusing (e.g. time of storage under
ammonium sulphate), the amount of protein applied
to the column, the total haemolytic activity
applied to the column or the duration of the
isoelectric focusing run.

The identity of each haemolytic component,
after removal of Ampholine by ammonium sulphate
precipitation, was investigated by testing for
haemolytic activity against the erythrocytes of
several mammalian species and by immunological
tests. Components 3, 4 and 5 had the marked
specificity for rabbit erythrocytes typical of
purified staphylococcal α-toxin whereas components
1 and 6 exhibited little species specificity;

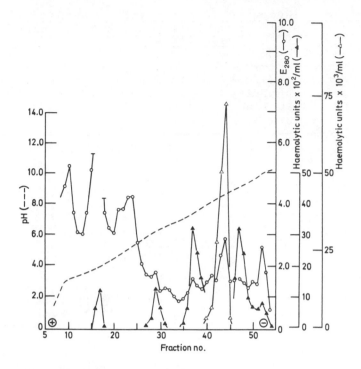

Figure 16.1 Isoelectric focusing of a crude ammonium sulphate precipitate of Staphylococcus aureus α-toxin; 795.0 mg were applied to an LKB 8102 column in a pH gradient of 3 to 10. The experiment was performed at 4°C at 800 V for 67 h. (Reproduced by courtesy of J. Med. Microbiol.,[11])

Table 16.4 Isoelectric points of the haemolytic components of S. aureus

Component no.	No. of determinations	Mean pI (± S.E.)
1	4	4.32 ± 0.24
2	11	6.26 ± 0.11
3	6	7.36 ± 0.03
4	26	8.55 ± 0.12
5	16	9.15 ± 0.07
6	5	10.01 ± 0.05

Table 16.5 Recovery of haemolytic components of
S. aureus in six large-scale isoelectric focusing
experiments

Protein applied (mg)	Haemolytic activity applied (H.U.)	Distribution of recovered activity (%)					
		Component no.					
		1	2	3	4	5	6
1 128	9.0×10^6	0.2	1.3	-	98.5	-	-
780	2.5×10^6	-	0.6	1.1	98.3	-	-
262	8.8×10^5	-	0.4	1.4	92.7	3.9	1.6
795	8.3×10^6	1.0	1.3	4.8	87.3	4.5	1.1
794	5.3×10^6	2.0	0.4	-	94.0	2.1	1.5
594	1.6×10^6	0.1	0.6	5.7	91.0	-	2.6

component 2 occupied an intermediate position in
haemolysis tests. Neutralisation tests with
standard α-antitoxin showed that within experimental
error, the haemolytic activities of components 2, 3,
4 and 5 were quantitatively neutralised while the
activity of components 1 and 6 was not neutralised
even at high concentrations of antitoxin. In double
diffusion tests (Figures 16.2 and 16.3) the main
line of precipitation obtained with component 4
against α-antitoxin gave a reaction of identity with
components 2 and 3 and a reaction of partial
identity with component 5. Components 1 and 6 did
not show reactions of identity with the main line of
precipitation. These findings indicate that
components 2, 3, 4 and 5 represent multiple forms of
staphylococcal α-toxin and the forms were designated
α_A (pI value 8.55 ± 0.12), α_B (pI value 9.15 ± 0.07),
α_C (pI value 7.36 ± 0.03) and α_D (pI value
6.28 ± 0.11).

In experiments in which high activity fractions
of α_A were pooled and refocused, between two and
four α-toxin forms reappeared (Table 16.6). The
main component was again α_A accounting for 66 to 96%
of the recovered activity. The amounts of α_B were
higher when several α_A fractions were pooled for
refocusing than if the two peak fractions of α_A were
selected for refocusing (Table 16.6). However, α_B
was always present and its appearance in experiments
in which fractions in the pH range 8.2 to 8.5 were
refocused suggests that it was not merely a
contaminant of the α_A fractions. The converse,

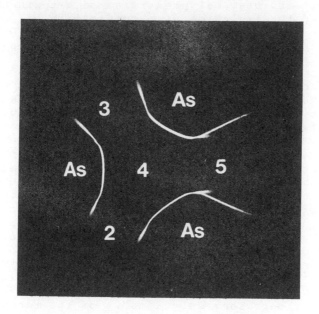

<u>Figure 16.2</u> Double radial immunodiffusion pattern
demonstrating the antigenic relationship of
components 2, 3, 4 and 5. AS, Standard antiserum
(CPP76/33, Wellcome Research Laboratories,
Beckenham, Kent); 2, component 2 (pI value
6.28 ± 0.11); 3, component 3 (pI value 7.36 ± 0.03);
4, component 4 (pI value 8.55 ± 0.12); 5, component
5 (pI value 9.15 ± 0.07). (Reproduced by courtesy
of <u>J. Med. Microbiol.</u>)

namely the formation of α_A from α_B, was demonstrated
by refocusing single peak fractions of α_B; in this
case α_B accounted for 67% and α_A for 33% of the
recovered activity. As mentioned earlier, this
observation of reversible interconversion is
important in assessing possible causes of multiple
forms. It is also important to note that when α_A
was refocused in the presence of 6 M urea, the
α-toxin activity was recovered as a single peak
having a pI value of 8.5.
     Before discussing possible reasons for the
appearance of multiple forms of staphylococcal
α-toxin, it is necessary to pin-point the areas of
agreement and disagreement in the findings of
different authors. The most recent in a series of
studies of this toxin is the work of Six and
Harshman[12]. In a comprehensive investigation of the

physical and chemical properties of α-toxin they
reported the isolation by a combination of ammonium
sulphate precipitation, gel filtration and
preparative gel electrophoresis, of two main forms
termed A and B in milligram quantities. On
isoelectric focusing form A had a pI value of 7.25
and accounted for 15% of the activity; form B had a
pI value of 8.4 and accounted for 84% of the
activity. It was stated briefly that 'No evidence
for interconversion of the forms was obtained'.
Despite the confusing use of different systems of
nomenclature and some discrepancies regarding minor
forms, there is general agreement that the main form
of staphylococcal α-toxin has a pI of around 8.5.
Comparison of the values reported for the minor
forms of α-toxin (Table 16.3) reveals strong
evidence for the existence of a minor form having a
pI of 7.1 to 7.4, and also suggests that another
more anodic form exists. There is also good
agreement[9,11] that concentrated culture filtrates
contain a minor α-toxin form having a pI value of
9.1 to 9.2. It is important to note that such minor
forms may represent only 1 to 2% of the recovered
activity and that for this reason it is essential to
use accurate and sensitive assays when screening for
the presence of multiple forms.

     McNiven et al.[11] obtained enough of the forms
of α-toxin with pI values of 8.5 and 9.1 to carry
out refocusing experiments in the presence and
absence of urea. The important conclusions relating
to possible causes for the existence of these two
forms were:

  (i)   refocusing of the 8.5 form always gave rise
         to small amounts of the 9.1 form,
  (ii)   refocusing of the 9.1 form yielded a mixture
         of the 8.5 and 9.1 forms,
  (iii) the 8.5 form when refocused in 6 M urea did
         not give rise to multiple forms,
  (iv)   in SDS disc gel electrophoresis, both the 8.5
         and the 9.1 forms contained a major protein
         component having a molecular weight of
         36 000 and a minor component having a
         molecular weight of 170 000.

     Taken together, these observations suggest that
the two forms do not differ in primary protein
structure. They are also inconsistent with changes
in covalent structure resulting either from the
removal of positively charged groups (e.g.
deamidation) or the introduction of negatively
charged groups. Moreover, Wadström[9] was unable to
demonstrate heterogeneity with respect to molecular
weight in mixtures of the different α-toxin

components examined by gel filtration, and McNiven et al.[11] could find no difference in the molecular weights of the components with pI values of 8.5 and 9.1 by SDS disc gel electrophoresis. The most probable explanation would seem to be that the 8.5 and the 9.1 components represent conformationally different forms of staphylococcal α-toxin similar to the two forms of colicin E_2 (ref. 29). From the distribution of the two forms after refocusing it appears likely that the 8.5 component is the most kinetically and thermodynamically stable form[1]. It is not possible from available data, however, to exclude the possibility that during purification the toxin molecule binds low molecular weight material or undergoes slight proteolysis leading to the formation of an equilibrium between the 8.5 and 9.1 forms. It is interesting to note that Six and Harshman[12] have shown that α-toxin 'binds' up to 25 to 30 molecules of Tris per molecule of toxin. It is encouraging that this group is currently performing a detailed physico-chemical analysis of their A and B forms of α-toxin which have identical molecular weights, very similar amino acid compositions, identical amino acid sequences at the N-terminal ends of the molecules and yield similar peptides on treatment with cyanogen bromide. Such investigations, together with conformational analysis studies, are essential if the appearance of multiple forms is to be adequately explained.

<u>Staphylococcal enterotoxins</u>   Preparative isoelectric focusing has revealed the presence of multiple forms of enterotoxins A, B and C_2. However, these have been less well characterised than the various forms of α-toxin.

Enterotoxin A, found to be homogeneous by several criteria, was resolved into four forms having pI values of 8.14, 7.68, 7.26 and 6.64 by preparative isoelectric focusing[20]; the major form had a pI value of 7.26. No refocusing experiments were carried out and the separated forms were not characterised. It is not possible, therefore, to discuss the possible causes of heterogeneity of enterotoxin A.

Two groups have reported multiple forms of enterotoxin B. In 1971 Chang and Dickie[21] reported the existence of two major electrophoretic forms of enterotoxin B; these had pI values of 8.55 and 8.25. Minor components were detected at pHs 7.8 and 8.0. Both major forms were biologically and serologically identical and had the same molecular weight (24 500). In refocusing experiments, the form with

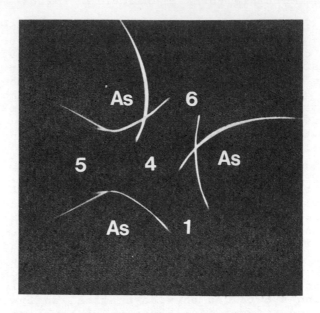

Figure 16.3 Double radial immunodiffusion pattern demonstrating the antigenic relationship of components 1, 4, 5 and 6. AS, Standard antiserum (CPP76/63, Wellcome Research Laboratories, Beckenham, Kent); 1, component 1 (pI value 4.32 ± 0.24); 4, component 4 (pI value 8.55 ± 0.12); 5, component 5 (pI value 9.15 ± 0.07); 6, component 6 (pI value 10.01 ± 0.05). (Reproduced by courtesy of J. Med. Microbiol.)

Table 16.6 Refocusing of α_A fractions of staphylococcal α-toxin

No. of fractions pooled	pH range of pooled fractions	Distribution of recovered haemolytic activity			
		α_A	α_B	α_C	α_D
5	7.7 - 8.5	66.2	33.8	-	S*
3	8.2 - 8.7	93.5	6.5	S*	-
2	8.2 - 8.5	94.8	5.2	-	-
2	8.5 - 8.7	93.4	6.6	-	-

* S denotes shoulder not fully resolved.

a pI value of 8.55 gave rise to a mixture of the
8.55 and 8.25 forms; by contrast, the 8.25 form did
not yield the 8.55 form on refocusing. This type of
observation, namely the formation of more anodic
components on refocusing, is common and has been
reported for many proteins. Such findings are
usually explained in terms of deamidation of the
labile amide groups of glutamine and/or asparagine
residues. Although early work[30-32] suggested that
deamidation was responsible for the heterogeneity of
bovine milk lactoperoxidase and cytochrome C, it has
proved exceedingly difficult to produce conclusive
chemical evidence of deamidation (e.g. see Awdeh,
Williamson and Askonas[33]). Midelfort and Mehler[34]
demonstrated that the microheterogeneity of rabbit
muscle aldolase was caused by deamidation in vivo
of an asparagine residue near to the C terminus of
each subunit.

Results conflicting with those of Chang and
Dickie[21] have been reported by Metzger, Johnson and
Collins[22], who studied the behaviour of enterotoxin
B in narrow-range pH gradients. The four forms
isolated by this group had pI values of 9.56, 9.4,
9.05 and 8.5. The main form (pI value 9.4) was
found to be stable on refocusing. Metzger et al.[22]
pointed out that Chang and Dickie[21] measured the
pHs of their fractions at room temperature and not
at 4°C and that the latter pooled several fractions
in refocusing experiments. Both criticisms are
valid, but unfortunately Metzger et al.[22] base their
conclusions on the $E_{280\ nm}$ profiles and did not
determine the biological activity of the
fractionated toxin. This is unsatisfactory since
significant amounts of biological activity often
account for only a small proportion of the total
protein.

Multiple forms of a third staphylococcal
enterotoxin, C_2 have been described[23,24]. The first
study described the resolution of purified
enterotoxin C_2 into three forms with pI values of
6.65, 5.9 and 5.0. These were biologically and
serologically identical and had the same molecular
weight (30 000). No refocusing experiments were
performed and deamidation was again suggested as an
explanation for the appearance of multiple forms.
In a more detailed study of the toxin in pH 5 to 8
gradients, up to eight immunologically identical
components with pI values of 7.35, 6.95, 6.75, 6.55,
6.20, 5.95, 5.7 and 5.50 were found[24]. Like McNiven
et al.[11], they observed that the proportions of
individual forms varied in different experiments.
The 6.95, 5.95 and 6.75 components were refocused

and each gave rise to a mixture of three or four
components. In almost every case the additional
forms were more anodic than the form subjected to
refocusing. Although deamidation is mentioned as a
possible reason for heterogeneity, the components
were not characterised and refocusing in the
presence of 6 M urea was not performed.

Other staphylococcal toxins The description of
multiple forms of other staphylococcal toxins is at
present poorly documented. Staphylococcal β-toxin
(sphingomyelinase C) appears to exist in a single
cationic form having a pI value of 9.0 to 9.4. A
minor acidic component (pI value 3.0) of β-toxin
was found to be associated with insoluble acidic
material[13] and this is probably an artefact. As so
often reported for other proteins when the main
β-toxin component (pI value 9.4), prepared by
isoelectric focusing in broad pH gradients, was
refocused in narrow gradients (pH 8.0 to 10.0),
microheterogeneity was demonstrated[13] with peaks
appearing at pH 9.8, 9.4, 9.2 and 8.8, but this
finding was not studied further.

It is only recently that staphylococcal γ-toxin
has been generally accepted as a distinct entity
despite the fact that evidence of this was presented
as long ago as 1956[35]. In the only isoelectric
focusing study of this toxin so far[16] it was found
to have a pI value of 9.5. The detailed
characterisation of a staphylococcal γ-toxin must
await the preparation of concentrated high potency
material.

There have been many attempts to characterise
staphylococcal δ-toxin. However, by 1970 so many
conflicting results had been reported that
Bernheimer[10] concluded that different groups might
not have been studying the same substance. A
possible reason for this confusion is that δ-toxin
can exist in varying states of aggregation[17]. From
Table 16.3 it can be seen that the main δ-toxin
component was found to be a basic protein[16,17] (pI
value 9.5 to 9.6) and McNiven et al.[11] concluded
that a haemolytic component which focused at pH 10.0
was probably δ-toxin. An acidic form of δ-toxin
(pI value 5.0) has also been described[17].
Protein-protein interactions may explain the
existence of two forms of δ-toxin since a
considerable difference in the molecular weights of
the 9.5 form (68 000) and the 5.0 form (200 000)
has been reported[17].

The most recently discovered staphylococcal
toxin, epidermolytic toxin, has been reported to

have a pI of approximately 7.0 (refs. 25,36). Recently
Arbuthnott et al. (unpublished observations), using
ammonium sulphate-precipitated epidermolytic toxin,
have detected a second component having a pI value
of 6.2.

16.2.2 The Toxins of Clostridium Species

In common with Staphylococcus aureus, members of the
genus Clostridium produce many extracellular toxins
and enzymes. However, by contrast with the
staphylococcal toxins which are almost all basic
proteins focusing in the pH 7.0 to 10.0 region, the
clostridial products are acidic proteins focusing in
the pH 4.0 to 7.0 region. The clostridial toxins
include the most potent exotoxins known, including
the neurotoxins of Cl. tetani and Cl. botulinum.
Although these toxins were crystallised many years
ago and have since been well characterised, there
have been only two reports of isoelectric focusing
studies of the botulinum toxin. It is in the study
of the less well characterised toxins of
Cl. perfringens (welchii) of toxinological type A
that the technique of preparative isoelectric
focusing has been most used (Table 16.7). This is
because it has proved particularly difficult to
separate the numerous extracellular products of
this organism by other methods. Recent work[39-41,44]
has established the value of isoelectric focusing in
the purification of Cl. perfringens type A α-toxin
which is known to be a phospholipase C (E.C.
3.1.4.3). This toxin, which is also both haemolytic
and lethal, has been widely used in investigations
of the structure and function of biological
membranes. It is important to emphasise that
commercially available preparations of
Cl. perfringens phospholipase C contain numerous
contaminating activities including θ-toxin,
hyaluronidase (μ-toxin), collagenase (κ-toxin),
neuraminidase, deoxyribonuclease, α-glucosidase,
endo-β-N-glucosaminidase, phosphatase and
sulphatase[39]. Many of these factors may affect
membranes and the use of Cl. perfringens
phospholipase C in membrane studies can only be
justified if highly purified preparations are used.
     Recently, food poisoning strains of
Cl. perfringens type A were shown to produce an
enterotoxin causing fluid accumulation in the small
intestine of experimental animals. Tests in human
volunteers established that this factor induces the
symptoms of clostridial food poisoning. Preparative
isoelectric focusing has, again, proved useful in
the purification and characterisation of this toxin.

Table 16.7 Isoelectric points of clostridial toxins

Toxin	Reported pIs	Reference
Cl. perfringens α-Toxin	5.2 5.5	Bernheimer, Grushoff and Avigad[37]
	5.3 5.6	Sugahara and Ohsaka[38]
	4.7 5.7	Möllby, Nord and Wadström[39]
	5.25 5.5	Smyth and Arbuthnott[40, 41]
Cl. perfringens θ-Toxin	6.56	Smyth and Arbuthnott[41]
	5.7—5.9 6.2-6.3 6.5-6.6 6.8-6.9	Smyth[42]
	6.8	Möllby and Wadström[44]
Cl. perfringens Enterotoxin	4.3	Hauschild and Hilsheimer[45]

Table 16.7 (contd.)

Toxin	Reported pIs	Reference
Cl. perfringens Hyaluronidase (μ-toxin)	4.73	Smyth and Arbuthnott[41]
	4.7	Möllby, Nord and Wadström[39]
Cl. perfringens Collagenase (κ-toxin)	4.54	Smyth and Arbuthnott[41]
Cl. botulinum Type A toxin	4.5, 8.5	Galdiero, Tufano and Cerciello[46]
Cl. botulinum Type B toxin	5.25	Beers and Reich[47]

The toxins of Cl. perfringens type A In 1962
Ispolatovskaya and Levdikova[48] observed that
partially purified preparations of α-toxin eluted
from carboxymethyl cellulose columns as two well
defined peaks. Starch gel electrophoresis of
lyophilised preparations revealed up to five bands
of α-toxin activity[49]. Preparative isoelectric
focusing[37,38] indicated the existence of two forms
of α-toxin with pI values of 5.2 to 5.3 and 5.5 to
5.6. These authors were concerned only with
describing the presence of multiple forms. The
detailed study of Smyth and Arbuthnott[40,41] was
undertaken to investigate the relationship of these
forms to one another and to develop a method which
would yield milligram quantities of highly purified
α-toxin free from the other toxins of
Cl. perfringens. Again, since this represents one
of the most comprehensive isoelectric focusing
studies of clostridial toxins, the main findings
will be presented here.

   The material used consisted of ammonium
sulphate-precipitated culture filtrates of two
strains (S 107 and BP 6K) of Cl. perfringens type A
and a lyophilised sample (AGX 1846) kindly supplied
by Wellcome Research Laboratories, Beckenham, Kent.
In broad pH gradients the α-toxin focused as a
single peak (pI value 5.2) and was separated from
the bulk of the collagenase, hyaluronidase and
θ-toxin activities. However, the recovery of
biological activity was low and when fractions were
pooled, contaminating amounts of other activities
were detected. This led to the selection of narrow
pH gradients (pH 4 to 6) for purification studies.
In such gradients as much as 3.87 g of crude
material were applied to the 440 ml column. A high
degree of resolution was achieved and up to 80% of
the α-toxin activity could be recovered (Figure
16.4). Most of this appeared in fractions within
the pH range 5.1 to 5.6 with a peak of activity at
pH 5.5; a pronounced shoulder was present on the
anodic side of the α-toxin peak. In other
experiments, this shoulder was clearly resolved into
a second peak having a pI value of 5.25. Refocusing
of pooled fractions from the main α-toxin component
yielded two peaks of activity, a major component (pI
value 5.49) termed α_A and a minor component (pI value
5.25) termed α_B. Collagenase, hyaluronidase,
neuraminidase and θ-toxin could not be detected
in α_A preparations. An identical pattern was
obtained with the AGX 1846 batch of toxin supplied

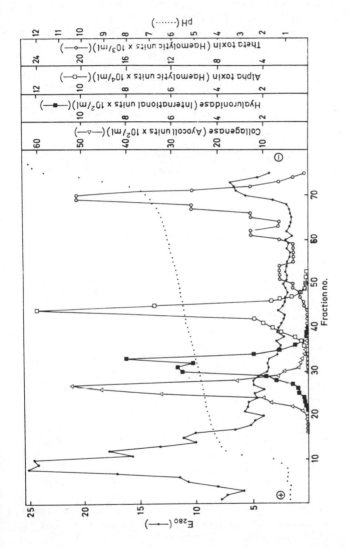

Figure 16.4 Separation of α-toxin, θ-toxin, collagenase and hyaluronidase from *Cl. perfringens* BP6K by isoelectric focusing in a pH gradient of 4 to 6. 650 mg of 35–50% saturation ammonium sulphate precipitate of culture filtrate were applied to an LKB 8101 column. The experiment was performed at 4°C at 800 V for 70 h. (Reproduced by courtesy of J. Med. Microbiol., [42])

by Wellcome Research laboratories and was comparable to the material used by Bernheimer et al.[37]. Both α_A and α_B were found to contain the hot-cold haemolytic activity, phospholipase C and lethal activities typical of Cl. perfringens α-toxin. Moreover, the ratios of these activities were of the same order for both components and compared well with the ratio of the three activities in the material applied to the isoelectric focusing column.

Batch AGX 1846, when focused in the presence of 6 M urea, exhibited a single peak with an average pI value of 5.52 ± 0.6, corresponding to the α_A form. Refocusing of this component in the absence of urea again gave rise to two components with pI values typical of α_A and α_B.

These findings, when viewed in relation to the results of other workers, indicate good agreement regarding the heterogeneity of Cl. perfringens α-toxin as revealed by preparative isoelectric focusing. Three independent groups[37-41] have detected two forms corresponding to α_A and α_B. A fourth group[39] reported the presence of two α-toxin components in commercial preparations of Cl. perfringens phospholipase C; their component with a pI value of 5.7 could correspond to α_A but the pI value 4.7 form of the enzyme is considerably more acidic than α_B.

The results of Smyth and Arbuthnott[40,41] indicate that α_B disappears in the presence of 6 M urea and reappears on removal of urea suggesting that the change in isoelectric point responsible for the formation of α_B is reversible. This, together with the fact that α_A and α_B are immunologically identical, excludes the possibility that these forms differ in primary structure. Protein-protein interactions seem unlikely since both Bernheimer et al.[37] and Smyth and Arbuthnott[40,41] find that α_A and α_B have the same molecular weight; furthermore, they have argued against deamidation, carbamylation and loss of carbohydrate moieties as possible reasons for multiple forms.

A reduction in heterogeneity in the presence of 6 M urea was taken to suggest that multiple forms observed in the absence of urea were conformationally related[5,6]. On this basis it is possible to speculate that α_B represents a conformer of α_A in which positive charges are shielded following folding of the molecule. However, the effect of ammonium sulphate, which is used both in the initial fractionation of culture filtrates and in the removal of Ampholines after isoelectric

focusing, remains to be investigated. It is
interesting to note here that Möllby and Wadström[44],
who avoided the use of ammonium sulphate, detected
only one component (pI value 5.7) in purified
preparations of Cl. perfringens α-toxin. It is
possible that certain concentration procedures, such
as ammonium sulphate precipitation or
lyophilisation, may induce conformational changes in
the toxin molecule. Moreover, the possibility that
ligand binding is involved in this process cannot be
excluded.

Of the other clostridial toxins listed in
Table 16.7, the θ-toxin shows most evidence of
multiple forms. Although Smyth and Arbuthnott[41]
reported a value of 6.56 for the pI of the main
θ-toxin component, inspection of the elution profile
shown in Figure 16.4 suggests the existence of
multiple forms. In a more detailed study of this
toxin, Smyth[42] has found evidence of four forms
having pI values of 5.7 to 5.9, 6.2 to 6.3, 6.5 to
6.6 and 6.8 to 6.9.

16.2.3 Miscellaneous Bacterial Toxins
As pointed out earlier, to date most isoelectric
focusing studies on bacterial toxins have been of
staphylococcal and clostridial toxins. A few
reports relating to the haemolytic toxins of other
organisms are listed in Table 16.8.

Table 16.8 Isoelectric points of various haemolysins

Toxin	Reported pIs		References
Streptolysin O	6.5		Bernheimer et al.[37]
	6.1 (major)	7.6 (minor)	Smyth and Fehrenbach[43]
Cereolysin	6.5		Bernheimer et al.[37]
Aeromonas haemolysin	4.3; 5.5		Wretlind et al.[50]

The oxygen-labile haemolysin of Streptococcus
pyogenes (streptolysin O) has properties in common
with other oxygen-labile haemolysins, namely,
pneumolysin, tetanolysin, Cl. perfringens θ-toxin,
and the cereolysin of Bacillus cereus. All are

neutralised by hyperimmune anti-streptolysin O, all
are activated by reducing agents and all are
inhibited by cholesterol. The pI of streptolysin O
when determined by Bernheimer et al.[37], was 6.5;
a value of 6.1 for the major form of streptolysin O
has also been reported[43]. It is worth noting that
cereolysin also had a pI value of 6.5[37] and as
mentioned previously, the main component of
Cl. perfringens θ-toxin also has a pI in this
region. These findings emphasise the similarities
in the properties of the oxygen-labile haemolysins.
     Table 16.8 includes the pI values of the
components with haemolytic activity from Aeromonas
hydrophila; unlike all the other bacteria so far
mentioned, this organism is gram-negative.

16.3   CONCLUSIONS

This article summarises preparative isoelectric
focusing studies of bacterial toxins. These
proteins are of interest both because of their
physico-chemical properties and their potent
biological activities. As more information is
obtained about their mode of action at the molecular
level it is likely that they will be used
increasingly as tools in the study of cell structure
and physiology.
     Some have been more thoroughly studied than
others, but it is possible to generalise that
preparative isoelectric focusing is of growing
importance as an aid to the purification of
bacterial toxins and that this technique has
revealed in many instances the existence of multiple
forms. There are, however, important discrepancies
between the findings of different research groups
and our knowledge of the causes of multiple forms
is fragmentary. In particular it seems that the
manner in which toxins are treated prior to
isoelectric focusing may induce changes in the
structure of the 'native' toxin molecule. Thus,
although there is good evidence that multiple forms
are not merely artefacts of isoelectric focusing,
it is more difficult to exclude the possibility that
the appearance of multiple forms is a consequence of
the method in which the crude toxin is pre-treated.
     Attempts have been made in a few cases (e.g.
staphylococcal α-toxin, staphylococcal enterotoxins,
Cl. perfringens α-toxin) to investigate the
relationship between the different forms. It is
encouraging that several authors now see the need
to prepare individual components in amounts which
will allow both chemical and conformational analysis.

REFERENCES

1. EPSTEIN, C.J. and SCHECHTER, A.N., 'An Approach
   to the Problem of Conformational Enzymes'.
   Ann. N.Y. Acad. Sci., 151, 85-101 (1968)
2. International Union of Pure and Applied
   Chemists - International Union of Biochemistry,
   'Commission on Biochemical Nomenclature. The
   Nomenclature of Multiple Forms of Enzymes.
   Recommendations'. Biochem. J., 126, 769-771
   (1971)
3. GLICK, J.M., KERR, S.J., GOLD, A.M. and SHEMIN,
   D., 'Multiple Forms of Colicin E3 from E. coli
   CA-38 (Col E3, Col I)'. Biochemistry, 11,
   1183-1188 (1972)
4. BACCANARI, D.P. and CHA, S., 'Succinate
   Thiokinase. VI. Multiple Interconvertible Forms
   of the Enzyme'. J. Biol. Chem., 248, 15-24
   (1973)
5. UI, N., 'Isoelectric Points and the
   Conformation of Proteins. I. Effect of Urea on
   the Behaviour of some Proteins in Isoelectric
   Focusing'. Biochim. Biophys. Acta, 229,
   567-581 (1971)
6. UI, N., 'Isoelectric Points and the
   Conformation of Proteins. II. Isoelectric
   Focusing of α-Chymotrypsin and its Inactive
   Derivatives'. Biochim. Biophys. Acta, 229,
   582-589 (1971)
7. VESTERBERG, O., WADSTRÖM, T., VESTERBERG, K.,
   SVENSSON, H. and MALMGREN, B., 'Studies on
   Extracellular Proteins from Staphylococcus
   aureus. I. Separation and Characterization of
   Enzymes and Toxins by Isoelectric Focusing'.
   Biochim. Biophys. Acta, 133, 435-445 (1967)
8. WADSTRÖM, T., 'Studies on Extracellular
   Proteins from Staphylococcus aureus. II.
   Separation of Deoxyribonucleases from
   Staphylococcus aureus by Isoelectric Focusing.
   Purification and Properties of the Enzymes'.
   Biochim. Biophys. Acta, 147, 441-452 (1967)
9. WADSTRÖM, T., 'Studies on Extracellular
   Proteins from Staphylococcus aureus. IV.
   Separation of α-toxin by Isoelectric Focusing'.
   Biochim. Biophys. Acta, 168, 228-242 (1968)
10. BERNHEIMER, A.W., 'Cytolytic Toxins of
    Bacteria'. In: Microbial Toxins, Vol. 1, Ed.
    S.J. Ajl, S. Kadis and T.C. Montie, Academic
    Press, New York, 183-212 (1970)
11. MCNIVEN, A.C., OWEN, P. and ARBUTHNOTT, J.P.,
    'Multiple Forms of Staphylococcal α-Toxin'.
    J. Med. Microbiol., 5, 113-122 (1972)

12. SIX, H.R. and HARSHMAN, S., 'Physical and Chemical Studies on Staphylococcal α-Toxins A and B'. Biochemistry, 12, 2677-2683 (1973)

13. WADSTRÖM, T. and MÖLLBY, R., 'Studies on Extracellular Proteins from Staphylococcus aureus. VI. Production and Purification of β-Haemolysin in Large Scale'. Biochim. Biophys. Acta, 242, 288-307 (1971)

14. MAHESWARAN, S.K. and LINDORFER, R.K., 'Physico-chemical and Biological Properties of Purified Staphylococcal beta Hemolysin'. Bact. Proc., Abstr. M95 (1971)

15. BERNHEIMER, A.W., AVIGAD, L.S. and KIM, K.S., 'Staphylococcal Sphingomyelinase (β-Hemolysin)'. Ann. N.Y. Acad. Sci., in press (1974)

16. MÖLLBY, R. and WADSTRÖM, T., 'Separation of gamma-Hemolysin from Staphylococcus aureus, Smith 5R'. Infect. and Immun., 3, 633-635 (1971)

17. KREGER, A.S., KIM, K.S., ZABORETSKY, F. and BERNHEIMER, A.W., 'Purification and Properties of Staphylococcal delta Hemolysin'. Infect. and Immun., 3, 449-465 (1971)

18. MAHESWARAN, S.K. and LINDORFER, R.K. 'Purification and Partial Characterisation of Staphylococcal delta Hemolysin'. Bact. Proc. Abstr. M23 (1970)

19. MÖLLBY, R. and WADSTRÖM, T., 'Studies on Hemolysins from Staphylococcus aureus by the Method of Isoelectric Focusing'. In: Protides of the Biological Fluids, Proceedings of the 17th Colloquium, Bruges, Section C1, Ed. H. Peeters, Pergamon Press, Oxford, 465-469 (1970)

20. SCHANTZ, E.J., ROESSLER, W.G., WOODBURN, M.J., LYNCH, J.M., JACOBY, H.M., SILVERMAN, S.J., GORMAN, J.C. and SPIRO, L., 'Purification and some Chemical Properties of Staphylococcal Enterotoxin A'. Biochemistry, 11, 360-366 (1972)

21. CHANG, P.C. and DICKIE, N., 'Fractionation of Staphylococcal Enterotoxin B by Isoelectric Focusing'. Biochim. Biophys. Acta, 236, 367-375 (1971)

22. METZGER, J.F., JOHNSON, A.D. and COLLINS, W.S., 'Fractionation and Purification of Staphylococcus aureus Enterotoxin B by Electrofocusing'. Biochim. Biophys. Acta, 257, 183-186 (1972)

23. CHANG, P.C., YANO, Y., DIGHTON, H. and DICKIE, N., 'Fractionation of Staphylococcal Enterotoxin C_2 by Isoelectric Focusing'. Canad. J. Microbiol., 17, 1367-1372 (1971)

24. DICKIE, N., YANO, Y., ROBERN, H. and STAVRIE, S., 'On the Heterogeneity of Staphylococcal Enterotoxin C_2'. Canad. J. Microbiol., 18, 801-804 (1972)

25. MELISH, M.E., GLASGOW, L.A. and TURNER, M.D., 'The Staphylococcal scalded Skin Syndrome : Isolation and partial Characterisation of the Exfoliative Toxin'. J. Infect. Dis., 125, 129-140 (1972)

26. MADOFF, M.A. and WEINSTEIN, L., 'Purification of Staphylococcal alpha-Hemolysin'. J. Bacteriol., 83, 914-918 (1962)

27. KITAMURA, S., SHELTON, J. and THAL, P.A., 'Isolation and Characterisation of Staphylococcus alpha-Hemolysin'. Ann. Surg., 160, 926-935 (1964)

28. BERNHEIMER, A.W. and SCHWARTZ, L.L., 'Isolation and Composition of Staphylococcal alpha Toxin'. J. Gen. Microbiol., 30, 455-468 (1963)

29. HERSCHMAN, H.R. and HELINSKI, D.R., 'Purification and Characterisation of Colicin E_2 and Colicin E_3'. J. Biol. Chem., 242, 5360-5368 (1967)

30. CARLSTRÖM, A., 'Induced Heterogeneity of Lactoperoxidase'. Acta Chem. Scand., 20, 1426-1427 (1966)

31. CARLSTRÖM, A. and VESTERBERG, O., 'Isoelectric Focusing and Separation of the Subcomponents of Lactoperoxidase'. Acta Chem. Scand., 21, 271-278 (1967)

32. FLATMARK, T. and VESTERBERG, O., 'On the Heterogeneity of Beef Heart Cytochrome C. IV. Isoelectric Fractionation by Electrolysis in a Natural pH Gradient'. Acta Chem. Scand., 20, 1497-1503 (1966)

33. AWDEH, Z.L., WILLIAMSON, A.R. and ASKONAS, B.A., 'One Cell - one Immunoglobulin. Origin of Limited Heterogeneity of Myeloma Protein'. Biochem. J., 116, 241-248 (1970)

34. MIDELFORT, C.F. and MEHLER, A.H., 'Deamidation in vivo of an Aspargine residue of Rabbit Muscle Aldolase'. Proc. Nat. Acad. Sci. (U.S.A.), 69, 1816-1819 (1972)

35. SMITH, D.D., 'α- and γ-Lysin Production by R Variants of Staphylococcus aureus'. Nature, 178, 1060-1061 (1956)

36. ARBUTHNOTT, J.P., KENT, J., LYELL, A. and
    GEMMELL, C.G., 'Studies of Staphylococcal
    Toxins in Relation to Toxic Epidermal
    Necrolysis (the Scalded Skin Syndrome)'.
    Brit. J. Derm., 86, Supplement 8, 35-39 (1972)
37. BERNHEIMER, A.W., GRUSHOFF, P. and AVIGAD, L.S.,
    'Isoelectric Analysis of Cytolytic Bacterial
    Proteins'. J. Bacteriol., 95, 2439-2441 (1968)
38. SUGAHARA, T. and OHSAKA, A., 'Two Molecular
    Forms of Clostridium perfringens α-Toxin
    associated with Lethal, Hemolytic and
    Enzymatic Activities'. Jap. J. Med. Sci.
    Biol., 23, 61-66 (1970)
39. MÖLLBY, R., NORD, C-E. and WADSTRÖM, T.,
    'Biological Activities contaminating
    Preparations of Phospholipase C (α-Toxin) from
    Clostridium perfringens'. Toxicon, 11,
    139-147 (1973)
40. SMYTH, C.J. and ARBUTHNOTT, J.P.,
    'Characteristics of Clostridium perfringens
    type A α-Toxin Purified by Isoelectric
    Focusing'. J. Gen. Microbiol., 71,
    Proceedings, ii, (1972)
41. SMYTH, C.J. and ARBUTHNOTT, J.P.,
    'Properties of Clostridium perfringens
    (welchii) type A α-Toxin (Phospholipase C)
    Purified by Electrofocusing'. J. Med.
    Microbiol., in press (1974)
42. SMYTH, C.J., 'Multiple Forms of Clostridium
    perfringens θ-Toxin (θ-Haemolysin):
    Physical Properties and Biological
    Characteristics'. Proc. Soc. Gen. Microbiol.,
    1, 56 (1974)
43. SMYTH, C.J. and FEHRENBACH, F.J., 'The
    Streptolysin O, NADase and Esterase of Groups
    A, C and G Streptococci. Proc. Soc. Gen.
    Microbiol., 1, 56-57 (1974)
44. MÖLLBY, R. and WADSTRÖM, T., 'Purification of
    Phospholipase C (alpha-Toxin) from
    Clostridium perfringens'. Biochim. Biophys.
    Acta, 321, 569-584 (1973)
45. HAUSCHILD, A.H.W. and HILSHEIMER, R.,
    'Purification and Characteristics of the
    Enterotoxin of Cl. perfringens type A'.
    Canad. J. Microbiol., 17, 1425-1433 (1971)
46. GALDIERO, F., TUFANO, M.A. and CERCIELLO, T.,
    'Isoelectric Focusing of Clostridium botulinum
    type A Toxin'. Arch. Mikrobiol., 74, 101-102
    (1970)

47. BEERS, W.H. and REICH, E., 'Isolation and Characterisation of <u>Cl. botulinum</u> type B Toxin'. <u>J. Biol. Chem.</u>, <u>244</u>, 4473-4479 (1969)

48. ISPOLATOVSKAYA, M.V. and LEVDIKOVA, G.A., 'Further Purification and Immunochemical Properties of Lecithinase, the Lethal Factor of <u>B. perfringens</u> Toxin'. <u>Biochemistry</u>, <u>27</u>, 533-536, - in Russian, English translation from <u>Biokhimiya</u>, <u>27</u>, 631-635 (1962)

49. ISPOLATOVSKAYA, M.V., 'The Possible Existence of Several Exolecithinases in <u>Clostridium welchii</u>'. <u>Biochemistry</u>, <u>29</u>, 744-746 - in Russian, English translation from <u>Biokhimiya</u>, <u>29</u>, 869-872 (1964)

50. WRETLIND, B., MÖLLBY, R. and WADSTRÖM, T., 'Separation of Two Hemolysins from <u>Aeromonas hydrophila</u> by Isoelectric Focusing'. <u>Infect. Immun.</u>, <u>4</u>, 503-505 (1971)

17. FRACTIONATION OF HUMAN SALIVARY PROTEINS BY ISOELECTRIC FOCUSING

J.A. Beeley

17.1 INTRODUCTION

Isoelectric focusing is a powerful technique for the fractionation of salivary proteins. In contrast to many biological fluids (e.g. serum) which contain numerous proteins and produce isoelectric focusing patterns which are so complex as to be difficult to interpret[1], saliva contains relatively few proteins (20 to 30) and is well suited to fractionation by this method.

The first report of the separation of salivary proteins by isoelectric focusing was made in 1969; parotid, submandibular and mixed secretions were fractionated in polyacrylamide gel rods and excellent resolution was obtained[2]. Since then, saliva has been fractionated by isoelectric focusing on thin layers of polyacrylamide gel and in density gradient columns.

17.2 SAMPLE PREPARATION AND METHODS

The principle of isoelectric focusing depends on the presence of a sample of low ionic strength[3,4]. Saliva, however, has a relatively low protein concentration (approx. 0.5 - 1.5 mg/ml) and a high content of inorganic ions (e.g. Na^+, K^+, PO_4^-, HCO_3^-, Cl^- etc.); it is therefore necessary both to desalt and concentrate the sample prior to isoelectric focusing. These procedures can be accomplished simultaneously by means of a Diaflo ultrafiltration cell (Amicon, N.V., Oosterhoot (N.B.), Holland). Large volumes of saliva (>20 ml) can readily be brought to a protein concentration suitable for analysis by this technique (10 to 50 mg/ml). With small volumes of saliva (<5 ml), however, it is not

technically possible by this method to reduce the
sample volume sufficiently to give the required
protein concentration. It is necessary to
freeze-dry the sample and dissolve it in a small
volume of water. A recent alternative method of
preparation of small samples of saliva for
isoelectric focusing involves the use of a B-15
Minicon micro-concentrator (Amicon, N.V.), which
enables large numbers of samples of saliva to be
rapidly desalted and reduced to a volume of 0.05 ml
in one step without the need for ancillary
equipment. Desalting of saliva by dialysis results
in the loss of certain minor components from the
sample[2].

A pH gradient of 3 to 10 has been found to
give the best resolution of salivary proteins.
Narrower range gradients, although improving the
resolution of certain areas of the pH spectrum,
give much less satisfactory results overall.

Isoelectric focusing has been used for the
resolution of salivary proteins on both analytical
and preparative scales. At the analytical level,
rods or thin layers of polyacrylamide gel served as
the stabilising support, whereas at the preparative
level, columns of solution stabilised by sucrose
have been used.

17.3   ISOELECTRIC FOCUSING OF SALIVARY PROTEINS IN
       POLYACRYLAMIDE GELS

Before the advent of isoelectric focusing, analysis
of the protein constituents of saliva usually
involved discontinuous gel electrophoresis.
Although this technique gives good resolution of the
major components, it is limited by the direction of
migration of the proteins and gives only partial
resolution of the minor constituents. Furthermore,
the bands lack the sharpness of those formed on
isoelectric focusing[5,6].

Human parotid, submandibular and mixed salivas
have been resolved by isoelectric focusing on gel
rods[2] and thin layers (Figure 17.1). The advantages
of gel rods are that they allow the comparison of
large numbers of samples, that the bands are free
from distortion due to rippling of the gel, and that
a solution of relatively low protein concentration
can be studied by mixing the protein-containing
solution with the gel monomer prior to
polymerisation. Thin-layer gels[7] have many other
advantages, including the direct comparison of
different samples on a single gel, direct
measurement of isoelectric points by means of an

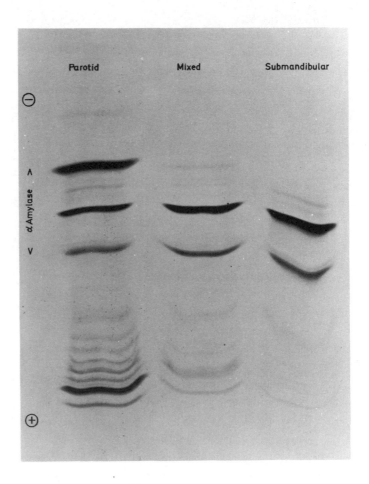

Figure 17.1 Isoelectric focusing of salivary proteins on a thin layer of polyacrylamide gel, pH 3 to 10. The experiment was performed for 4 h with a final potential of 15 V/cm. T and C values for the polyacrylamide gel were 6% and 2.45% respectively. Samples were applied on filter paper strips close to the anode end of the gel. The protein bands were stained with Lissamine Green.

antimony electrode[8], prevention of exposure of the
sample to extremes of pH, etc. (see Chapters 6 and 7).
    Lissamine Green[1] has been generally used as the
protein stain; recently, though, a method which
employs an aqueous acid extract of Coomassie
Brilliant Blue and eliminates the need for fixing,
removal of ampholytes and destaining, has also been
used[9]. Glycoproteins can be detected by the use of
the P.A.S. stain[5].
    The bands on the gels which correspond to the
isoenzymes of α-amylase can readily be identified
by means of starch slide zymograms[10]. Up to seven
isoenzymes can usually be detected, the patterns in
the parotid and mixed secretions being very similar.
By means of an antimony electrode, the pI values of
the major isoenzymes have been shown to be
approximately 6.66, 6.59, 6.36, 6.25, 5.93 and
5.78. The isoenzymes of parotid saliva have been
subdivided into two 'families', 'family' A (which is
carbohydrate-containing) consisting of three major
isoenzymes, and 'family' B (which contains no
detectable carbohydrate) consisting of two
isoenzymes[11,12]. By means of thin-layer gel
isoelectric focusing and the antimony electrode, it
is tentatively suggested that the isoelectric points
of the isoenzymes of 'family' A appear to be 6.66,
6.59 and 5.93, and the values for 'family' B, 6.25
and 5.78. Identification of the isoenzymes of
α-amylase is unfortunately made difficult by the
changes in the proportions of individual isozymes
and the formation of new forms on storage[12]. In
addition, isoenzyme patterns vary from individual
to individual.
    Four specific salivary proteins purified from
human parotid saliva have been tested for
homogeneity by isoelectric focusing in gel rods[13].
    Parotid saliva from patients with connective
tissue disorders has been studied by isoelectric
focusing in gel rods. Saliva from patients with
Sjögren's syndrome and from those with rheumatoid
arthritis alone showed additional bands at the
anodal end of the gel when compared with saliva
from normal control subjects[14]. These abnormal
bands precipitate out at their isoelectric pHs and
are therefore readily detected by densitometry.
    Preparation of large numbers of small saliva
samples for isoelectric focusing has in the past
been time consuming and laborious; the introduction
of the new B-15 Minicon micro-concentrator
(mentioned above) should make such work considerably
easier in the future. Furthermore, the
availability of an improved thin-layer apparatus[15]

which enables many samples to be run simultaneously and includes a cooling platten, should enable variations in salivary proteins from different individuals to be studied more easily.

A further development of the technique of thin-layer isoelectric focusing involved electrophoresis in a second dimension into antibody-containing agarose. Saliva from two individuals with differing isoamylase patterns was studied, using rabbit antiserum to human parotid amylase as the antibody. The technique demonstrated semi-quantitatively multiple forms of salivary amylase[16] which were apparently immunologically identical.

17.4   COLUMN DENSITY GRADIENT ISOELECTRIC FOCUSING OF SALIVARY PROTEINS

Human parotid saliva has also been studied by isoelectric focusing in sucrose density gradient columns. A general spectrum of the proteins present was produced using a broad pH gradient (pH 3 to 10)[17,18]. Amylase activity was located between pH 6.2 and 6.5, lysozyme at about pH 11.0, two glycoproteins at pH 9.4 and 10.7, and an unidentified protein at between pH 3 and 5. Carrier ampholyte and sucrose were removed from fractions from the column by Sephadex G50 chromatography. The composition of the peaks was studied by disc gel electrophoresis which showed that all of the peaks contained several molecular species.

Density gradient isoelectric focusing in broad pH gradients, however, does not resolve the isoenzymes of α-amylase. In order to separate these isoenzymes, a narrower range pH gradient is necessary. Using a pH gradient of 5 to 7, five isoenzymes of α-amylase were observed in a purified parotid amylase preparation[19,20]. Chromatography of the preparation on DEAE-Sephadex gave rise to two peaks, one containing two isoenzymes and the other, three. The isoenzymes of α-amylase from parotid and submandibular salivas have been separated without any prior purification steps using a mixture of carrier ampholytes containing equal proportions of pH 4 to 6 and 5 to 8 Ampholines. Both types of saliva were found to contain at least four isoenzymes, three of which had identical isoelectric points[21].

There appear to be discrepancies in the isoelectric points reported for the isoenzymes of α-amylase. This is probably due to the complex nature of the material and instability of the isoenzyme pattern rather than simply variation from laboratory to laboratory. A more detailed study of this problem is much needed.

There is only one report of isoelectric focusing of proteins from sublingual saliva. The technique was used as a final step in the purification of a sublingual glycoprotein with an isoelectric point of 2.0[22]. In view of the high viscosity and difficulty in collecting sublingual saliva, studies on this secretion are difficult.

17.5 CONCLUSIONS

Isoelectric focusing has proved to be an invaluable technique in the fractionation of salivary proteins. The proteins present can be studied with or without prior purification. Technical improvements in isoelectric focusing in thin-layer polyacrylamide gels are likely to give improved resolution. One of the uses of this approach might be to give a more detailed knowledge of the protein patterns of the secretions of glands from healthy individuals with a view to characterisation of abnormalities. Sucrose density gradient isoelectric focusing is the method of choice for at least partial purification of salivary proteins for more detailed structural studies.

ACKNOWLEDGEMENTS

The author wishes to thank Dr. P.J. Keller and Dr. D.L. Kauffman for the provision of purified human parotid α-amylase.

REFERENCES

1. DALE, G. and LATNER, A.L., 'Isoelectric Focusing in Polyacrylamide Gels'. Lancet, i, 847-848 (1968)
2. BEELEY, J.A., 'Separation of Human Salivary Proteins by Isoelectric Focusing in Polyacrylamide Gels'. Arch. oral Biol., 14, 559-561 (1969)
3. SVENSSON, H., 'Isoelectric Fractionation, Analysis and Characterisation of Ampholytes in Natural pH Gradients. I. The Differential Equation of Solute Concentrations at a Steady State and its Solution for Simple Cases'. Acta Chem. Scand., 15, 325-341 (1961)
4. SVENSSON, H., 'Isoelectric Fractionation, Analysis and Characterisation of Ampholytes in Natural pH Gradients. II. Buffering Capacity

I

and Conductance of Isoionic Ampholytes'.
Acta Chem. Scand., 16, 456-466 (1962)

5. CALDWELL, R.C. and PIGMAN, W., 'Disc
    Electrophoresis of Human Saliva in
    Polyacrylamide Gel'. Arch. Biochem. Biophys.,
    110, 91-96 (1965)

6. STEINER, J.C. and KELLER, P.J., 'An
    Electrophoretic Analysis of Human Parotid
    Saliva'. Arch. oral Biol., 13, 1213-1221
    (1968)

7. BEELEY, J.G., 'Ovomucoid Heterogeneity Examined
    by Flat Bed Isoelectric Focusing'. Biochim.
    Biophys. Acta, 230, 595-598 (1971)

8. BEELEY, J.A., STEVENSON, S.M. and BEELEY, J.G.,
    'Polyacrylamide Gel Isoelectric Focusing of
    Proteins: Determination of Isoelectric Points
    Using an Antimony Electrode'. Biochim. Biophys.
    Acta, 285, 293-300 (1972)

9. MALIK, N. and BERRIE, A., 'New Stain Fixative
    for Proteins Separated by Gel Isoelectric
    Focusing Based on Coomassie Brilliant Blue'.
    Anal. Biochem., 49, 173-176 (1972)

10. ALLEN, B.J., ZAGER, N.I. and KELLER, P.J.,
    'Human Pancreatic Proteins: Amylase,
    Proelastase, and Trypsinogen'. Arch. Biochem.
    Biophys., 136, 529-540 (1970)

11. KAUFFMAN, D.L., ZAGER, N.I., COHEN, E. and
    KELLER, P.J., 'The Isoenzymes of Human Parotid
    Amylase'. Arch. Biochem. Biophys., 137,
    325-339 (1970)

12. KELLER, P.J., KAUFFMAN, D.L., ALLAN, B.J. and
    WILLIAMS, B.L., 'Further Studies on the
    Structural Differences Between the Isoenzymes
    of Human Parotid α-Amylase'. Biochemistry,
    10, 4867-4874 (1971)

13. BENNICK, A. and CONNELL, G.E., 'Purification
    and Partial Characterisation of Four Proteins
    from Human Parotid Saliva'. Biochem. J., 123,
    455-464 (1971)

14. CHISHOLM, D.M., BEELEY, J.A. and MASON, D.K.,
    'Salivary Proteins in Sjögren's Syndrome:
    Separation by Isoelectric Focusing in
    Acrylamide Gels'. Oral Surg., 35, 620-630
    (1973)

15. KARLSSON, C., DAVIES, H., ÖHMAN, J. and
    ANDERSON, V., 'LKB 2117 Multiphor. I.
    Analytical Thin Layer Gel Electrofocusing in
    Polyacrylamide Gel'. LKB Application Note
    No. 75, LKB Produkter AB, Stockholm Bromma,
    Sweden, (1973)

16. SKUDE, G. and JEPPSSON, J.-O., 'Thin Layer
    Electrofocusing Followed by Electrophoresis in
    Antibody Containing Gel'. Scand. J. Clin. Lab.
    Invest., 29, Suppl. 124, 55-58 (1972)
17. ARNEBERG, P., 'Electrofocusing of Parotid
    Salivary Proteins'. J. Periodont. Res., 4,
    166 (1969)
18. ARNEBERG, P., 'Fractionation of Parotid Salivary
    Proteins by Isoelectric Focusing in a Wide pH
    Range'. Scand. J. Dent. Res., 80, 134-138
    (1972)
19. ANDJIC, J., HAYEM, A., CARLIER, A. and BONTE,
    M., 'Isolation of Salivary Amylase by
    Isoelectric Focusing' - in French . C.R. Acad.
    Sci. Paris, Ser. D., 270, 407-409 (1970)
20. CARLIER, A., HAYEM, A., BONTE, M., ANDJIC, J.
    and HARVEY, R. 'Amino Acid Composition of Five
    Human Salivary Iso-amylases' - in French .
    C. R. Acad. Sci. Paris, Ser. D., 271,
    2204-2205 (1970)
21. BIRKHED, D. and SÖDER, P.-Ö., 'The Presence of
    Iso-α-Amylases in Human Saliva'. Arch. oral
    Biol., 18, 203-210 (1973)
22. ROLLA, G. and JONSEN, J., 'A Glycoprotein
    Component from Human Sublingual - Submaxillary
    Saliva'. Caries Res., 2, 306-318 (1968)

18. ISOELECTRIC FOCUSING STUDIES OF β-LACTAMASES

M. Matthew

18.1 INTRODUCTION

The β-lactamases (E.C. 3.5.2.6.) are bacterial
enzymes which hydrolyse the β-lactam bond in the
nuclei of penicillins and cephalosporins, thus
destroying their antibiotic properties. Different
organisms produce enzymes which either act
preferentially on penicillins or cephalosporins or
which have a wide spectrum of activity[1]. The genes
specifying these enzymes may be carried on the
chromosome or on an extrachromosomal plasmid known
as an R-factor (resistance transfer factor)[2].
R-factors may be transferred from one species or
genus to another and an organism may be host to more
than one type of R-factor. It is therefore possible
that an organism may make several different
β-lactamases. This communication describes the
use of isoelectric focusing for the study of enzymes
from several genera of Enterobacteria. The strains
had previously been examined for their ability to
use a number of penicillins and cephalosporins as
substrates for β-lactamase and for the effects of
different inhibitors. Their biochemical and
metabolic characteristics had also been determined.

18.2 METHODS

Debris was removed from intracellular extracts by
centrifuging sand-ground preparations at 1500 g for
10 min and ultrasonicated preparations at 21 000 g
for 30 min. Three β-lactamases were purified by gel
filtration and ion-exchange chromatography[3,4]. For
isoelectric focusing, samples were loaded towards
the anode end of a thin-layer polyacrylamide gel[5]
containing pH 3 to 10 Ampholine. After focusing, pH

248

measurements were made by means of a miniature
flat-ended combination glass electrode。 Bands with
β-lactamase activity were located by damping the gel
with cephalosporin analogue 87/312 (ref. 6), the
concentration of which was 0.5 mg/ml in 0.1 M sodium
phosphate, pH 7。 The compound is yellow, but
becomes pink when the β-lactam bond is broken so
that bands with β-lactamase activity show up pink on
a yellow background。 The gel was damped by
overlaying it with a sheet of Whatman No. 54 paper
that had been soaked in substrate solution。

The length of time during which one takes
photographs depends entirely on the range of
activities present on the plate, e.g. for 2 i.u。 one
photographs immediately after damping with substrate,
and for 0.0002 i.u。 after about 30 min delay。
Serial photographs were taken to record the
positions of bands with different activities as they
appeared and before they diffused. The lower limit
of sensitivity was about 0.0002 i.u. in a single
band。 Samples with up to a 16 000-fold difference
in activity could be loaded and read on a single
plate.

18.3 RESULTS

Because the error in pH measurement of different
runs was ± 0.2 pH units, the identity of different
samples was always checked by loading them in
adjacent tracks and looking for confluence of bands。
An intracellular extract usually focused to give a
pattern of multiple β-lactamase bands。 These were
identical whether obtained from cells ground with
sand or from a partially purified preparation of
cells disrupted by ultrasonication followed by
ultracentrifugation. Using purified enzymes, it
was evident that β-lactamase preparations focused
as a characteristic and reproducible group of bands,
usually consisting of one main band and a number of
satellite bands。

Within a single genus and species,
preparations from a number of strains focused to
give identical patterns of β-lactamase activity;
these were therefore classed together. Figure 18.1
illustrates the classes which have so far been
distinguished in 31 strains of Escherichia coli.
Loadings were adjusted so that a qualitative
comparison could be made between principal
β-lactamase bands of different isoelectric focusing
classes. As a result, some of the weaker bands,
detected in other experiments, do not appear and
their positions have therefore been marked by bars。

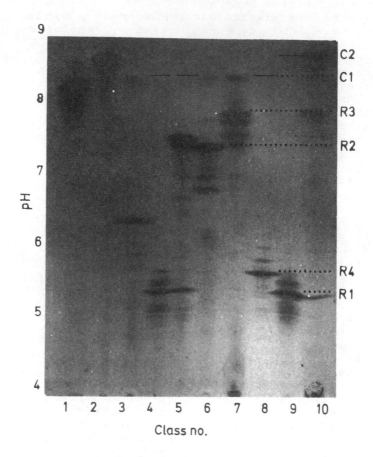

<u>Figure 18.1</u> Isoelectric focusing patterns of the
β-lactamases of <u>Escherichia coli</u>. The experiment
was performed in a thin layer of polyacrylamide gel
using pH 3 to 10 Ampholines and a final potential
of 20 V/cm. T and C values for the polyacrylamide
gel were 7.7 and 2.6 respectively. Each sample was
an intracellular extract and contained the same
total enzyme activity. Bars mark the positions of
known bands which show up after a longer exposure of
enzyme to substrate/stain. The enzyme patterns were
classed from 1 to 10 (see text). C.1 and C.2 denote
chromosomally specified enzymes; R.1, R.2, R.3 and
R.4 denote R-factor specified enzymes

   In <u>E. coli</u> the classes depend on the
combination of β-lactamases specified by
chromosomes and R-factors[1]; the main bands of their

isoelectric focusing patterns have been assigned
the letters C and R respectively. This division of
strains into classes by isoelectric focusing of
β-lactamase is in accordance with their division by
the criteria of substrate specificity, inhibitor
profile and metabolic characteristics, with the
exception that these criteria failed to
discriminate between classes 4, 8 and 9.

Class 1. These strains are antigenic type K-12
and are represented in the Figure 18.1 by D31 (track
1 on gel), which makes a chromosomal
cephalosporinase (main band C.1, pI value 8.3). C.1
is also present in classes 3 to 8.

Class 2. The β-lactamase has a main band C.2,
pI value 8.5, which is also present in classes 9 and
10. The relationship between the isoelectric
focusing patterns of classes 1 and 2 resembles that
between the enzymes of the genus Enterobacter which
are thought to be chromosomally mediated. The
β-lactamase patterns of different strains often have
a number of bands in common but which differ in
their relative intensities. Class 1 and 2 strains
are also bacteriologically very similar. It
therefore seems likely that the class 2 β-lactamase
is chromosomal.

Class 3. This is represented at present by
only one organism, the TEM strain (class 4) which
has been cured of its R-factor, and now has the
major band at a pI value of 6.3.

Class 4. Although these organisms make the
chromosomal β-lactamase C.1, their characteristic
penicillinase activity is mediated by the enzyme
specified by the TEM R-factor (main band R.1, pI
value 5.4). This enzyme has a group of bands
identical with that of the β-lactamase specified by
the R_{GN14} and R.1 R-factors. Identical groups have
been found in strains of Enterobacter, Klebsiella
and Proteus.

Class 5. Class 5 organisms make the C.1 and
R.1 β-lactamases and another enzyme (main band pI
value 7.6) which may be specified by an additional
R-factor.

Class 6. The C.1 β-lactamase is relatively
inactive and the pattern is dominated by that of the
penicillinase specified by the R-factor R_{GN238}
(main band R.2, pI value 7.4). This R.2 enzyme was
also found in Klebsiella, and when the R-factor
specifying it was transferred to E. coli K-12, the
resulting organism had a β-lactamase pattern
identical with others in class 6.

Class 7. Class 7 is represented by one
organism, an E. coli K-12 into which the Salmonella

R-factor R_{1818} was transferred. This specifies a
broad-spectrum enzyme (main band R.3, pI value 8.1).

    Class 8. This organism is an E. coli K-12 into
which the Pseudomonas R-factor RPI has been
transferred. The enzyme it specifies (major band
R.4, pI value 5.6) is identical with the TEM
β-lactamase in molecular weight, substrate
specificity, inhibitor profile and cross-reaction
with antiserum raised against the purified TEM
enzyme; these can be distinguished only by
isoelectric focusing.

    Class 9. The principal enzyme is R.1. These
organisms differ from those of class 4 only because
they make β-lactamase C.2 instead of C.1.

    Class 10. Class 10 is analogous to class 5 in
that the pattern includes a chromosomal main band
C.2 (this is replaced by C.1 in class 5), the R.1
main band, and a third main band of pI value 8.0.

18.4 CONCLUSION

On isoelectric focusing, each type of β-lactamase
forms a clearly recognisable group of bands which is
not influenced qualitatively by the presence of
other β-lactamases produced by the same strain.
These β-lactamase patterns have been used to
classify organisms; this classification is in
accordance with a classification based on the usual
bacteriological criteria, but can separate strains
which have not been distinguished by available
methods. The properties of a β-lactamase may be
predicted if its isoelectric focusing bands match
those of an enzyme that has a known band pattern.

ACKNOWLEDGEMENTS

Miss A.M. Harris grew the strains, examined their
bacterial characteristics and prepared the
intracellular extracts. Purified enzymes P99 and
K1 were prepared by Dr. M.G. Boulton from
Enterobacter cloacae P99 and Klebsiella aerogenes
1082E, respectively; TEM was prepared from
Escherichia coli K12-R$_{TEM}$ by Professor M.H.
Richmond.

REFERENCES

1. RICHMOND, M.H. and SYKES, R.B. 'The
     β-lactamases of Gram-negative Bacteria and
     their Possible Physiological Role'. Adv.
     Microb. Physiol., 9, 31-88 (1973)

2. HAYES, W. The Genetics of Bacteria and their
    Viruses, 2nd edn., Blackwell, Oxford (1969)
3. ROSS, G.W. and BOULTON, M.G., 'Purification of
    β-lactamases on QAE-Sephadex'. Biochem.
    Biophys. Acta, 309, 430-439 (1973)
4. DATTA, N. and RICHMOND, M.H., 'The Purification
    and Properties of a Penicillinase whose
    Synthesis is Mediated by an R-factor in
    Escherichia coli'. Biochem. J., 98, 204-209
    (1966)
5. AWDEH, Z.L., WILLIAMSON, A.R. and ASKONAS, B.A.,
    'Isoelectric Focusing in Polyacrylamide Gel and
    its Application to Immunoglobulins'. Nature
    (Lond.), 219, 61-67 (1968)
6. O'CALLAGHAN, C.H., MORRIS, A., KIRBY, S.M. and
    SHINGLER, A.H., 'Novel Method for Detection of
    β-lactamases by using a Chromogenic
    Cephalosporin Substrate'. Antimicrob. Agents
    Chemother., 1, 283-288 (1972)

I*

19. THE USE OF ISOELECTRIC FOCUSING IN THE ANALYTICAL AND PREPARATIVE FRACTIONATION OF CHROMATIN NONHISTONE PROTEINS

A.J. MacGillivray and D. Rickwood

19.1 INTRODUCTION

Chromatin, the DNA-protein complex isolated from eukaryotic nuclei, is generally accepted as being representative of interphase chromosomes. There is now considerable evidence to indicate that the nonhistone proteins of the complex control which specific portions of the DNA are available for transcription in different tissues. Other investigations suggest that some of these regulatory proteins are phosphoproteins, the phosphate groups of which are metabolically unstable[1]. There is obviously considerable interest in the isolation and identification of these specificity-determining factors, but no marked tissue differences have been found in a number of studies of chromatin nonhistone proteins[2-4]. Because these proteins are insoluble in dilute buffers, most of these investigations have employed electrophoresis in sodium dodecyl sulphate (SDS), a system which separates polypeptides only on the basis of differences in molecular weight. In this communication we describe a two-dimensional polyacrylamide gel procedure which we have used to judge the true complexity of these proteins[5].

19.2 SUMMARY OF METHODS

Nuclear phosphoproteins were labelled in vitro by incubation of purified nuclei with $[\gamma-^{32}P]$-ATP[4]. Chromatin was then isolated from the nuclei and dissociated in a solution containing 2 M NaCl, 5 M urea, and 1 mM sodium phosphate, pH 6.8. The nonhistone proteins were isolated by chromatography on hydroxylapatite, the bulk of the proteins (fraction H2) being eluted with 0.05 M sodium phosphate, pH 6.8 and the remaining 30% (fraction H3) with 0.2 M sodium phosphate, pH 6.8 (ref. 2). The proteins were concentrated by dialysis against Carbowax 20M (G.T. Gurr, High Wycombe, Bucks) and reduced in 8 M urea in 0.3 M Tris-HCl buffer, pH 8.3, containing 50 mM dithioerythritol (DTE) for 2 h at 37°C followed by dialysis against 8 M urea containing 2.5 mM DTE. The reduced proteins (0.5 - 1.0 mg) were then subjected to isoelectric focusing for 16 h at 4°C in 90 x 5 mm gel rods containing 4% (w/v) acrylamide, 8 M urea, 1 mM DTE and 2% (w/v) pH 3.5 to 10 Ampholines. Each gel was then incubated at 45°C in solutions of 8 M urea containing 1 mM DTE and progressively decreasing amounts of phosphate buffer, pH 7.0 and SDS, after which it was placed on top of 15% (w/v) acrylamide gels overlayed with 2.5% gels, both containing 0.1% (w/v) SDS, 4 M urea and 1 mM DTE in a thin-layer apparatus similar to that described by Hultin and Sjoqvist[6]. SDS-electrophoresis was then carried out at 10°C for 1 h at 15 mA per gel and then for a further 2.5 h at 40 mA per gel. The gels were extracted from their trays and stained at 65°C with Coomassie Blue[7]. ^{32}P-labelled proteins were detected by autoradiography.

19.3 RESULTS

Using this method we have found that the proteins of the H2 fraction of chromatin consist of a heterogeneous mixture of components of molecular weight range 15 000 to 200 000, having isoelectric points between pH 4.5 and 9.0 (Figure 19.1a). The H3 fraction, on the other hand, appears to be a less complex group of proteins with isoelectric points in the range pH 2 to 6. Both H2 and H3 proteins consist of a mixture of phosphorylated and non-phosphorylated polypeptides with little similarity being found between the protein species of the two fractions from any tissue. However, comparison of the components of H2 and H3 fractions by this two-dimensional technique showed that many of the phosphorylated proteins are common to mouse liver, kidney and brain chromatin with only a few molecular species being tissue-specific.

In order to investigate the chemical and functional properties of individual nonhistone protein species we have attempted to achieve separations similar to those demonstrated by the two-dimensional gel technique but on a preparative scale. Since isoelectric focusing of nonhistone protein preparations in the conventional LKB

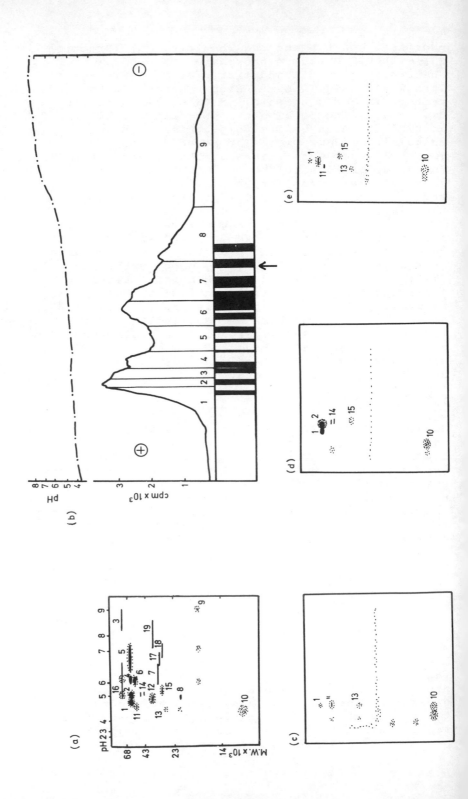

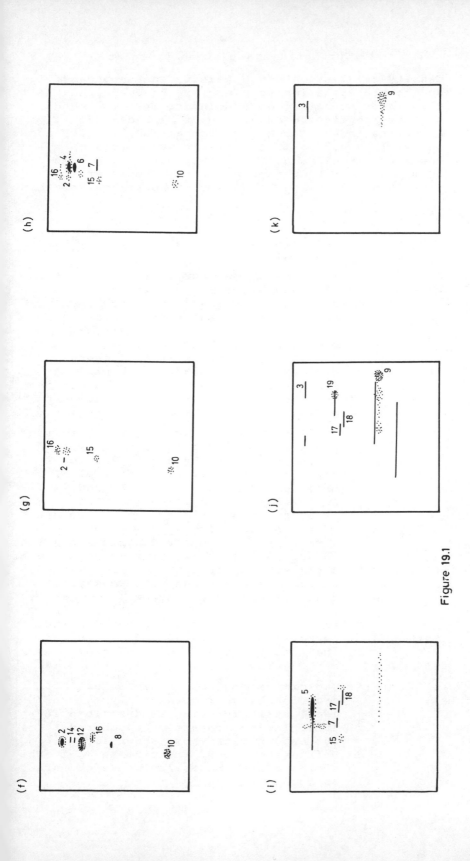

Figure 19.1

density gradient column apparatus was unsuccessful
due to precipitation problems, we have adapted the
thin-layer technique of Radola[8] to meet our needs.
A slurry consisting of 3.82 g of Sephadex G50
Superfine in 40 ml 8 M urea containing 1 mM DTE and
1% (w/v) pH 3.5 to 10 Ampholines was spread on a
200 x 200 mm glass plate. After drying for some
30 min at room temperature so that the layer lost
some 3% of its weight, samples of nonhistone protein

Figure 19.1   Isoelectric focusing of mouse liver H2
               proteins.

       (a)   Two-dimensional acrylamide gel pattern
               of mouse liver H2 proteins. The
               horizontal ordinate indicates the
               separation by isoelectric focusing in
               the first dimension, the vertical
               ordinate that obtained by
               SDS-electrophoresis in the second
               dimension. Stained protein bands are
               indicated as lines or filled areas and
               ^{32}P-labelled components are shown by
               grains.

       (b)   Isoelectric focusing in a thin layer of
               Sephadex G50. The layer was prepared
               as described in the text. 2.5 mg of
               ^{32}P-labelled H2 proteins in 1 ml of 8 M
               urea, containing 2.5 mM DTE, and 1%
               Ampholines were applied in 50 µl
               aliquots in a strip across the centre
               of the plate using a 22 x 22 mm
               coverslip. The upper diagram shows the
               pH gradient (——•——) obtained after 18 h.
               A transfer strip (200 x 35 mm) was
               prepared and stained with Coomassie
               Blue. The middle diagram (———) shows
               the profile of ^{32}P-radioactivity in
               this strip, whilst the lower diagram
               represents the stained protein bands.
               The arrow indicates the point of
               application of the sample.

     (c-k)   Two-dimensional gel analysis of
               fractions 1 to 9 obtained by
               isoelectric focusing as described in
               (b). The components are numbered to
               correspond with those shown for
               unfractionated H2 proteins in (a). The
               scales of pH and molecular weight are
               as for (a).

preparations in a solution of 8 M urea, 1 mM DTE and
1% (w/v) Ampholines were inserted into the Sephadex
and isoelectric focusing was performed on a cooled
metal block at 10°C for 16 h at 7.5 V/cm followed by
a further period of 2 h at 15 V/cm. Protein was
detected by staining a transfer strip of Whatman 3MM
paper with Coomassie Blue[8] and the radioactivity
located by an Actigraph III Strip Scanner
(Nuclear-Chicago Corporation, Illinois, U.S.A.).
For example, Figure 19.1b shows the result of
isoelectric focusing 2.5 mg of mouse liver H2
proteins in such a system. The layer was divided
into nine fractions as indicated and the proteins
recovered from the Sephadex by incubation for 16 h
at 37°C in a solution of 6 M guanidine
hydrochloride, 0.3 M Tris-HCl buffer, pH 8.3 and
10 mM DTE, followed by centrifugation. After
dialysis against 8 M urea containing 2.5 mM DTE,
each extract was examined by the two-dimensional
gel technique outlined above. The components of
fractions 1 to 9 show a progressive shift towards a
more basic range of proteins, indicating that the
Sephadex thin-layer technique yields a good
separation of the H2 proteins based on their
isoelectric points (Figure 19.1c-k). This may be
contrasted with the separation obtained on
QAE-Sephadex, when some proteins bind to the
ion-exchanger in an anomalous way[5].

   The proteins so separated by isoelectric
focusing can be further fractionated by gel
filtration. As an example of this, we have been
particularly interested in a low molecular weight,
highly phosphorylated component of pI value
approximately 4.5 which we have found in the H2
fraction of all the chromatins we have so far
examined. In our two-dimensional gels this
component does not coincide with any single stained
protein band and accounts for at least 20% of the
radioactivity in the H2 fraction (Figure 19.1a,
spot 10). It represents the major phosphorylated
component in fractions 1 to 4 of the Sephadex
thin-layer isoelectric focusing system with
indications that it is heterogeneous with respect o
charge (Figure 19.1c-f). Due to its low molecular
weight this material is well separated from other
components in such isoelectric focusing fractions or
in a fraction obtained by chromatography of reduced
H2 proteins on QAE-Sephadex[5]. This phosphorylated
component has now been isolated from such fractions
by gel filtration on a column of Sepharose 6B
(780 x 22 mm) run in 6 M guanidine hydrochloride
adjusted to pH 6.0 with NaOH and containing 1 mM

DTE[5]. Analyses show that this component is in fact
a phosphoprotein, the $[^{32}P]$ being recovered as
phosphoserine and phosphothreonine[9].

REFERENCES

1.   MACGILLIVRAY, A.J. and RICKWOOD, D., 'The Role
     of Chromosomal Proteins as Gene Regulators'.
     In: Biochemistry of Differentiation and
     Development, Biochemistry Series, Vol. 9
     Ed. J. Paul, Medical and Technical Publishing
     Co. Ltd., Oxford, in press (1974)
2.   MACGILLIVRAY, A.J., CAMERON, A., KRAUZE, R.J.,
     RICKWOOD, D. and PAUL, J., 'The Nonhistone
     Proteins of Chromatin. Their Isolation and
     Composition in a Number of Tissues'.
     Biochim. Biophys. Acta, 277, 384-402 (1972)
3.   WU, F.C., ELGIN, S.C.R. and HOOD, L.E.,
     'Nonhistone Chromosomal Proteins of Rat
     Tissues. A Comparative Study by Gel
     Electrophoresis'. Biochemistry, 12,
     2792-2797 (1973)
4.   RICKWOOD, D., RICHES, P.G. and MACGILLIVRAY,
     A.J., 'Studies of the in vitro Phosphorylation
     of Chromatin Nonhistone Proteins in Isolated
     Nuclei'. Biochim. Biophys. Acta, 299,
     162-171 (1973)
5.   MACGILLIVRAY, A.J. and RICKWOOD, D., 'The
     Heterogeneity of Mouse Chromatin Nonhistone
     Proteins as evidenced by Two Dimensional
     Polyacrylamide Gel Electrophoresis and Ion
     Exchange Chromatography'. Eur. J. Biochem.,
     41, 181-190 (1974)
6.   HULTIN, T. and SJOQVIST, A., 'Two dimensional
     Polyacrylamide Gel Electrophoresis of Animal
     Ribosomal Proteins Based on Charge Inversion'.
     Anal. Biochem., 46, 312-316 (1972)
7.   VESTERBERG, O., 'Staining of Protein Zones after
     Isoelectric Focusing in Polyacrylamide Gels'.
     Biochim. Biophys. Acta, 243, 345-348 (1971)
8.   RADOLA, B.J., 'Isoelectric Focusing in Layers of
     Granulated Gels. 1. Thin layer Isoelectric
     Focusing of Proteins'. Biochim. Biophys. Acta,
     295, 412-425 (1973)
9.   MACGILLIVRAY, A.J. and RICKWOOD, D.,
     manuscript in preparation

20. THE BEHAVIOUR OF GELATIN PREPARATIONS IN
THE ACIDIC REGION OF THE pH GRADIENT

C.R. Maxey and M.R. Palmer

20.1 INTRODUCTION

Gelatin is a heterogeneous protein derived from collagen, which occurs in connective tissue. The collagen can be denatured at high or low pH to produce respectively alkali-processed gelatin with a low average isoelectric point (pI), or acid-processed gelatin with a high isoelectric point. The methods normally used to determine the pI of gelatin give average values only. In theory, isoelectric focusing should make possible measurements of the pIs of the individual subcomponents of gelatin. However, the application of this technique to gelatin, which is unusually heterogeneous, has revealed limitations which have not become apparent in previous work on proteins with fewer components.

20.2 METHODS

The thin-layer polyacrylamide gel technique of Awdeh et al.[1] was used with minor modifications.
Glass plates (204 x 166 mm), coated with a thin layer of gelatin, were prepared as follows. They were first washed with a solution of 0.1% (w/v) sodium hydroxide, rinsed with water, and then washed in a solution of 0.3% (w/v) chromic potassium sulphate (dodeca hydrate), acidified with 0.3% (v/v) concentrated sulphuric acid. Finally, they were rinsed with distilled water and allowed to dry. The plates were then dipped in coating solution. After draining, they were dried at room temperature. The coating solution, made up on the day of use, contained 7 g gelatin, 0.7 ml 5% (w/v) saponin solution, and 7.5 ml 5% (w/v) chromic

261

potassium sulphate (dodeca hydrate), made up to 1
litre with water. Similar coated plates may be
obtained from Ilford Ltd., Ilford, Essex, U.K.
(attn: Mr. J. Ehrlich). It is advisable to bake the
coated plates overnight in an oven at 110°C to
complete the hardening process. There is no
evidence that the thin gelatin coating dissolves off
into the polyacrylamide layer, and interferes with
the subsequent analysis of the samples. The
polyacrylamide gel adhered well to these plates and
no trouble was encountered with detached
polyacrylamide layers.

Most experiments were done using a 5%
polyacrylamide gel, made up as follows. 2.5 g
acrylamide, 0.08 g N,N'-methylenebisacrylamide, and
2.0 ml pH 3 to 10 Ampholine were made up to 50 ml
with distilled water and degassed under reduced
pressure; 1.0 ml 0.004% riboflavin was added to
initiate polymerisation. The solution was cast
between the coated plate and another plate in the
usual way. Focusing of alkali-processed gelatin
was usually accomplished in 6 h, with a potential of
approx. 27 V/cm for the last 4.5 h. The experiment
described in section 20.3.1 was done using a 3%
polyacrylamide gel with sucrose present to
strengthen it[2]. The gel was made up as follows.
1.5 g acrylamide, 0.055 g N,N'-methylenebisacrylamide,
7.5 g sucrose, and 1.5 ml 40% (w/v) pH 3 to 10
Ampholine were made up to 50 ml with distilled
water, and treated as above. Focusing of the
alkali-processed gelatin for this experiment was
accomplished overnight, the increased viscosity of
the media necessitating the increased time.

Sample solutions were placed directly on the
polyacrylamide gel, and were kept from spreading by
placing glass cover-slips on top. Application by
means of filter paper produced streaking.

For visualisation of protein bands, the
polyacrylamide layers were soaked in 15% (w/v)
trichloroacetic acid solution for about 15 min,
which resulted in precipitation of gelatin
components as white opaque bands (precipitation did
not occur with 8% (w/v) trichloroacetic acid). It
was not possible to remove the Ampholine and then
stain with a protein dye such as Amido Black,
because the gelatin was leached out before all the
Ampholine had been removed. pH determinations were
made directly on the polyacrylamide gel with a
flat-ended pH electrode at room temperature.
Average pIs were obtained by the mixed-bed
ion-exchange method[3].

The gelatin used in a number of experiments described below was designated SC200, and was supplied by Croda Food Products Ltd., 123 Grange Road, Bermondsey, London S.E.1. It was a photographic grade limed-ossein, alkali-processed, gelatin with an average pI of 4.85, Bloom jelly strength of 287 g, and the viscosity of a 6.67% (w/v) solution at 40°C was 51 mP. The relative proportions of different molecular weight components have been measured by SDS polyacrylamide disc electrophoresis. (The molecular weight values were confirmed by light scattering measurements and Sephadex gel chromatography.) The results are: 100 000 and below: 66%; > 100 000 - 200 000: 13%; > 200 000 - 500 000: 11%; > 500 000: 10% (ref. 4). The material with a molecular weight 200 000 and below moves readily in a 5% polyacrylamide gel while much of that with a molecular weight greater than 500 000 does not move at all. The 11% in between moves only slowly and probably does not come to equilibrium in the time allowed for the focusing.

20.3   RESULTS

20.3.1   General
A representative experiment is shown in Figure 20.1. A set of bands in the pH range 4.5 to 5.5 were common to all the gelatin samples except for the acid-processed gelatin, which had an average pI of 7.2. From viscosity measurements, the approximate molecular weight of the trypsin-hydrolysed samples was about 20 000, and of the acid-hydrolysed sample 40 000 (ref. 5). The gelatin of pI 7.2 is the precursor for the chemically modified gelatin of pI 5.3. These features are discussed in more detail below.

The apparent heterogeneity came as a surprise. It is generally assumed that the pH gradient on isoelectric focusing is relatively smooth, and there was no reason to expect marked discontinuities in the distribution of pIs for gelatin. Thus a number of experiments were carried out to determine the nature of the bands, their reproducibility, and other factors affecting them.

20.3.2   Unreacted Gelatins
Experiments were performed in a pH gradient from 3 to 10 on a series of gelatins with average pIs of 4.85, 4.90, 4.98, 5.10 and 5.23. The results showed bands with the range of pIs of the individual samples extending over 0.5 to 0.7 pH units. The

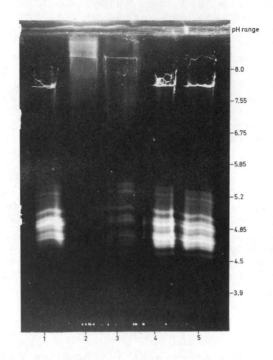

Figure 20.1 Isoelectric focusing of a range of gelatin samples in pH 3 to 10 Ampholine. 1, SC200 gelatin; 2, acid-processed ossein gelatin, pI 7.2 (precursor for sample 3); 3, phthalated gelatin, pI 5.3; 4, trypsin-hydrolysed gelatin; 5, acid-hydrolysed gelatin. Precise experimental details are given in section 20.2

bands were in exactly the same position for all the gelatins. Small changes in the range of bands were consistent with the difference in average pI.

20.3.3 Hydrogen Bonding

Gelatin is extensively aggregated by hydrogen bonds at temperatures below $35^{\circ}C$. As isoelectric focusing is carried out at about $5^{\circ}C$, it was necessary to show that the gelatin had reached an equilibrium position in the pH gradient. Samples were placed on a plate at the beginning of the run and then at hourly intervals during it. The results showed no significant difference, except for the 2 h sample, which was not completely focused. As the samples jelled when they were put on the cold plate, the hydrogen bonds must have been disrupted before the gelatin molecules would pass through the

polyacrylamide gel matrix. The normal focusing
time of 6.5 h is therefore sufficient to obtain
optimal resolution. In a separate experiment it was
shown that the gelatin focused in the same bands
when the samples were placed at opposite ends of
the plate at the beginning of the run.

20.3.4 Hydrolysed Gelatin

A series of samples of gelatin (SC200) were
hydrolysed with trypsin, collagenase, hydrochloric
acid and sodium hydroxide. Both enzymes were from
Koch-Light Laboratories, Colnbrook, Bucks:
collagenase, form II, batch no. 43348, reported to
contain very little proteolytic and peptidase
activity; trypsin, ex-bovine pancrease, twice
recrystallised, batch no. 42788. Trypsin attacks
gelatin in the band portions, while collagenase
attacks the interband portions[6]. (The gelatin
chains have a number of 'band' sections where the
amino acid residues with ionisable side chains
accumulate. The portions in between are called
'interband', and contain very few amino acid
residues with ionisable side chains.) It is
reasonable to assume that acid and alkali attack the
gelatin chain more randomly than enzymes, although
not in an identical manner[7]. Samples of different
viscosities were taken at various times during the
hydrolysis and subjected to isoelectric focusing.
The molecular weight of the hydrolysed gelatin
ranged down to about 10 000, at which value it
would not precipitate with trichloroacetic acid.
Apart from a slight decrease in the average pI, the
band patterns were the same for all samples and
independent of the method or degree of hydrolysis.

20.3.5 Chemically Modified Gelatins

Gelatin can be reacted so that the amino groups on
the lysine and hydroxylysine residues, or the
carboxylic acid groups on the aspartic and glutamic
acid residues are substituted. Such procedures
change the pI of the gelatin. If a gelatin with a
high pI (having a proportion of its aspartic and
glutamic acid residues amidated) is reacted to block
the lysine amino groups, the pI can be lowered.
     The acid-processed gelatin (acid-ossein from
Croda Food Ingredients Ltd.) had its pI reduced from
7.2 to 5.3 by reaction with phthalic anhydride.
This replaced the lysine amino groups with
carboxylic acid-containing groups. The total number
of charged groups on the molecule was then much
lower but the ratio of the groups was similar to
that of an alkali-processed gelatin such as SC200.

On focusing (Figure 20.1), the sample of modified
gelatin had exactly the same bands (around pH 5) as
SC200. The bands are absent from the precursor,
most of which moved only slightly in the high pH
region.

20.4 DISCUSSION

Differences between the average pI of gelatin
samples are shown clearly by the isoelectric
focusing method. Also the average pIs of the main
components of a mixture of gelatins with different
pIs can be measured by this method.

However, the bands obtained between about pH
4.5 and 5.5 by the thin-layer isoelectric focusing
method on gelatins are an artefact of the method.
They do not reflect a series of pI fractions in the
gelatin itself. This conclusion is based on the
fact that the bands appear in the same positions
for a great variety of gelatins, including
hydrolysed and chemically modified gelatins. In
order to clarify this conclusion it is necessary to
consider the structure of gelatin and the various
chemically reacted samples that have been tested.

Collagen is made up of units of tropocollagen
covalently cross-linked together. The tropocollagen
units consist of three polypeptide chains (α chains)
each of approximately 100 000 molecular weight,
covalently linked and hydrogen-bonded to form a
triple helix. Two of the chains (α_1) are the same,
but the third (α_2) is slightly different in
composition. To make gelatin, collagen is treated
with alkali or acid to break the covalent
cross-links and hydrogen bonds without degrading the
polypeptide chains. In practice, some cross-links
remain and some chains are broken so that commercial
gelatin contains a high proportion of multi-chain
molecules joined in various combinations and at
various points, and degraded to various extents to
produce large and small fragments. Disc
electrophoresis shows that at least 30 different
molecular weight fractions below 500 000 are
obtained from normal alkali-processed gelatin[8]. In
alkali-processed gelatin most, but not all, of the
side chain amide groups of asparagine and glutamine
are hydrolysed[9]. In acid-processed gelatins, most
of these side chain amide groups remain
unhydrolysed. Thus the different molecular weight
fractions of the alkali-processed gelatin will each
have differing numbers of asparagine and glutamine
residues.

As the amino acid sequence does not have a

precisely regular repeating structure[10] there will
be a large number of molecules, each with a slightly
different net charge, in normal gelatin. The fact
that only about 15 discrete bands were observed in
ordinary alkali-processed gelatin was therefore
unexpected.

The gelatin was further chemically reacted.
The two enzymes used hydrolyse the gelatin at
different positions. The hydrolysis will result in
an increased number of gelatin fragments and these
fragments will have different net charges. The
hydrolysis with acid and with alkali would be
expected to break the chains differently, and thus
would produce fragments with slightly different net
charges. If the bands obtained by isoelectric
focusing really corresponded to groups of gelatin
molecules with almost identical pIs, then hydrolysis
ought to cause the bands to spread and eventually
merge with each other. This does not occur.

When the average pI of acid-processed gelatin
is reduced from 7.2 to 5.3 by chemical reaction, the
net charge on the reacted gelatin must be on average
the same as for alkali-processed gelatin with a pI
at about this pH. However the total number of acid
and basic groups is less. It is very unlikely that
individual molecules of the chemically modified
gelatin will have identical charge balances to the
molecules of the alkali-processed gelatin. Thus
chemically reacted gelatin ought to give different
pI bands; this again does not happen.

The bands cannot therefore reflect the real
distribution of pIs of the molecular components in
these differently treated gelatins. They must
therefore represent an artificial distribution of
the pI components on the isoelectric focusing plate.

This evidence points to a stepwise pH gradient,
at least in the pH 5 region, where most of the work
described above has been done. Micro-pH steps,
about 15 per pH unit, would explain the bands
obtained by the various preparations of gelatin
tested. The overall pH gradient would not be
affected by the micro-steps, and the method of pH
measurement used in this work, either cutting small
discs and measuring the pH of the eluate, or
measuring directly with flat-ended pH electrodes,
would not detect micro-steps. The many gelatin
fractions would be expected to concentrate on the
rising part of the pH step to give a series of bands.
The relatively few components of other proteins with
a pI around 5 would position themselves
appropriately on the micro-pH steps to give the
different patterns obtained.

There is no evidence that gelatin complexes
with the focused Ampholine bands. For example,
Ampholine does not affect the jelling of gelatin.
The correlation between the overall position of the
gelatin bands on the isoelectric focusing plate and
the average pI of the samples is very good. A
gelatin-Ampholine complex would be expected to
affect this overall position of the gelatin on the
plate if it was strong enough to force it into
bands.

20.5 CONCLUSIONS

The evidence presented in this paper suggests that,
at least in the pH 5 region, the pH gradient formed
by Ampholine in thin layers of polyacrylamide is not
smooth but is in the form of micro-pH steps. This
conclusion is based upon the fact that the
heterogeneous protein, gelatin, always gives the
same bands despite being subjected to a wide range
of chemical reactions.

The isoelectric focusing technique gives
valuable information about the major pI components
of gelatin and, for example, indicates the extent of
the hydrolysis of the asparagine and glutamine side
chains to aspartic and glutamic acid. However, the
bands are artefacts of the method.

Lines of possible further work include the
focusing of different but equally heterogeneous
protein preparations, and the extension of the
present experiments to cover a wider pH range, as
well as direct measurement of the pH gradient with
a micro-pH probe.

ACKNOWLEDGEMENTS

Much of the practical work reported in this paper
was performed by Mr. R.B. Rampersad. The molecular
weight distribution of the gelatin was determined by
Dr. I. Tomka. We had many useful discussions with
Mr. A.M. Kragh.

REFERENCES

1. AWDEH, Z.L., WILLIAMSON, A.R. and ASKONAS, B.A.,
    'Isoelectric Focusing in Polyacrylamide Gel and
    its Application to Immunoglobulins'. Nature,
    219, 66-67 (1968)
2. KARLSSON, C., DAVIES, H., ÖHMAN, J. and
    ANDERSON, U.-B., 'LKB 2117 Multiphor. I.
    Analytical Thin Layer Gel Electrofocusing in
    Polyacrylamide Gel'. LKB Application Note,No.75

LKB Produkter AB, S-161 25 Bromma 1, Sweden
(March 1973)

3. JANUS, J.W., KENCHINGTON, A.W. and WARD, A.G.,
'Rapid Method for the Determination of the
Isoelectric Point of Gelatin using Mixed-bed
Ion Exchange'. Research, 4, 247-248 (1951)

4. TOMKA, I. (personal communication)

5. STAINSBY, G., WOOTTON, J.W. and WARD, A.G.,
'The Relations Between Molecular Weight,
Viscosity, and Gelling Properties for Gelatin
Prepared using Controlled Conditions'.
Gelatin and Glue Research Association, Research
Report, A29 (1962)

6. FUNAKOSHI, H. and NODA, H., 'Estimation of the
Average Length of the Interband Regions in
Collagen Polypeptide Chain'. Biochim. Biophys.
Acta, 86, 106-121 (1964)

7. SAUNDERS, P.R. and WARD, A.G., 'Mechanical
Properties of Degraded Gelatins'. Nature, 176,
26-27 (1955)

8. BARTLEY, J.A. (personal communication)

9. EASTOE, J.E., 'The Chemical Composition of
Gelatin. II. The Amino Acid Composition of
Gelatin, Collagen, and Reticulin'. Gelatin
and Glue Research Association, Research Report,
A13 (1954)

10. TRAUB, W. and PIEZ, K.A., 'The Chemistry and
Structure of Collagen'. Adv. Prot. Chem., 25,
243-352 (1971)

21. pH-DEPENDENT STATES OF A VIRAL COMPONENT FROM FOOT-AND-MOUTH DISEASE VIRUS

P. Talbot

Foot-and-mouth disease viruses are grouped into seven serotypes, each containing numerous strains. These strains show a wide spectrum of electrophoretic mobilities[1] which are a unique heritable property of the virion. There is a relationship between electrophoretic mobility and the serotype of a virus strain which may reflect the phylogenetic divergence of the seven serotypes from an ancestral prototype.

When this phenomenon was investigated further by isoelectric focusing, difficulties were encountered due to a tendency for the focused viral material to precipitate at its isoelectric point. Accordingly, a horizontal trough apparatus was developed (see Chapter 5) for use in this study. This incorporates features which circumvent impairment of resolution due to isoelectric precipitation of focused material and also allows samples to be inserted at selected points in a pre-formed pH gradient.

Foot-and-mouth disease virus of type O (strain 1) was radioactively labelled by incorporation of $[^{14}C]$-amino acids from an algal protein hydrolysate and purified according to the method of Brown & Cartwright[2]. Samples of purified radioactively labelled virus were inserted into pre-formed broad-range pH gradients and subjected to isoelectric focusing. At the end of the run, the gradient was fractionated and the pH and radioactivity of each fraction were measured.

The radioactivity profile obtained was found to depend on the pH at the point of insertion of the sample into the pre-formed pH gradient (Figure 21.1).

270

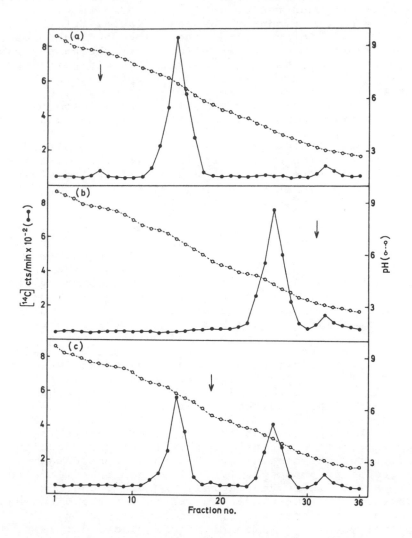

Figure 21.1   Isoelectric focusing of foot-and-mouth
disease virus, type O (strain 1) labelled with
$[^{14}C]$-amino acids and inserted into pre-formed pH
gradients at different points.   The points of
insertion are indicated by arrows.   (a) pH 8.7;
(b) pH 3.2; (c) pH 5.6.   (o————o), Radioactivity
(cts/min x 10^{-2}); (o- - -o), pH.   Isoelectric
focusing was performed at 4°C for 72 h.   Final
voltage 1000 V, d.c

If the sample was inserted at an alkaline pH (pH 8
to 9), a single major component was observed after
isoelectric focusing and was located in a zone
corresponding to pH 6.9. However, when a replicate
sample was inserted at acidic pH (pH 3 to 4), a
single major component was again found, but this
time it was located in a zone corresponding to pH
4.3. Both components were formed if the sample was
inserted into the pH gradient at the mid-point (pH
5 to 6). In each case a minor component was
observed in a zone corresponding to pH 3.1.

The two major components, when isolated by
isoelectric focusing and subsequently re-focused in
a second pre-formed pH gradient, were shown to be
interconvertible. The pH 6.9 component isolated
after insertion of the original sample at alkaline
pH when inserted at acid pH for re-focusing yielded
the pH 4.3 component. The reverse was found if the
pH 4.3 component was re-focused after insertion at
an alkaline pH.

Foot-and-mouth disease viruses are acid-labile
picornaviruses and the pH ranges in which both the
major components were located are close to, or
below, the pH at which these viruses degrade. When
these viruses are degraded below pH 7.0, the viral
RNA is released, with the formation of 12S protein
subunits and a protein aggregate which sediments
more rapidly[3]. Each 12S subunit contains three of
the four protein species found in the virus and
corresponds to one face of its icosahedral capsid[4].
The rapidly sedimenting protein aggregate consists
of the fourth protein species, which exhibits the
serological and biophysical properties of a group
protein within the foot-and-mouth disease virus
group[5].

The finding that both major components isolated
by isoelectric focusing consisted of 12S subunits
supported the conclusion that they represented viral
degradation products. The minor component located
at pH 3.1 sedimented rapidly and was found to
contain the fourth protein species of the virus when
subsequently examined by electrophoresis in
polyacrylamide gels containing sodium dodecyl
sulphate. The identity of the two major components
was confirmed by a similar series of experiments
using radioactively labelled 12S subunit purified by
sucrose density gradient centrifugation. When this
material was examined by isoelectric focusing,
results identical to those described in Figure 21.1
were obtained: two interconvertible major components
were found. The minor component was not found
since the fourth protein is absent from purified 12S

preparations.

When strains of other serotypes of foot-and-mouth disease virus were similarly examined, the pH zones in which the two interconvertible forms of the 12S subunit were located differed slightly between serotypes of the virus. As might be expected from its properties as a group protein, the minor component, consisting of the fourth virus protein, was located in the same pH zone regardless of serotype.

The existence of two interconvertible pH-dependent forms of the 12S subunit of foot-and-mouth disease virus is comparable with the observations of Mandel on poliovirus[6]. Poliovirus is an acid-stable picornavirus and the virion can exist in one of two interconvertible pH-dependent forms having different isoelectric points. It was considered that this provided evidence to support the existence of two resonating forms of the poliovirus capsid protein. It is probable that this applies also to the 12S subunit of foot-and-mouth disease virus. The inability of the 12S subunit to raise virus-neutralising antibody in animals, although it contains the protein carrying the major immunising antigen, may be a reflection of a conformational hindrance of the antigenic site.

Isoelectric focusing thus offers a method of investigation of the relationship between conformational states and the immunological properties of the structural proteins of a virus; it also has potential in serotype differentiation.

REFERENCES

1. PRINGLE, C.R., 'Electrophoretic Properties of Foot-and-mouth Disease Virus Strains and the Selection of Intra-strain Mutants'. J. Gen. Virol., 4, 541-555 (1969)
2. BROWN, F. and CARTWRIGHT, B., 'Purification of Radioactive Foot-and-mouth Disease Virus'. Nature (Lond.), 199, 1168-1170 (1963)
3. BURROUGHS, J.N., ROWLANDS, D.J., SANGAR, D.V., TALBOT, P. and BROWN, F., 'Further Evidence for Multiple Proteins in the Foot-and-mouth Disease Virus Particle'. J. Gen. Virol., 13, 73-84 (1971)
4. TALBOT, P. and BROWN, F., 'A Model for Foot-and-mouth Disease Virus'. J. Gen. Virol., 15, 163-170 (1972)
5. TALBOT, P., ROWLANDS, D.J., BURROUGHS, J.N., SANGAR, D.V. and BROWN, F., 'Evidence for a Group Protein in Foot-and-mouth Disease Virus

Particles'. J. Gen. Virol., 19, 369-380
(1973)
6. MANDEL, B., 'Characterization of Type 1
Poliovirus by Electrophoretic Analysis'.
Virology, 44, 554-568 (1971)

22. CLUES TO PROTEIN STRUCTURES FROM ISOELECTRIC FOCUSING

M.J. Hobart

22.1 INTRODUCTION

The methods described below give indirect clues as to the structure of proteins, but are clearly inferior in reliability and precision to current methods of protein chemistry. They have been collected and applied in response to a situation which may be common to a number of fields of investigation: availability of simple specific zymogram assays, and lack of highly purified material in sufficiently large quantity to permit conventional analysis.

Isoelectric focusing in thin polyacrylamide gel slabs[1] offers a combination of very high resolving power, ease of comparison between samples, technical simplicity and economy of sample. It is a powerful method for the detection of changes in charge on protein molecules.

22.2 METHODS AND RESULTS

22.2.1 Determination of Shift Due to Unit Charge Change

Before specific chemical modifications to proteins can be converted into numerical values of residues affected, it is necessary to determine experimentally the effect of changing the charge of the molecule by a single unit. Trace acetylation of free amino groups is a convenient method for producing small changes in charge, each group blocked representing unit charge change. Maleation produces changes of two units of charge for each residue blocked[2].

Trace acetylation was carried out by adding 1 M acetic anhydride in dimethylsulphoxide (DMSO) to

275

serum samples which had been dialysed against 0.1 M
Tris-HCl buffer pH 8.0, to give final concentrations
of 1, 2, 3, 5 and 10 mM. Equal volumes of the five
acetylated samples were mixed together, and the band
patterns of the C6 and C7 components of complement
examined. After such treatment, both components
showed new bands extending the pattern of
non-acetylated material to regions of lower pH. The
absence of new bands in the pH region between those
which usually occur showed that these native
components were separated by a single unit of
charge. Similar patterns of charge alteration have
been noted for haemoglobin.

22.2.2 Enumeration of Polypeptide Chains
Transamination of the α-amino group of the
N-terminal amino acid of a polypeptide chain may be
achieved under relatively mild conditions, yielding
a less charged α-keto acid[3]. Provided that the
N-terminus is available for reaction (i.e. not
blocked or buried in the interior of the molecule),
and that at the pI of the protein the α-amino group
is usually charged, then unit shift of the
isoelectric point may be expected for each
polypeptide chain which has participated in
transamination. The number of chains enumerated by
counting the shifts in the band pattern of a protein
which has been transaminated will usually be a
minimum figure for the reasons given above.
Haemoglobin treated in this way showed a shift to a
lower pI value.

22.2.3 Enumeration of Free Thiol Groups and Interchain Disulphide Bridges
Feinstein[4], and Feinstein and Stott[5], have used
charged alkylating reagents to measure the thiol
groups on proteins. Iodoacetamide does not alter
the charge of the protein, whereas iodoacetic acid
makes it more acidic and ethyleneimine (D. Beale,
personal communication) makes it more basic.
Complement components C2, C6 and C7 exhibited no
change in pI values on treatment of whole serum with
10 mM iodoacetate or ethyleneimine at pH 8.0.
However, reduction of whole serum (in 0.1 M Tris-HCl
buffer, pH 8.0) with 5 mM dithiothreitol followed by
alkylation with iodoacetate or ethyleneimine,
produced a shift of the whole band pattern of C6 by
at least one space, and of C7 by at least two spaces.
This indicates the probable presence of at least
one interchain disulphide bridge in each molecule.
The C2 component was inactivated by this treatment.

22.2.4 <u>Symmetry and Subunit Structures</u>
Isoelectric focusing is unique among electrolytic
methods for protein separation in not requiring
buffer pools in the electrode compartments and,
therefore, it permits the use of media with
non-uniform solute composition. It is possible to
compare directly the pI values of proteins in the
presence and absence of high molarity urea solutions
by preparing a thin-layer gel containing a
concentration gradient of urea.

Urea gradient thin-layer gels are poured
between glass plates arranged so that the urea
gradient is oriented at 90° to the final direction
of current flow (<u>Figure 22.1</u>). Acrylamide solution
containing 8 M urea is poured in first, followed by
solutions containing decreasing amounts of urea.

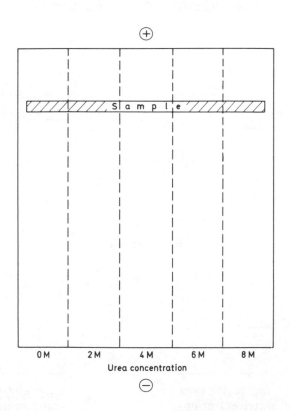

Figure 22.1 Urea concentration is oriented at 90°
              to the direction of current flow

K

With care, a discontinuous gradient of urea
concentration may be obtained, stabilised by the
differences in density between successive layers of
solution. The sample is applied uniformly across
the gel and focusing is carried out in the normal
way, though it may be necessary to prolong the
separation time due to the lower mobility of
proteins in strong urea.

Covalently linked structures cannot be dissociated
by urea. If denaturation is not accompanied by a
change in pI, the protein band will be straight
(Figure 22.2a), but if there is a change, it may
occur sharply at a critical urea concentration
(Figure 22.2b) or may be more gentle (Figure 22.2c).

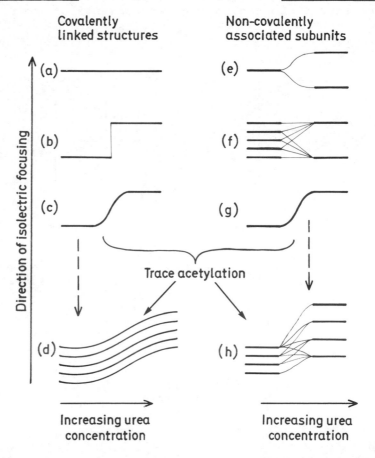

Figure 22.2 Diagrammatic representation of possible
patterns of polypeptide bands obtained by thin-layer
gel isoelectric focusing of native or trace-
acetylated proteins in the presence of discontinuous
            urea concentration gradients

In general, covalently linked protein molecules will give a continuous band extending across the width of the gel.

Proteins made up of non-covalently associated subunits are often dissociated by strong urea. The undissociated band may give rise to a number of free subunit bands as the urea concentration increases (Figure 22.2e).

Many proteins are made up of a number of similar subunits, the 'hybrids' giving rise to a number of isoenzymes (e.g. lactate dehydrogenase). In such cases, as the urea concentration increases, clear band patterns in the absence of urea give way to a zone of confusion in which interdigitating bands may be seen, before emerging into a zone where the bands of the fully dissociated subunits are seen (Figure 22.2f). The existence of a confused portion of the pattern of a protein normally showing several bands will usually indicate the presence of a subunit structure, but its absence is not conclusive evidence for the protein being a single covalent structure.

It is to be expected that proteins which exist as oligomers of identical subunits would give rise to a pattern in a urea gradient gel indistinguishable from that of a covalently united structure (Figure 22.2g) since in many cases the pI of the oligomer will be identical with that of its isolated subunits. Therefore, the band will not be split as the molecule dissociates. Identical subunits can be made non-identical by random charge changes such as those which occur when the protein is trace-acetylated; the bands of such artificial 'isoenzymes' give rise to a complex pattern (Figure 22.2h) similar to that described above. Trace acetylation of a covalently united structure, however, will give rise to a set of bands which will remain parallel (Figure 22.2d).

22.3 DISCUSSION

It must be emphasised that the methods described in this paper are not claimed to offer anything other than clues to the structure of proteins, and should not be used as alternatives to conventional techniques of protein chemistry.

Nevertheless, they offer a number of advantages: they are easy to apply, require small quantities of material and, as has been pointed out by Stott and Feinstein[5], those involving alterations of charge offer the opportunity to examine the behaviour of sub-populations in the sample. Thus, as only half of the molecules show a feature (for instance the presence of two free thiol groups), this will be more clearly apparent using methods which separated the sub-populations than with methods which produce only a mean result.

ACKNOWLEDGEMENTS

I am most grateful to Professor P.J. Lachmann, Dr. A. Feinstein and Dr. M. Salaman for helpful discussion.

REFERENCES

1. AWDEH, Z.L., WILLIAMSON, A.R. and ASKONAS, B.A., 'Isoelectric Focusing in Polyacrylamide Gel and its Application to Immunoglobulins'. Nature (Lond.), 219, 66-67 (1968)
2. STARK, G.R., 'Recent Developments in Chemical Modification and Sequential Degradation of Protein'. Adv. in Protein Chemistry, 24, 261-308 (1970)
3. DIXON, H.B.F., 'Transamination of a Protein in the Presence of Acetate, Glyoxylate and Nickel ions'. Biochem. J., 103, 38p.
4. FEINSTEIN, A., 'Use of Charged Thiol Reagents in Interpreting the Electrophoretic Patterns of Immunoglobulin Chains and Fragments'. Nature (Lond.), 210, 135-137 (1966)
5. STOTT, D.I. and FEINSTEIN, A., 'Biosynthesis and Assembly of IgM. Free Thiol Group Present on the Intracellular Subunits'. Europ. J. Immunol., 3, 229-235 (1973)

23. HETEROGENEITY OF HEPATITIS B ANTIGEN

C.R. Howard and A.J. Zuckerman

The close association between hepatitis B antigen
and human hepatitis B virus (serum hepatitis virus)
has now been firmly established[1]. Early studies
involving staining and flotation experiments
showed hepatitis B antigen to be lipoprotein which
was immunologically distinct from normal low density
serum lipoproteins[2]. Examination of serum
containing this antigen in the electron microscope
by the negative staining technique revealed a
remarkably heterogeneous population of virus-like
particles. The principal antigenic constituent was
a small pleomorphic spherical particle, measuring
approx. 20 nm in diameter but with a range of
between 16 and 25 nm. The presence of tubular
forms, with a constant diameter of 20 nm and often
a length of several hundred nanometers, was a
characteristic feature[3]. The third type of particle
was also spheroidal, measuring approx. 42 nm in
diameter, with an inner core of 28 nm in diameter,
surrounded by a 2 nm shell and an outer coat about
7 nm in thickness[4]. All three types of particles
are aggregated by specific hepatitis B antibody,
suggesting that there is at least one common
antigenic determinant on the surface of each
morphological entity. The mobility of hepatitis B
antigen by immunoelectrophoresis in agar gel was
found to follow closely that of α_2-globulin[5]. Kim
and Tilles[6] reported that purified antigen, derived
from the serum of individual patients with acute
hepatitis B infection, migrated in an
electrophoretic field either in the α_2-β-globulin
region or in the β-globulin region with some
trailing; this confirmed their earlier findings of

281

electrophoretic heterogeneity of serum samples
obtained from such patients[7]. An antigen-positive
serum from a patient suffering from post-transfusion
hepatitis was examined by isoelectric focusing in
large-pore polyacrylamide gel slabs[8]. The antigen
in the pH range 4.8 to 5.0, was detected by
subjecting slices of gel, after isoelectric focusing,
to immunoelectrophoresis. By contrast, the pattern
of bands found in stained gels suggested focusing of
the antigen over a much wider pH range. Also,
antigenic activity was not correlated with the
morphology of the particles nor with a particular
antigenic subtype specificity.

The close association of hepatitis B antigen
with normal serum components, confirmed in our
laboratory by radioimmunoassay of fractionated
material, has been an acknowledged difficulty in the
development of centrifugation techniques for
separation of the antigen in pure form from serum.
Since, unlike other separation techniques, there is
almost complete recovery of total protein after
separation by isoelectric focusing, we applied this
technique to the purification of hepatitis B
antigen. Serum containing antigen with the
subdeterminants ad+y- and which was morphologically
constituted almost entirely of small spherical
particles, was subjected to isoelectric focusing in
a sucrose density gradient in the apparatus
described by Vesterberg and Svensson[9] containing
carrier ampholytes (Ampholine) at a final
concentration of 1% (w/v). The cathode was protected by a 2% ethanolamine solution in water and the
anode by 1.4% (w/v) ortho-phosphoric acid in 60%
(w/v) sucrose. Antigenic activity was found in
those peaks of serum proteins which possessed
isoelectric points in the pH range 4.0 to 7.0.
Antigenic activity was not detected in association
with separated gamma-globulins. This is in
accordance with the well known epidemiological and
clinical experience that the use of gamma-globulin
clinically is free from the risk of transmitting
hepatitis and with the failure to detect hepatitis B
antigen (a marker associated with infectivity) by
electron microscopy after Cohn fractionation of
human plasma known to contain the antigen[10]. The
low molecular weight serum proteins were removed by
gel filtration on Sephadex G200 and were
concentrated by ultrafiltration. Hepatitis B
antigen was then separated from the remaining
unwanted serum protein by isoelectric focusing in a
sucrose gradient as already described. Two discrete
bands of hepatitis B antigen were found[11] with

isoelectric points of 3.65 and 4.33. Normal serum
proteins were not detected in the two bands by the
double radial micro-Ouchterlony immunodiffusion
techniques using hyperimmune horse antiserum
against whole human serum. In addition, the protein
in both bands was aggregated by the addition of
concanavalin A after exhaustive dialysis against
phosphate-buffered saline. The effect was reversed
by the addition of α-methyl-D-mannoside. Each band
of separated hepatitis B antigen was found by immune
(using convalescent serum) electron microscopy[12]
to contain the intact small spherical particles,
20 nm in diameter. This implies that there is at
least one antigenic determinant common to both bands
of separated antigen. It has also been noted that
the small antigen particles fall into two groups[13],
measuring 19 nm and 25 nm in diameter, with a
corresponding difference in average molecular
weights (3.56 and 4.47 x 10^6, respectively). Two
isoelectric pH values were observed with iodinated,
purified hepatitis B antigen; one component had a pI
value of 4.0 and the other a pI value of 4.4. The
relative proportions of the two particle types were
dependent on the individual plasma from which the
antigen was purified, certain plasma containing
chiefly one or other of the particle types.

One sample of serum with antigenic
subdeterminants ay+d- was fractionated by
isoelectric focusing. The sample separated into two
bands of antigenic activity with pI values of 3.95
and 4.90, thus differing from those obtained
previously with the ad+y- subtype[11]. Considerable
difficulty arose in a number of experiments due to
isoelectric precipitation. This was overcome by
employing narrow-range pH gradients and by
increasing the applied voltage in small amounts at
regular intervals.

Isoelectric focusing of material labelled with
$\begin{bmatrix} 125 \\ I \end{bmatrix}$ by a modification of the chloramine T
method[14], revealed trace amounts of hepatitis B
antigen. Radioisotope labelling does not alter
appreciably the reactivity of hepatitis B antigen
and there is no significant alteration in buoyant
density (Howard and Zuckerman, unpublished
observations). However, the pI values of the peaks
of separated antigen were raised to 4.5 and 4.8
respectively. The relatively high phospholipid
content of the antigen suggested that its acidic
nature, as reflected in the low pI values so far
determined, might be due in part to the carboxyl
group in phosphatidyl serine. Analysis of
extracted lipid failed, however, to detect this

phospholipid[15,16]. Alternatively, the presence of
carbohydrate may influence the surface charge of
the lipoprotein moiety of the antigen, thereby
imparting a hydrophilic surface when in aqueous
solution[17]. It is also interesting to note that
some plant viruses behave similarly when focused in
polyacrylamide gels[18].

The apoprotein constituent of hepatitis B
antigen was found to be organised into a number of
definable polypeptides. Aliquots from peaks I and
II (Figure 23.1) of separated antigen activity were
solubilised by heating for 10 min at 80°C in the
presence of 1% (w/v) sodium dodecyl sulphate, 0.5 M
urea and 0.1% (w/v) dithiothreitol. The resulting
solution of denatured protein was then subjected to
disc electrophoresis in 10% SDS polyacrylamide gels
using 0.005 M Tris-glycine buffer, pH 8.0. After
staining with Coomassie Brilliant Blue, eight
identical polypeptides were discernable in samples
of material from both peaks I and II. The range of
molecular weights was approximately 2 000 to
300 000. Densitometry of the stained gels revealed
that at least one polypeptide (mol. wt. 100 000) was
a major component of the first peak, but it was
present only as a minor component in the second
peak. Conversely, the lowest molecular weight
polypeptide component of peak II was not present in
peak I. A similar analysis of the polypeptide
components of antigen bearing the ay+d-
subdeterminants has not yet been completed.

Further attempts have been made to
characterise the polypeptide composition of the
ad+y- subtype by procedures similar to those used
for the isolation of adenovirus subunits[19] and the
separation of the group-specific antigen of Rous
sarcoma virus[20]. Hepatitis B antigen labelled with
[125I] was heated for 2 h at 37°C in the presence of
4 M urea, 1% (w/v) 2-mercaptoethanol and 1% (w/v) of
a nonionic detergent Nonidet-P40 (B.D.H. Ltd., Poole,
England). The dissociated antigen was then
subjected to preparative isoelectric focusing in a
urea gradient of 4 to 8 M in the absence of sucrose
and containing carrier ampholytes (Ampholine) and
Nonidet-P40 at a final concentration of 1% (w/v) or
0.1% (w/v) respectively. The anode was protected by
2% (w/v) ortho-phosphoric acid solution in 8 M urea
and the cathode with 1.4% (w/v) ethanolamine in
water. A large peak of radioactive material with a
pI value of 5.9 was formed. This peak was
characterised further by SDS disc gel
electrophoresis as described above and the molecular
weight was estimated to be 100 000 and therefore

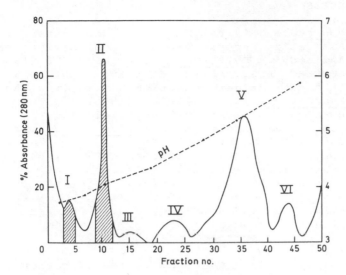

<u>Figure 23.1</u> The system had a volume of 110 ml and
contained 1% (w/v) Ampholine, pH range 3 to 10.
The duration of the experiment was 43 h and the
final potential was 600 V. pH measurements were
made at 20°C. Hepatitis B antigen activity was
detected by complement fixation,
immunoelectrophoresis and immune electron microscopy
and is indicated by the cross-hatched areas. These
fractions were pooled for analysis of constituent
        peptides. (From Howard and Zuckerman[11])

identified as the major polypeptide component of
peak I described above. This may be responsible in
part for the heterogeneity of the small 20 nm
antigen particles described earlier.
        The heterogeneity of hepatitis B antigen has
thus been confirmed by isoelectric focusing. This
technique offers a convenient method for further
analysis of the structure of antigens associated
with viral hepatitis.

ACKNOWLEDGEMENTS

The equipment for this work was provided by a grant
from Pfizer Ltd., and the hepatitis programme is
supported by grants from the Medical Research
Council, the World Health Organisation and the
Wellcome Trust. We are also indebted to Mrs. H.
Smith for invaluable technical assistance.

K*

REFERENCES

1. Memorandum. 'Viral Hepatitis and Tests for the
    Australia (Hepatitis-Associated) Antigen and
    Antibody'. Bull. W.H.O., 42, 957-992 (1970)
2. BLUMBERG, B.S., ALTER, H.J. and VISNICH, S.,
    'A "New" Antigen in Leukemia Sera'. J. Amer.
    Med. Assoc., 191, 541-546 (1965)
3. ZUCKERMAN, A.J., 'Viral Hepatitis and the
    Australia-Sh Antigen'. Nature (Lond.), 223,
    569 (1969)
4. DANE, D.S., CAMERON, C.H. and BRIGGS, M.,
    'Virus-like Particles in Serum of Patients with
    Australia Antigen-Associated Hepatitis'.
    Lancet, i, 659-698 (1970)
5. ALTER, H.J. and BLUMBERG, B.S., 'Further Studies
    on a "New" Human Isoprecipitin System
    (Australia Antigen)'. Blood, 27, 297-309
    (1966)
6. KIM, C.Y. and TILLES, J.G., 'Purification and
    Biophysical Characterization of Hepatitis B
    Antigen'. J. Clin. Invest., 52, 1176-1186
    (1973)
7. KIM, C.Y. and TILLES, J.G., 'Immunologic and
    Electrophoretic Heterogeneity of
    Hepatitis-Associated Antigen'. J. Infect.
    Dis., 123, 618-628 (1971;
8. JEANSSON, S., VESTERBERG, O. and WADSTRÖM, T.,
    'Separation of Australia-Antigen by Isoelectric
    Focusing in Acrylamide Gel'. Life Sciences,
    11, Part II, 929-937 (1972)
9. VESTERBERG, O. and SVENSSON, H., 'Isoelectric
    Fractionation, Analysis, and Characterization
    of Ampholytes in Natural pH Gradients. IV.
    Further Studies on the Resolving Power in
    Connection with Separation of Myoglobins'.
    Acta Chem. Scand., 20, 820-834 (1966)
10. ZUCKERMAN, A.J., TAYLOR, P.E., BIRD, R.G. and
    RUSSELL, S.M., 'The Australia
    (Hepatitis-Associated) Antigen in Fibrinogen
    and Other Fractions of Human Plasma'. J. Clin.
    Path., 24, 2-7 (1971)
11. HOWARD, C.R. and ZUCKERMAN, A.J.,
    'Electrofocusing of Hepatitis B Antigen'.
    J. Gen. Virol., 20, 253-256 (1973)
12. ZUCKERMAN, A.J., 'Electron Microscopy and Immune
    Electron Microscopy'. Bull. W.H.O., 42,
    975-978 (1970)
13. DREESMAN, G.R., HOLLINGER, F.B., SURIANO, J.K.,
    FUGIOKA, R.S., BRUNSCHWIG, J.P. and MELNICK,
    J.L., 'Biophysical and Biochemical
    Heterogeneity of Purified Hepatitis B Antigen'.

J. Virol., 10, 469-476 (1972)

14. HUNTER, W.M. and GREENWOOD, F.C., 'Preparation
    of Iodine-131 Labelled Human Growth Hormone of
    High Specific Activity'. Nature (Lond.), 194,
    495-496 (1962)

15. KIM, C.Y. and BISSELL, D.M., 'Stability of the
    Lipid and Protein of Hepatitis-Associated
    (Australia) Antigen'. J. Infect. Dis., 123,
    470-476 (1971)

16. TAKAHASHI, T., personal communication

17. BURRELL, C.J., PROUDFOOD, E., KEEN, G.A. and
    MARMION, B.P., 'Carbohydrates in Hepatitis B
    Antigen'. Nature (New Biol.), 243, 260-262
    (1973)

18. RICE, R.H. and HORST, J., 'Isoelectric Focusing
    of Viruses in Polyacrylamide Gels'. Virology,
    49, 602-604 (1972)

19. SHORTRIDGE, K.F. and BIDDLE, F., 'The Proteins
    of Adenovirus Type 5'. Arch. Virusforsch., 29,
    1-24 (1970)

20. HUNG, P.P., ROBINSON, H.L. and ROBINSON, W.S.,
    'Isolation and Characterization of Proteins
    From Rous Sarcoma Virus'. Virology, 43,
    251-266 (1971)

SECTION III

Applications in Immunology

24. ANTIBODY ISOELECTRIC SPECTRA

A.R. Williamson

24.1 INTRODUCTION

Antibody diversity is enormous. Specific antibody can be elicited against such an extensive range of antigenic determinants that one might be led to the conclusion that there is no limit to antibody diversity. Even when antibody is elicited in an animal by injection of a defined chemical grouping (hapten) conjugated to a protein the resultant hapten-specific antibody is a heterogeneous population of molecules.

Analytical isoelectric focusing has proved to be an invaluable tool in the study of the extent of heterogeneity of antibody of a given common specificity. This article serves to review the methods of detecting antibody isoelectric spectra and emphasises the need for caution in the interpretation of results. It will also describe how the techniques are being used to define the genetic control of antibody formation.

The properties of all immunoglobulins are similar and a technique with high resolving power is needed to distinguish between different members of the same family of immunoglobulin molecules. Many immunological methods have been devised making use of antisera specific for antigenic determinants on immunoglobulin molecules. Class and subclass specific determinants are easily defined (e.g. antisera specific for immunoglobulin M or immunoglobulin G); subtle differences down to single amino acid replacements are also detectable by antisera. This has allowed alleles to be defined at the genetic loci coding for immunoglobulin chains. In this way the genes coding for the constant regions of L and H chains have been identified.

However, each L and each H chain is encoded by two
genes (linked prior to transcription), namely a
constant region gene (C-gene) and a variable region
gene (V-gene). One of the problems of antibody
diversity has been to find suitable phenotypic
markers for the V-region so that the inheritance of
V-genes might be followed. The importance of the
problem is due to the need to define the genetic
basis of antibody diversity. Two opposite
viewpoints hold that either the pool of V-genes in
the germ-line is very small with somatic processes
leading to a diverse population of V-genes in the
population of lymphocytes potentially able to yield
antibody secretory cells, or the germ-line contains
a sufficiently large pool of V-genes to code for all
antibodies and each antibody-producing cell limits
its phenotype to one antibody. The latter germ-line
hypothesis predicts the inheritance of the ability
to make sets of antibody molecules of each
specificity. Isoelectric focusing has provided an
analytical tool for characterising individual
antibody molecules. The isoelectric spectrum of a
monoclonal antibody can be used as a phenotypic
marker for the four genes coding for its two
polypeptide chains.

Two years ago a chapter[1] in the Handbook of
Experimental Immunology began 'The application of
isoelectric focusing to immunology is in its
infancy. The future potential appears great'. That
chapter had not been published at the time
Electrofocusing '73 was held. The use of
isoelectric focusing in immunology is now more
widely accepted and it might be said to have come of
age. That is not to deny that there is plenty of
potential left to be developed.

24.2 DETECTION OF ANTIBODY SPECTRA AFTER ANALYTICAL ISOELECTRIC FOCUSING

Thin-layer polyacrylamide gel isoelectric focusing
was performed essentially as described by Awdeh,
Williamson and Askonas[2]. The details have been
described fully elsewhere[1,3]. We have continued to
use a very simple procedure. Gels of various
thicknesses are made as shown in Figure 24.1. The
thin-layer gel supported on the smaller of the glass
plates is inverted onto two carbon electrodes housed
in an airtight plastic refrigerator box. A single
power pack serves five such boxes from a multiple
outlet system (Figure 24.2). The current flow to
each box is monitored by a separate ammeter;
shrouded extra high tension connectors and plastic

Figure 24.1 Preparation of a thin-layer
polyacrylamide gel. The cell is constructed of two
glass plates separated by silicone rubber tubing of
the desired diameter and held together by bull-dog
clips. The larger plate is siliconised to
facilitate its removal after the gel has set. The
smaller plate which will carry the gel is a subbed
plate from Ilford. Use of these subbed plates
ensures easier handling of the gel during the
          development of spectra after focusing

trunking are used. This system is housed in a cold
room at 4°C. On a routine basis, over 100 samples
may be focused each day with good reproducibility.
     This methodology was developed originally for
examining antibody heterogeneity and has proven to
be the most useful format for comparison of
isoelectric spectra of many different samples.
Originally, antibodies were purified specifically by
interaction with antigen. These antibody
populations were usually very heterogeneous and

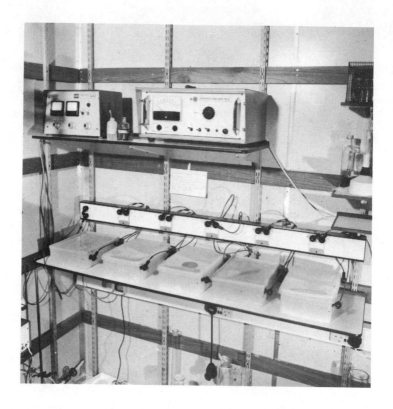

Figure 24.2 Multiple outlet system for running
five isoelectric focusing boxes simultaneously.
Five boxes, each accommodating one 160 mm x 200 mm
plate, are supplied by a single power pack
(LKB or MBI)

their spectra defied analysis in terms of the number
of contributing molecular species of antibody.
    In order to make use of a spectrum as a genetic
marker it was necessary to be able to visualise
antibody spectra directly after isoelectric focusing
of serum samples. For this purpose, interaction of
the focused bands with antigen gave the required
specificity and the use of radioactive antigen gave
high sensitivity[3]. Equally high sensitivity can be
obtained in the detection of anti-enzymes using
suitable zymogram methods. A special form of this
approach uses antibody-mediated enzyme function
mutants of β-galactosidase[4]. These enzyme molecules
are activated by interaction with antibody to a
particular determinant. Consequently, enzyme

activity is localised on these antibody bands and
there is no background problem. This is a potential
genetic marker for V-genes coding for antibodies
specific for the activating determinant. It is also
possible to use native β-galactosidase to develop
spectra of antibody specific for all determinants on
the molecule (Kipp, unpublished observations). In
order to wash away excess β-galactosidase not bound
to antibody bands, it is convenient to fix the
focused bands with glutaraldehyde prior to enzyme
overlay. Antibody activity survives this fixation
procedure as shown by Phillips and Dresser[5]. These
authors have used a layer of RBC in agar with
complement together with a developing serum to
visualise focused bands of lytic antibody. By
varying the specificity of the anti-immunoglobulin
in the developing serum they were able to identify
the class or subclass of the antibody in a given
band.

This constitutes a marked advance in
methodology and not just a minor modification.
Moreover, the method can be adapted to a variety of
antigens limited only by the ability to couple a
suitable form of the antigen to RBC[6]. As shown in
Figure 24.3, the haemolytic method can give
individual spectra for each subclass of
immunoglobulin G. The spectra shown in Figure 24.3
are of clonally selected DNP-binding antibodies
developed with DNP-coated sheep RBC and
anti-immunoglobulin G_1 or anti-immunoglobulin G_{2a}.
The use with proteins coupled to sheep RBC showed
that the haemolytic method reveals many clonal
products not visualised by overlaying the gel with
radio-iodinated protein and subsequent
autoradiography. This could be due to greater
sensitivity of the haemolytic method either in
detecting smaller amounts of antibody or in
detecting lower affinity antibody; neither of these
parameters has yet been fully explored. However,
the use of radio-labelled proteins may be limited by
the destruction of antigenic determinants by
iodination.

24.3 SPECTRUM OF A BIOSYNTHETICALLY HOMOGENEOUS
      ANTIBODY

Myeloma proteins afford the most readily studied
example of biosynthetically homogeneous
immunoglobulins. The myeloma tumour is a single
neoplastic plasma cell clone. It has been shown
that the original product of such a clone appears as
a single band on isoelectric focusing and that a

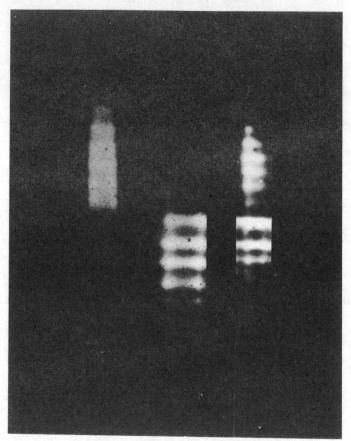

γG_{2a} γG_1 Autoradiograph

Figure 24.3 Isoelectric spectra of DNP-binding
antibodies visualised by lysis of DNP-coated sheep
red cells developed with either (a)
anti-immunoglobulin G_{2a}, or (b) anti-immunoglobulin
G_1 (ref. 6), or (c) by autoradiography of bound
radioactive hapten[3]. (From an experiment by A.J.
McMichael and J.M. Phillips)

series of post-synthetic changes leads to a
microheterogeneous isoelectric spectrum consisting
of several bands characteristic of myeloma protein
in serum[7]. For 5563 mouse G_{2a} myeloma protein the
initial H_2L_2 product focused as a band (O) carrying
two additional positive charges (or two fewer

negative charges) relative to the most basic myeloma band detected in serum. The pK_as of the two groups involved were approximately 7.5 and we speculated that some alteration of the N-termini of the H chains was involved in post-synthetic changes. Both L and H chains in the 5563 protein ultimately have a blocked N-terminus, namely pyrrolidone carboxylic acid. However, since the L chain has a finite lifespan in a pool of free L chains prior to incorporation into H_2L_2, changes may already occur in that pool. Glutamine, the precursor of pyrrolidone carboxylic acid was not found at the N-terminus of either H or L chains of band O and neither was leucine. Furthermore, Bevan (unpublished observations) was unable to detect N-terminal methionine which would be the original N-terminal amino acid. Recently a precursor of L chain has been demonstrated in several tumours[8-10]. This precursor is several amino acids longer than the mature L chain and in one case the additional amino acids have been shown to be at the N-terminus[8]. The conversion of 5563 band O to the form of immunoglobulin found in serum might well involve cleavage of a short peptide chain intermediate between the initiation point, methionine, and the eventual N-terminal amino acid, glutamine, which is cyclised when exposed.

The most basic myeloma component in serum is slowly converted to more acidic forms and this change can be attributed to the loss of amide groups[11]. This need not be the sole reason for microheterogeneity which in other cases can result from differences in the carbohydrate component. An understanding of the origin of the bands in the spectrum allowed the myeloma spectra to be used to interpret antibody spectra in clonal terms. It is now well documented that antibody produced by a single clone of B-lymphocyte-derived cells shows a characteristic microheterogeneous isoelectric spectrum. The best evidence comes from cloning experiments using the spleen cell transfer system in inbred mice[12]. In these experiments and in the case of restricted antibodies elicited in neonatal rabbits, antibodies having presumptive monoclonal spectra were shown by hapten binding studies to have identical patterns of heterogeneity. As is described in the following discussion of the use of isoelectric focusing, the spectrum of elicited antibody can be restricted by a variety of experimental procedures. Whichever method is used, the end result is that the spectrum of antibody is ultimately restricted to a limited pattern of bands

with a regular spacing pattern. The number and
spacing of the bands varies from spectrum to
spectrum. In rare cases only one band may be
discerned, but storage of such sera will usually
lead to the formation of further adjacent bands.
Also, with successive bleeding during the course of
a restricted antibody response, the number of bands
in the spectrum usually increases due to
post-synthetic changes in the antibody occurring in
serum rather than the production of different
antibodies by newly recruited clones.

An isoelectric spectrum as a marker for a clone
or as a genetic marker can only be exploited
usefully when the spectrum is simple. The spectrum
should preferably be monoclonal but of course two or
three clonal products can be distinguished in the
same serum. However, the more bands present in the
spectrum, the greater the degree of uncertainty in
defining the heterogeneity of the response in clonal
terms. It is decidedly unwise to place too much
emphasis on the assignment of groups of lines in a
complex spectrum as representing monoclonal
products. In the comparison of different complex
spectra, this misinterpretation can lead one to
conclude that there are common clones in the
different responses when in fact there are not.
This is emphasised when examining very complex
patterns. Often there is a regular repeat spacing
of the lines in such complex spectra[2]. This
apparent regularity may result from multiple protein
bands being spaced too closely to be resolved and
therefore forming single bands in some manner
influenced by the carrier ampholytes. It should be
stressed that this regularity is not observed when a
large number of monoclonal spectra are compared side
by side.

Under such conditions more than 5×10^4
different spectra can be distinguished[11]. The
methodology can, however, only show non-identity of
antibody molecules. It is <u>assumed</u> that where
antibody isoelectric spectra are indistinguishable
the antibodies are identical, but such a finding
cannot be considered as <u>proof</u> of identity.
Additional evidence for identity is not always
available.

24.4   ANTIBODY ISOELECTRIC SPECTRUM AS A CLONAL
       MARKER

One of the first uses for antibody spectra was as a
criterion for the selection and propagation of
single clones of antibody-forming cells[12]. A clone

is selected by the transfer of limited numbers of
spleen cells from an immunised donor mouse into a
series of irradiated syngeneic recipient mice.
Recipient mice then make clonally restricted
antibody as shown by isoelectric focusing.
Individual mice having monoclonal antibody spectra
are selected and that clone is propagated by serial
cell transfer into successive generations of
irradiated syngeneic mice[13,14].

The reproducibility of the antibody spectrum
through many transfers and a large expansion of the
clone shows that the product of such a clone derived
from a B-lymphocyte is genetically stable in the
same way as the myeloma protein produced by a
plasmacytoma. Thus, integration of particular V-
and C-gene pairs must occur early in differentiation
and must be a permanent event. Clonal selection
experiments therefore constitute a justification of
the use of the isoelectric spectrum as a genetic
marker for antibody.

Recently, cultured mouse myeloma cells were
screened for mutant clones producing myeloma protein
with an altered isoelectric focusing pattern[15]. The
frequency of variant clones was higher than expected
but cannot be taken as evidence for a somatic
mechanism of diversification of V-genes.

22.5 ANTIBODY ISOELECTRIC SPECTRA AS GENETIC MARKERS

Clonal selection experiments showed that there was
a very large number of different clones each making
a characteristic antibody which could bind the test
hapten (DNP-2,4-dinitrophenyl). The number of
unique monoclonal antibodies sharing a common
binding specificity can be determined by making
comprehensive transfers from primed donor mice.
This was done using NIP-BGG (4-hydroxy-3-iodo-5-
nitrophenacetyl-bovine gamma globulin) as the
immunogen; the number of NIP-binding antibodies
in CBA/H mice was estimated to be about 8000
(ref. 16). This is a minimum statistical
estimate corresponding to 5000 different V_H-V_L
combinations each giving a NIP-binding antibody
combining site. This result was interpreted in
terms of the minimum number of genes which could be
required to give this pool size. The random
association of the products of 70 V_H-genes and 70
V_L-genes would be sufficient. It was then open to
speculation as to how many of these genes are
present in the germ-line of CBA/H mice. We
interpreted the result as meaning that a large set

of V-genes was present in the germ-line of CBA/H
mice but that superimposed somatic diversification
could not be ruled out. The fact that the repeated
spectra between individual mice argued for a large
germ-line complement of genes was also stressed by
Hood[17]. On the other hand Jerne[18] chose to ignore
the repeat spectra and argued that the great
difference between the sets of antibodies expressed
in each donor mouse shows that antibody diversity
must have a somatic basis. Cunningham[19] also saw,
in the numbers, a need to propose somatic mutations.
Clearly this experimental result could be all things
to all men depending on their previous viewpoint.

The methodology is applicable to similar
systems and the pool sizes for antibodies of
different binding specificities could be mapped. At
present we have preliminary data from various hapten
systems and for one of these, the sulphanilic acid
group, there appears to be a more restricted pool
size than that which we found for NIP-binding
antibodies (Kipp, unpublished observations).

It is highly desirable to identify small pools
of antibodies of a given specificity. This pool
size will depend on the number of ways which are
open to a given animal to make antibody-combining
sites which will bind the chosen antigen. The
V-genes coding for these antibodies can then be
followed in breeding studies.

One such system is to use simple complete
antigens. The idea here is that the complete
antigenic determinant is defined, as opposed to just
defining the hapten which may be only a part of the
complete antigen. The series of molecules
α-DNP-oligo-L-lysine are immunogenic in guinea pigs
when the chain length $\geqslant 7$. We have studied the
response to α-DNP-decalysine and found that the
primary response, which can be detected as early as
day seven after immunisation, is clonally simple
with an average of less than two clones per
animal[20]. Comparison between animals showed that a
small number of clones were elicited many times
(Table 24.1). One clone occurred most frequently,
accounting for 39% of all monoclonal spectra. This
most frequently found spectrum is illustrated in
Figure 24.4. Five sera from different guinea pigs
each contain the one pattern in common. Overall,
only seven clones made up 76% of the clonal spectra
observed[21]. This means that only three V_L-genes
and three V_H-genes would be more than sufficient to
account for the bulk of the antibodies showing high
specificity for α-DNP-decalysine. Two points can
be made in favour of the presence of these genes in

the germ-line: (i) the high frequency of expression,
(ii) the rapid expression after primary
immunisation; both of these points would be harder
to reconcile with a somatic generation of diversity.
    The question as to whether the genes coding for
each of the antibodies are present in all guinea
pigs irrespective of expression is best answered by
breeding studies. Zitron (unpublished observations

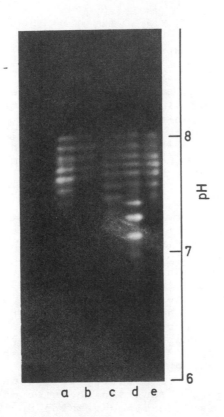

Figure 24.4 Spectra of antibodies specific for
α-DNP-decalysine found in sera of five different
animals. Antibodies were elicited in strain 2 or
strain 12 guinea pigs. The pH range was 5 to 10
(equal volumes of 5 to 8 and 7 to 10 Ampholine).
Final Ampholine concentration 2% (w/v). Spectra
were developed with radioactive hapten[1]. The
prototype monoclonal spectrum shown in track b is
considered to be present in the other four sera from
different animals. This is the monoclonal spectrum
seen most frequently in response to α-DNP-decalysine
                (see Table 24.1)

Table 24.1

Frequency (n)	Number[*] of clones (C)	C x n
20	1	20
4	1	4
3	5	15
1	12	12
Total	19	51

* Number of anti-α-DNP-decalysine clones (C) found in
all guinea pigs (i.e. poly-L-lysine responder and
poly-L-lysine non-responder animals) with a
frequency n. Sera from 33 guinea pigs immunised
with α-DNP-decalysine are included in this analysis.
Amongst the 51 monoclonal spectra compared, 19
different spectra were represented.
          Data from Williamson and Schlossman[21].

quoted in ref. 22) has shown that the set of V-genes
coding for specific clones are co-inherited by the
offspring of a given mating even when the parents
did not express those clones. Another point which
comes from this study is that the clones with a
high repeat frequency occur in both poly-L-lysine
(PLL) responder and PLL non-responder guinea pigs
with similar frequency. The PLL-gene controls
cell-mediated responses to PLL or any hapten carried
on that molecule[23]. Antibody responses are also
affected by the PLL-gene but clearly the V-gene
complement used for antibody formation is not linked
to the PLL-gene. Thus the question of how T-cell
specificity is determined remains open.

24.6 CONCLUSIONS

Isoelectric focusing is a powerful technique for
distinguishing between different antibodies of
similar specificity. Once the usefulness of this
approach is accepted the necessary cautions of
interpretation must also be stressed. Initially it
is sometimes difficult to convince others that a
monoclonal antibody may have a multi-band spectrum.
However there are dangers in assuming that, since
several monoclonal spectra consist of three bands,
all monoclonal spectra consist of three bands.

There is no magic to the number three: monoclonal antibody spectra often have more than three lines. Therefore it is not possible simply to divide the number of bands in the spectrum by three to obtain the number of clones. The number of lines can depend markedly on the sensitivity of the development method (see Figure 24.3).

We now have direct information from RNA-DNA hybridisation experiments that there are at least 5000 V_H-genes[24]. This means that our interpretation of the number of NIP-binding antibodies as being the products of a minimum of 70 V_L-genes and 70 V_H-genes is compatible with the pool size of germ-line V_H-genes. By implication there is probably also a large pool of V_L-genes.

Further studies using isoelectric spectra as genetic markers should be directed towards the stability of V-gene pools, the factors governing expression of V-genes and selective pressures on the evolution of V-genes.

REFERENCES

1. WILLIAMSON, A.R., 'Isoelectric Focusing of Immunoglobulins'. In: Handbook of Experimental Immunology, Ed. D.M. Weir, 2nd edn., Blackwell, Oxford, ch. 8, pp. 8.1-8.23 (1973)
2. AWDEH, Z.L., WILLIAMSON, A.R. and ASKONAS, B.A., 'Isoelectric Focusing in Polyacrylamide Gels and its Application to Immunoglobulins'. Nature, 219, 66-67 (1968)
3. WILLIAMSON, A.R., 'Antibody Isoelectric Spectra. Analysis of the Heterogeneity of Antibody Molecules in Serum by Isoelectric Focusing and Specific Detection with Hapten'. Europ. J. Immunol., 1, 390-394 (1971)
4. KÖHLER, G. and MELCHERS, F., 'Isoelectric Focusing Spectra of Antibodies which activate Mutant β-galactosidases'. Europ. J. Immunol., 2, 453-456 (1972)
5. PHILLIPS, J.M. and DRESSER, D.W., 'Isoelectric Spectra of Different Classes of Anti-erythrocyte Antibodies'. Europ. J. Immunol., 3, 524-527 (1973)
6. PHILLIPS, J.M. and DRESSER, D.W., 'Antibody Isoelectric Spectra Visualized by Antigen-coated Erythrocytes'. Europ. J. Immunol., 3, 738-740 (1973)
7. AWDEH, Z.L., WILLIAMSON, A.R. and ASKONAS, B.A., 'One Cell - one Immunoglobulin. Origin of Limited Heterogeneity of Myeloma Proteins'. Biochem. J., 116, 241-248 (1970)

8. MILSTEIN, C., BROWNLEE, G.C., HARRISON, T.M. and
    MATHEWS, M.B., 'A Possible Precursor of
    Immunoglobulin Light Chains'. Nature (New
    Biol.), 239, 117-120 (1972)
9. SWAN, D., AVIV, H. and LEDER, P. 'Purification
    and Properties of Biologically Active Messenger
    RNA for a Myeloma Light Chain'. Proc. Nat.
    Acad. Sci. (U.S.A.), 69, 1967-1971 (1972)
10. MACH, B., FAUST, C.H. and VASSALLI, P.,
    'Purification of 14S Messenger RNA of
    Immunoglobulin Light Chain that Codes for a
    Possible Light-chain Precursor'. Proc. Nat.
    Acad. Sci. (U.S.A.), 70, 451-455 (1973)
11. WILLIAMSON, A.R., SALAMAN, M.R. and KRETH, H.W.,
    'Microheterogeneity and Allomorphism of
    Proteins'. Ann. N.Y. Acad. Sci., 209, 210-222
    (1968)
12. ASKONAS, B.A., WILLIAMSON, A.R. and WRIGHT,
    B.E.G., 'Selection of a Single Antibody-forming
    Cell Clone and its Propagation in Syngeneic
    Mice'. Proc. Nat. Acad. Sci. (U.S.A.), 67,
    1398-1403 (1970)
13. ASKONAS, B.A. and WILLIAMSON, A.R., 'Factors
    affecting the Propagation of a B-cell Clone
    forming Antibody to the 2,4-dinitrophenyl
    Group'. Europ. J. Immunol., 2, 487-493 (1972)
14. WILLIAMSON, A.R. and ASKONAS, B.A.,
    'Senescence of an Antibody forming Cell Clone'.
    Nature, 238, 337-339 (1972)
15. COTTON, R.G.H., SECKER, D.S. and MILSTEIN, C.,
    'Somatic Mutation and the Origin of Antibody
    Diversity. Clonal Variation of the
    Immunoglobulin produced by MOPC21 Cells in
    Culture'. Europ. J. Immunol., 3, 135-140
    (1973)
16. KRETH, H.W. and WILLIAMSON, A.R., 'The Extent of
    Diversity of Anti-hapten Antibodies in Inbred
    Mice: Anti-NIP (4-hydroxy-5-iodo-3-nitrophenyl)
    Antibodies in CBA/H Mice'. Europ. J. Immunol.,
    3, 141-146 (1973)
17. HOOD, L., 'The Genetics, Evolution and
    Expression of Antibody Molecules'. Proc.
    Stradler Genetics Symp., 5, 73-142 (1973)
18. JERNE, N.K., 'The Immune System'. Scientific
    American, 229, 52-60 (1973)
19. CUNNINGHAM, A.J., 'Generation of Antibody
    Diversity: its Dependence on Antigenic
    Stimulation'. In: Contemporary Topics in
    Molecular Immunology, in press (1974)
20. SCHLOSSMAN, S.F. and WILLIAMSON, A.R.,
    Genetic Control of Immune Responsiveness, Eds.
    H.O. McDevitt and M. Landy, Academic Press,

N.Y., p.54 (1973)

21. WILLIAMSON, A.R. and SCHLOSSMAN, S.F.,
    'Antibody Diversity II. Inheritance of V-genes
    encoding Antibodies Specific for
    α-DNP-decalysine'. J. exp. Med., in press
    (1974)
22. ZITRON, I.M., 'Isoelectric-focusing and
    Antibody Diversity'. Transplantation and
    Allergy, in press (1973)
23. BENACERRAF, B. and McDEVITT, H.O.,
    'Histocompatibility-linked Immune Response
    Genes'. Science, 175, 273-279 (1972)
24. PREMKUMAR, E., SHOYAB, M. and WILLIAMSON, A.R.,
    'Germ line Basis for Antibody Diversity:
    Immunoglobulin V_H- and C_H-gene Frequencies
    Measured by DNA-RNA Hybridization'. Proc. Nat.
    Acad. Sci. (U.S.A.), 71, 99-103 (1973)

25. POLYMORPHISM OF THE SIXTH COMPONENT OF COMPLEMENT

C.A. Alper, M.J. Hobart and P.J. Lachmann

25.1 INTRODUCTION

Genetic markers have been described for three
components of the human complement system, namely
C3 (refs. 1 and 2), glycine-rich beta-glycoprotein
(GBG)[3], and C$\overline{1}$ inhibitor[4]. All were detected by
electrophoretic studies on whole sera, the
positions of GBG and C$\overline{1}$ inhibitor being identified
by specific antisera. Similar methods have been
used to show individual variations in the
electrophoretic mobilities of C4 (ref.5) and C6
(Alper, unpublished observations).
   Methods involving the use of specific
antisera for the detection of proteins separated by
electrophoresis demand substantial quantities of
these costly reagents, but may give excellent
quantitation of the different subcomponents. The
combination of thin-layer gel isoelectric focusing[6]
with simple specific in situ functional assays,
promises to be a convenient method for the
investigation of genetic markers of complement
components. These assays involve the
complement-mediated lysis of erythrocytes in the
presence of reagents specifically devoid of the
component under investigation, and for C6 and some
other components, depend on the sera of animals
genetically deficient of one of the complement
components.

25.2 METHODS AND MATERIALS

25.2.1 Isoelectric Focusing
This was carried out by the method of Awdeh et al.[5],
but was modified in that the gel contained 0.2 M
taurine (Osterman, personal communication). Taurine

$(NH_3^+-CH_2-CH_2-SO_3^-)$ is zwitterionic and has no net charge within the pH range of the run; it therefore serves to raise the osmotic pressure of the gel without contributing to its electrolyte concentration or to the viscosity of the liquid phase.

Samples of whole serum or plasma (5 μl) were applied to strips of Whatman 3MM paper (5 mm x 10 mm) located close to the anode and they were subjected to isoelectric focusing using pH 5 to 7 Ampholines at a final potential of 55 V/cm for 18 h.

25.2.2 Detection of C6

Agarose (Indubiose A 37, L'Industrie Biologique Francaise S.A. 35 Quai du Moulin de Cage 92 Gennevilliers, France) containing the C6 detecting system was poured directly onto the surface of the acrylamide gel after isoelectric focusing and, having set, was incubated at room temperature for ½ to 2 h. The detecting gel was prepared as follows (the standard abbreviations: E, erythrocytes; A, antibody; and Cn, complement components, have been used);

(i)   EAC43 (Antrypol) (Suramin B.P., F.B.A.
        Pharmaceuticals, Haywards Heath, Sussex)
        were prepared by stirring 10 ml 1% (v/v) EA
        with 1 ml yeast-treated human serum at 37°C
        for 75 s; 0.2 ml Antrypol (50 mg/ml) was
        added and the incubation was allowed to
        continue for 3 min. The sensitised cells
        were centrifuged at 2000 g for 5 min and
        washed twice in cold complement fixation
        test dilutent (CFD) supplied in tablet form
        by Oxoid Ltd., London, containing 0.7% (w/v)
        gelatin (Davis) and 0.002 M sodium azide.
        They were resuspended in 1 ml C6-deficient
        rabbit serum.

(ii)   The serum/cell mixture was added to 15 ml
        CFD containing 1.2% (w/v) agarose at 48°C,
        mixed and immediately poured onto the gel to
        a depth of 1 mm as an overlay on completion
        of isoelectric focusing.

A more detailed account of the C6 detection method has been published[6].

25.3 RESULTS

25.3.1 Preliminary Studies

A survey by isoelectric focusing of 133 individual sera submitted for biochemical screening at Hammersmith Hospital showed three common and

several less common C6 band patterns. Retrospective
study of sera (stored at -196°C) from ten
individuals showed that their patterns did not vary
over periods of between two and six months.

25.3.2 Family Studies

Members of 29 families have been studied.
Twenty-two included children with cystic fibrosis,
in five cases the proband was suffering from acute
myeloid leukaemia and in two cases from an (obscure)
immune deficiency syndrome.

It became clear on inspection of these sera,
that the results could most easily be explained on
the assumption that the patterns of bands are
controlled by a single locus and that one of the
frequently occurring alleles (C6A) controls the
production of a complex of bands of low pI, the
other (C6B) of high pI. Homozygotes for C6A have
the A pattern, and for C6B the B pattern (Figure
25.1) while the heterozygotes C6AC6B have all the
bands (pattern AB).

Unusual band patterns were observed in one
family: abnormally strong bands were observed in
positions which are usually occupied by weak bands.
The father (F) was homozygous C6BC6B. The mother
(M) had a grossly abnormal pattern with strong
bands extending far into the acidic range of pIs.
She had, in addition, a normal A band pattern and
was characterised genetically as C6AC6R (C6R
representing the 'rare' allele). The children
(S and D) showed all the abnormal bands of the
mother and the normal B bands of the father.

25.3.3 Reproduction of Patterns by in vitro Mixing

A mixture of sera homozygous for the acidic (A)
and basic (B) patterns consistently reproduced the
patterns of the heterozygote (A + B = AB). However,
a mixture of the sera of the parents of the
'unusual' family described in 25.3.2 failed to
reproduce the band patterns of the children, the
major difference being that there were no A bands
in the children's sera.

25.3.4 Structural Data

Sera were separated in gels containing 8 M urea
instead of taurine. When focusing was complete,
the gel was agitated in isotonic saline for 30 min,
drained and developed in the normal way. Less well
resolved versions of the conventional patterns were
revealed.

C6 partially purified from pooled sera showed
a pattern of bands similar to the AB pattern.

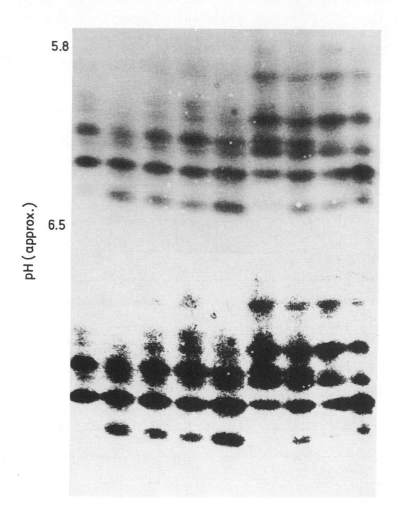

Figure 25.1 Haemolytic band patterns attributable
to C6. The upper and lower parts of the figure
differ only in their photographic contrast,
half-tones having been eliminated in the lower part,
which has not been retouched. The range of pI
values shown is between approx. pH 6.0 and 6.5;
the anode is at the top. A, B and AB, the three
most frequent patterns in individual sera,
representing the two homozygous states and the
heterozygous state, respectively; A + B, equal
volumes of A and B sera; F, M, S and D, sera of
     'unusual' family (see text section 25.3.2)

25.3.5 <u>Numerical Data</u>
<u>Mendelian ratios</u> Actual and predicted numbers of
progeny from the observed matings are shown in
<u>Table 25.1</u>.

Table 25.1   Inheritance of C6 allotypes

Mating	Numbers observed	Progeny		
		A	AB	B
AA x AA	3	9 (9)	O (O)	O (O)
AA x AB	17	17 (22.5)	28 (22.5)	O (O)
AB x AB	4	1 (2.5)	8 (5)	1 (2.5)
AB x BB	1	O (O)	1 (0.5)	O (0.5)
BB x BB	O	-	-	-

Expected numbers of progeny shown in brackets.

<u>Gene frequencies and Hardy-Weinberg equilibrium</u>
Pooled data from both family and 'random' samples
have been used in calculating gene frequencies.
264 individuals were examined. The gene and
predicted and observed phenotypic frequencies are
shown in <u>Table 25.2</u>.

Table 25.2   Gene and phenotype frequencies

Gene frequency	C6A 0.646		C6B 0.333			C6 (all.) 0.0208
Phenotype	A	AB	B	AR	BR	R
Fr. (pred.)	0.417	0.431	0.111	0.027	0.014	0.0004
Fr. (obs.)	0.417	0.436	0.106	0.023	0.019	O

23.3.6   <u>Sex Linkage and Disease State</u>
There was no evidence for sex linkage of the genetic
marker, nor was there any obvious correlation
between disease states and C6 allotypes. The C6
patterns are not obviously distorted in any sera
from diseased subjects.

25.4   DISCUSSION

This paper describes a new genetic polymorphism of
serum proteins, the fourth to be discovered for a
complement component. There are two common alleles

and a number of rare patterns, at least one of which
is a third allele. If all the rare variants
hitherto observed are also alleles, there are at
least seven C6 alleles in man.

Although the gene and phenotype frequencies
quoted in Table 25.2 are drawn from a very small and
potentially unrepresentative population sample, the
agreements between the predicted and observed
phenotype frequencies are remarkably good. This
suggests a widespread balanced polymorphism at the
C6 locus.

There is no evidence that the locus controlling
the patterns is related to the genes coding for the
polypeptide chain(s) of the molecule, though it
appears from the studies in urea and of partially
purified C6 that the structural features giving rise
to the band patterns are part of the covalent
structure of the molecule. The physico-chemical
origin of the many-banded pattern is unknown, as is
the nature of the difference between the common
alleles. Since the strongest bands in the normal C6
patterns are separated by a single unit of charge
(Hobart, Salaman and Lachmann, unpublished
observations), the normal A and B patterns may
represent a 'frame shift' of a single unit of
charge. The unusual patterns are characterised by
a smaller shift, which might be due to the
substitution of a charged amino acid by an
uncharged residue or to differences in molecular
weight or conformation.

It will be interesting to search for genetic
linkages involving the C6 marker locus, especially
with other complement components. The evolutionary
origin of multi-enzyme triggered cascades such as
the complement or clotting systems is intriguing.
It is likely that the proteins making up the systems
have survived because they have an integrated
function within the developed cascade. It is
attractive, therefore, to believe that the triggered
cascade systems evolved explosively, perhaps by a
process of multiple gene duplication. Expansion
may have occurred either by tandem duplication or by
polyploidation. In the case of tandem duplication,
one may hope to find linkage between markers on
different complement components. However, in the
case of polyploidation, chromosome mapping of
markers on complement components and other genetic
systems would be necessary before searching for
evidence of evolutionary relationships.

ACKNOWLEDGEMENTS

I am most grateful to Dr. R. Harris for helpful
discussion, and to Dr. R. Harris and Dr. R. Haslam
for providing test sera.

REFERENCES

1. ALPER, C.A. and PROPP, R.P., 'Genetic
    Polymorphism of the Third Component of Human
    Complements (C'3)'. J. Clin. Invest., 47,
    2181-2191 (1968)
2. AZEN, E.A. and SMITHIES, O. 'Genetic
    Polymorphism of C3 (β1C-Globulin) in Human
    Serum'. Science, 162, 905-907 (1968)
3. ALPER, C.A., BOENISCH, T. and WATSON, L.,
    'Genetic Polymorphism in Human Glycine-rich
    Beta-glycoprotein'. J. Exp. Med., 135, 66-80
    (1972)
4. BACH, S., RUDDY, S., MACLAREN, J.A. and AUSTEN,
    K.F., 'Electrophoretic Polymorphism of the
    Fourth Component of Human Complement C4 in
    Paired Maternal and Foetal Plasmas'.
    Immunology, 21, 729-740 (1971)
5. AWDEH, Z.L., WILLIAMSON, A.R. and ASKONAS, B.A.,
    'Isoelectric Focusing in Polyacrylamide Gel and
    its Application to Immunoglobulins'. Nature
    (Lond.), 219, 66-67 (1968)
6. LACHMANN, P.J., HOBART, M.J. and ASTON, W.P.,
    'Complement Technology'. In: Handbook of
    Experimental Immunology, Ed. D.M. Weir,
    Blackwell Scientific Publications, Oxford,
    p.5.1-5.17 (1974)

26. EXAMINATION OF ANTI-D IgG IMMUNOGLOBULIN

J.G. Templeton and G.R. Milne

26.1 INTRODUCTION

The characterisation of blood group antibodies has
been hindered by the heterogeneity of
immunoglobulin fractions of serum and by the
limitations of the methods used to separate them.
While the electrophoretic heterogeneity of human
immunoglobulin has been well demonstrated by
isoelectric focusing[1], work carried out specifically
on blood group antibodies has been limited[2].
Cellulose chromatography has, however, shown that
differences exist between the charge on some
antibody molecules and the bulk of the IgG
immunoglobulin, and that such differences also exist
among different specific antibody molecules[3]. A
number of independent reports in different fields
suggested that further study of blood group
antibodies would be profitable. It has been
demonstrated that the IgG heavy chain subclasses can
be separated by isoelectric focusing[4]. Although all
of the four subclasses have been shown to contain
Anti-D IgG immunoglobulin[5], the relative amounts of
Anti-D found in the subclasses are widely different
from the proportions of the subclasses present in
normal serum[6]. However, to date no significance has
been ascribed to this fact. This report contains
the results of our preliminary investigations into
this problem.

26.2 EXPERIMENTAL PROCEDURE

26.2.1 Isoelectric Focusing
The technique was essentially that outlined in the
LKB 8100 apparatus instruction manual although a
number of minor modifications were introduced. The

cathode solution comprised 1% (v/v) ethylene diamine
in 60% (w/v) sucrose, while 0.33% (w/v) phosphoric
acid was used as the anode solution. Equal volumes
of pH 6 to 8 and pH 8 to 10 Ampholine were mixed to
form a pH gradient of pH 6 to 10 at a concentration
of 1.33% (w/v) Ampholine. Isoelectric focusing was
carried out at 5°C for a total of 100 h with a
starting potential of 600 V. This was increased in
steps to 1000 V after 24 h. After isoelectric
focusing for 24 h with no sample present, the
protein was applied at the centre of the gradient by
means of a catheter[7]. The column was emptied at a
rate of 1.5 ml/min and the pH of each fraction
measured using a Radiometer Digital pH Meter type
PHM 52. The removal of Ampholine and sucrose was
accomplished by dialysis against phosphate buffered
saline (9 vols of isotonic saline + 1 vol of 0.066 M
Na_2HPO_4; 0.066 M KH_2PO_4 pH 6.8) for 48 h.

26.2.2 Assay of Immunoglobulins

The autoanalyser technique detailed by Rosenfield
and Haber[8] was used to measure levels of Anti-D
immunoglobulin. Hyland immunodiffusion plates were
used to quantitate IgG and IgA levels in pooled
fractions.

26.2.3 Elution of Anti-D from Sensitised Cells[9]

1 ml of washed packed R_2R_2 cells was agitated
continually with 1 ml of Anti-D plasma for 2 h at
37°C. After centrifuging the mixture at 1000 g for
10 min the supernatant fluid was removed and the
sensitised cells washed three times with isotonic
saline at room temperature. Then 1 ml of saline was
added to the washed cells, which were incubated at
56°C for 5 min with repeated shaking. The
supernatant fluid which contained eluted Anti-D
activity was removed after centrifugation. Such
preparations will be referred to as 'eluates'.

26.3   RESULTS AND DISCUSSION

The initial work was carried out on IgG
immunoglobulin fractions prepared from pooled
donations of Anti-D plasma (supplied by the
Scottish National Blood Transfusion Association
Protein Fractionation Centre at Edinburgh and the
Lister Institute of Preventive Medicine at Elstree).
It was felt that this would provide a base-line
with which other Anti-D plasmas could be compared.
Also the amount of total plasma protein which can be
separated by isoelectric focusing is limited due to
precipitation of certain proteins at their

isoelectric points (pIs). For this reason analysis
of a preparation which was largely IgG
immunoglobulin, the fraction where our interest lay,
seemed likely to yield maximum information. The
Anti-D profile of an IgG immunoglobulin preparation
containing 230 μg Anti-D/ml and 6.5 g protein/100 ml
showed considerable heterogeneity. The pI maximum
of the Anti-D was at pH 9.25 with minor peaks at
pH 8.9, 8.75 and 6.0. A different preparation,
containing 50 μg Anti-D/ml and 10 g protein/100 ml,
exhibited an Anti-D profile with peaks at similar
pH values. Since, at pH values greater than 8
sucrose acts like an acid, a check was made to
assess whether the isoelectric profile of Anti-D was
affected by sucrose. Reversal of polarity indicated
that the pI maximum at pH 9.25 was independent of
the sucrose concentration.

It might be dangerous to comment too fully on
the significance of the minor Anti-D peaks. The
accuracy of Anti-D quantitation is normally quoted
at ± 17% (ref. 10); therefore these peaks might be
artefacts. However, the similarities which
existed between these two experiments led to the
hypothesis that these minor peaks might represent
the subclasses of IgG immunoglobulin. Until
recently Anti-D was thought to occur only in the
IgG 1, IgG 3 and IgG 4 subclasses[11]. The proportion
of the IgG 1 subclass in normal sera is about 61%
with the 3 and 4 subclasses contributing 5% and 4%
respectively[6]. It has been shown that the IgG 1
subclass has high levels of activity around pH 9.0
(ref. 4) which agrees well with our findings that
the main Anti-D component was isoelectric at pH
9.25. The IgG 3 subclass is reported as being
isoelectric between pH 8.4 and pH 8.95 with the IgG
4 subclass isoelectric around pH 6.0 (ref. 4). The
minor peaks on the Anti-D profile of the IgG
immunoglobulin preparations were found close to
these pH regions.

Figure 26.1 shows the separation of 1 ml of
plasma from a sensitised donor and contained 400 μg
Anti-D/ml and 5.5 g protein/100 ml. The
fractionation of an 'eluate' containing 0.45 μg
Anti-D/ml is also shown. Three main areas of Anti-D
were detected in the plasma; one between pH 8.5 and
9.5, the second between pH 7.7 and 8.0 and the third
between pH 3.0 and 6.0. In the 'eluate' no Anti-D
activity was found between pH 7.7 and 8.0
corresponding to the plasma fractionation.

The first area of Anti-D activity has a main
peak at pH 9.2 close to the pI maximum of pH 9.25
found for the IgG immunoglobulin preparations. A

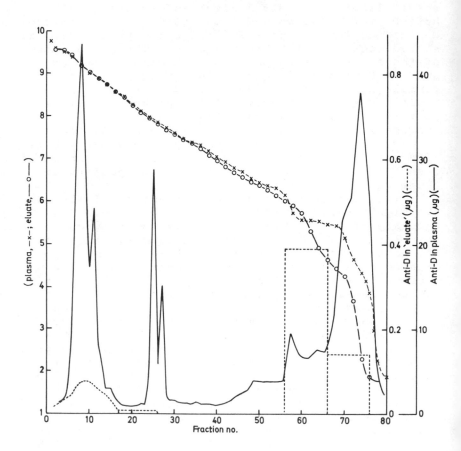

Figure 26.1 Preparative density gradient
isoelectric focusing of 1 ml plasma containing
400 μg Anti-D/ml and 1 ml 'eluate' from this plasma
containing 0.45 μg Anti-D/ml. The density gradient
consisted of sucrose (0 to 60%, w/v); the Ampholine
concentration was 1.33% (w/v). Runs were performed
at 5°C. After a period of 24 h 'pre-focusing',
during which the voltage was slowly increased to
1000 V, the sample was introduced and focusing
continued for a further 76 h. Fractions of 1.25 ml
were collected. pH measurements were carried out
on these fractions, which were then assayed for
Anti-D immunoglobulin. 'Eluate' fractions were
pooled prior to Anti-D quantitation

smaller peak at pH 8.9 and an inflexion point at pH 8.7 agrees well with the results for the IgG fractions and could indicate the presence of the IgG 3 subclass. The Anti-D activity in the 'eluate' showed a pI maximum at pH 9.15. This could indicate a slight alteration in the nature of the Anti-D, although the elution technique is known to be particularly gentle. However, the pI maxima found in the 'eluate' and the plasma differ by only one fraction and can be explained in terms of the error involved in Anti-D quantitation.

It is perhaps a little more difficult to explain the second area of Anti-D activity with a maximum at pH 7.9. Little Anti-D activity was detected at this pH value in the 'eluate' indicating perhaps that this particular species had a higher binding constant than the others. None of the IgG subclasses have so far been reported as having a pI at pH 7.9 although the isoelectric range of the IgG 2 subclass extends from pH 8.4 downwards, with a maximum between pH 6.8 and pH 7.3 (ref. 4). As has already been mentioned, Anti-D was thought to occur only in subclasses 1, 3 and 4 but recent work has demonstrated the presence of IgG 2 Anti-D in about 25% of the sera from repeatedly boosted subjects[5]. Although the donor whose plasma is under investigation has not received booster injections, the Anti-D concentration is so high that it seems possible that an unusual Anti-D component is present.

The third area of Anti-D activity between pH 6 and 3 probably corresponds to the IgG 4 subclass, isoelectric around pH 6.0. However, maximum activity was detected at pH 4.5 and it may be that the slight precipitation which occurred in this region would cause a shift in apparent pI. It might be argued that this peak was caused directly by the precipitation of protein and was in fact an artefact. However, the 'eluate', which exhibited no precipitation, showed considerable Anti-D activity between pH 6.0 and 4.6. A larger proportion of Anti-D was found in the 'eluate' in this region compared to the area around pH 9.0 than would be expected from the plasma profile, indicating a possible difference in the binding constants between the IgG 4 and IgG 1 subclasses.

Another theory is that the activity could be due to IgA immunoglobulin, which was detected in the plasma aliquots between pH 6.0 and 4.6. About 10% of all Anti-D sera contain both IgG- and IgA-Anti-D[9]. No IgA was, however, detected in the 'eluate' and this explanation needs closer examination.

A number of questions remain to be answered,

L*

but it is hoped that further work with specific IgG
subclass antisera will confirm the hypothesis.
Also, further fractionation on narrower ranges of
Ampholine should allow better separation of each of
the pH regions of Anti-D activity.

REFERENCES

1. VALMET, E., 'Demonstration of the
    Microheterogeneity of Human Serum
    Gamma-Globulin by Isoelectric Focusing'.
    Science Tools, 15, No. 1, 8-11 (1968)
2. PERRAULT, R., 'Cold IgG Autologous Anti-LW. An
    Immunological Comparison with Immune Anti-LW'.
    Vox Sang., 24, 150-164 (1973)
3. FRAME, M. and MOLLISON, P.L., 'Charge Differences
    between Human IgG Isoantibodies associated with
    Specificity'. Immunology, 16, 277-283 (1969)
4. HOWARD, A. and VIRELLA, G., 'The Separation of
    Pooled Human IgG into Fractions by Isoelectric
    Focusing and their Electrophoretic and
    Immunological Properties'. Protides of the
    Biological Fluids, Proc. 17th Coll., Bruges,
    1969, Ed. H. Peeters, Elsevier, Amsterdam,
    449-453 (1970)
5. MORELL, A., SKVARIL, F. and RUFENER, J.L.,
    'Characterisation of Rh Antibodies formed
    after Incompatible Pregnancies and after
    Repeated Booster Injections'. Vox Sang., 24,
    323-330 (1973)
6. MORELL, A., SKVARIL, F., STEINBERG, A.G.,
    LOGHEM, VAN, E. and TERRY, W.D., 'Correlation
    between the Concentrations of the Four
    Subclasses of IgG and Gm Allotypes in Normal
    Human Sera'. J. Immunol., 108, 195-206 (1972)
7. FREEDMAN, M.H., 'The Use of Preparative
    Isoelectric Focusing for the Further
    Purification of Rabbit Anti-hapten Antibodies'.
    J. Immunol. Methods, 1, 177-198 (1972)
8. ROSENFIELD, R.E. and HABER, G.V., 'Detection and
    Measurement of Homologous Human Haemagglutinins'.
    Automation in Analytical Chemistry. Technicon
    Symposia 1965, p. 503-506 (1966)
9. MOLLISON, P.L. Blood Transfusion in Clinical
    Medicine, 5th edn., Blackwell Scientific
    Publications, Oxford p. 453 (1972)
10. JUDD, W.L., and JENKINS, W.J., 'Assay of Anti-D
    using the Technicon Auto-Analyser and the
    International Standard Anti-D Typing Serum'.
    J. Clin. Path., 23, 801-804 (1970)
11. FRAME, M., MOLLISON, P.L. and TERRY, W.D.,
    'Anti-Rh Activity of Human γG4 Proteins'.
    Nature (Lond.), 225, 641-643 (1970)

27. ISOELECTRIC PATTERNS IN IgG MYELOMA PROTEINS: POSSIBLE BIOCHEMICAL AND CLINICAL INFERENCES

M.T. Cwynarski, J. Watkins and P.M. Johnson

27.1 INTRODUCTION

It is clear that paraproteinaemia is not confined to patients with malignant immuno-proliferative disorders[1,2]. In a study of the serum of 9420 blood donors, Kohn and Srivastava[3] found an incidence of 0.2% of apparently benign paraproteinaemia. With only one exception, all the paraproteins were of the IgG class. Isoelectric focusing has revealed that 'monoclonal' IgG paraproteins possess a limited, discrete charge heterogeneity[4,5]. This communication presents a study of IgG paraproteins obtained from patients with various gammopathies, both malignant and benign, in an attempt to correlate the characteristic charge heterogeneity pattern of the protein with the pathology of the monoclonal disease. Forty-four patients were included in the study; of these 22 had multiple myeloma as assessed by the MRC Trials Criteria[6], one had a presumptive diagnosis of multiple myeloma, five had neoplastic disease other than multiple myeloma and 16 were considered to have benign paraproteinaemia associated with various clinical conditions (including seven with rheumatic disease).

27.2 ISOELECTRIC FOCUSING PATTERNS OF IgG PARAPROTEINS

Isoelectric focusing of either serum or of IgG isolated by DEAE-cellulose chromatography was carried out on thin layers of polyacrylamide gel using apparatus essentially similar to that described by Leaback and Rutter[5].
   Polyacrylamide gels were prepared either as

described by Leaback and Rutter[5] (T = 3%, C = 2.7%)
or as described by Awdeh, Williamson and Askonas[4]
(T = 5%, C = 2.7%). Gels were polymerised with
ammonium persulphate and incorporated Ampholine
carrier ampholytes, pH range 3 to 10 at a
concentration of 2% (w/v). Isoelectric focusing was
carried out as described by the respective
authors[4,5] and the resolved proteins were stained by
means of bromophenol blue[7]. The differences in gel
composition produced no differences in the
isoelectric pattern for each sample. Individual
sera gave characteristic and reproduceable
isoelectric patterns, which were not influenced by
storage at -20°C (in some cases for up to five
years) or by repeated freezing and thawing for
assay purposes.

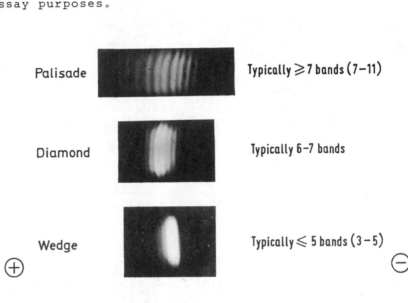

Palisade   Typically ≥ 7 bands (7–11)

Diamond   Typically 6–7 bands

Wedge   Typically ≤ 5 bands (3–5)

$\oplus$ $\ominus$

Figure 27.1 Isoelectric focusing patterns of
monoclonal IgG. The three types of band pattern,
together with an indication of the number of bands
which are observed on isoelectric focusing of
monoclonal IgG in polyacrylamide gels[4,5] are shown.
The gels were stained with bromophenol blue. pH 3
to 10 Ampholine was used

Basically three types of IgG patterns emerged
(Figure 27.1). Two of the patterns, palisade and
diamond, exhibited Gaussian-type distributions of
band intensities whereas the third pattern, a wedge,
showed a skewed distribution. The wedge pattern
always showed increasing band intensity (skew) in

the direction of increasing pI. The distinction
between the palisade and the diamond was not always
clear; nevertheless, each type of pattern consisted
of a characteristic number of bands (Figure 27.1).
The most common pattern was the wedge; about half of
the patients (24 out of 44) exhibited this pattern,
while the palisade and diamond occurred with
approximately equal frequency in the remaining
cases.

27.3 FACTORS INFLUENCING ISOELECTRIC PATTERN OR PATTERN FREQUENCY

We were unable to find any correlation of pattern
type with age, sex, serum IgG levels, heavy chain
subclass, urinary Bence-Jones protein or, indeed,
the disease itself (benign or malignant).
Insufficient information was available to make any
assessment of the correlation of pattern type with
duration of the disease and our series was too small
to study genetic trends in terms of Gm and Inv
markers. However, there was a striking association
of wedge patterns in samples containing kappa light
chain type protein (14 out of 17 examined), in
contrast to the almost uniform distribution of
patterns amongst those containing lambda type chain
(Table 27.1). This may reflect the molecular
conformation of the light chain in either the kappa
or the lambda paraproteins and might correlate with
a report that antibody affinity to certain antigens
is dependent on light chain type[8].

Table 27.1

Isoelectric focusing band pattern	No. of patients showing light chains of the following type	
	κ	λ
Palisade	1/17	7/22
Diamond	2/17	6/22
Wedge	14/17	9/22

27.4 STARCH GEL ELECTROPHORESIS PATTERNS OF IgG PARAPROTEINS

A report by Fahey[9], drawing attention to the
heterogeneity of myeloma proteins when studied by
starch gel electrophoresis, led us to re-examine

IgG myeloma proteins

this technique in parallel with isoelectric
focusing.

   Horizontal starch gel electrophoresis[10] of
serum at pH 8.9 with a discontinuous glycine borate
buffer system[11] gave either single- or multi-band
patterns of monoclonal IgG. The multi-band patterns
ranged from faint to strongly defined bands in
palisade, diamond or wedge patterns, which were
remarkably similar to those observed for the same
samples resolved by isoelectric focusing
(Figure 27.2). There appeared to be a correlation
between the band pattern on starch gel
electrophoresis and a clinical diagnosis of
malignancy. With our technique, patients with
proven malignancy predominantly produced single-band
patterns on starch (Figure 27.2). The data are
summarised in Table 27.2; unfortunately only 21 of
our original sera were available for study by this
technique.

Table 27.2

Starch gel patterns of paraproteins (monoclonal IgG)	No. of patients of tumour type	
	Malignant	Benign
Single band	9/13	2/8
Multiple bands	4/13	6/8

   The total incidence of multi-band proteins in
this series is similar to that found by Fahey[9].
However, all of the proteins characterised by Fahey
were obtained from clinically diagnosed myelomas
whereas in this study the majority of multi-band
proteins were obtained from individuals without
neoplasia. The difference in resolution between our
series and that of Fahey's can probably be
attributed to differences in starch gel technique[9].
The heterogeneity in our series appears to be
predominantly manifested by the benign paraproteins.
In fact, one patient showing a multi-band starch
gel pattern and included with the malignant group on
a presumptive diganosis of multiple myeloma, was
later shown not to fulfil the requirements of the
MRC Trial Criteria and is probably benign.

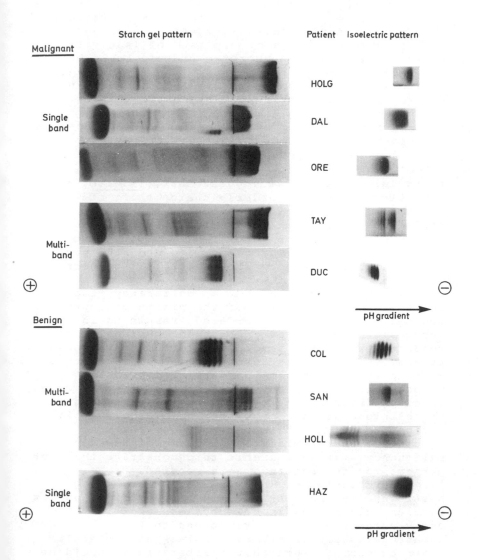

<u>Figure 27.2</u> Charge heterogeneity patterns of
monoclonal IgG separated by starch gel
electrophoresis and polyacrylamide gel isoelectric
focusing. The different IgG band patterns obtained
by starch gel electrophoresis[10,11] (see arrows) of
serum from patients with malignant or benign
paraproteinaemia are compared with pattern types
obtained by isoelectric focusing[4,5] (see <u>Figure 27.1</u>)

27.5   ORIGINS OF LIMITED CHARGE HETEROGENEITY
       PATTERNS IN IgG PARAPROTEINS

Experiments by Awdeh, Williamson and Askonas[12] with
mouse plasma cell tumour 5563 have demonstrated that
the initial intracellular synthesis was of an IgG
protein showing only a single band on isoelectric
focusing, whereas the secreted protein could be
resolved into three components. These experiments
show that the heterogeneous isoelectric pattern
arises as a result of a post-synthetic charge
alteration to a single molecular species. It is
interesting that the newly formed molecular species
all had pI values lower than the intracellular IgG
and did not, as might have been expected, have pI
values on either side of that of the original
molecular species. We suggest that, in vivo, there
is a progressive and orderly charge shift of the
molecules with time in both benign and malignant
states; a natural ageing process. Such changes in
charge state could be described by the observed
palisade and diamond patterns. Indeed, the pattern
of normal heterogeneous IgG is itself a type of
extended palisade.
      It seems possible that as malignancy progresses
the charge heterogeneity of the plasma cell products
becomes increasingly disordered, resulting in a
progressive loss of discrete bands on isoelectric
focusing, since the bands tend to fuse into zones of
broader mean pI value, producing a wedge spectrum.
Such molecular interactions are also probably
responsible for the characteristic curling of wedge
spectrum paraproteins resolved by electrophoresis
on cellulose acetate or starch gel (Figure 27.2,
patient Holg). On this basis, wedge patterns
should occur predominantly in cases of advanced
malignancy. We were unable to demonstrate this but
perhaps too few patients were studied.
      The relationship between molecular
heterogeneity and multiple electrophoretic bands is
complex (see review article by Ressler[13]).
Post-synthetic charge alterations to IgG
paraproteins are likely to involve intramolecular
rearrangements. Such charge alterations should be
detectable by isoelectric focusing but would be
unlikely to be resolved on media generally employed
for electrophoretic techniques. Nevertheless, a
number of reports (reviewed by Fahey[9]) have
described charge heterogeneity of some myeloma
proteins resolved by starch gel electrophoresis.
Because of the similarities between patterns
obtained by starch gel electrophoresis and
isoelectric focusing we suggest that this represents

a second type of charge heterogeneity, seen most
commonly in benign cases. Conceivably, this could
be related to differences in protein-bound
oligosaccharides, with charge differences arising
due to the presence of different numbers of sialic
acid residues; both quantitative and qualitative
variations in carbohydrate content are known to
occur in IgG myeloma proteins.

Finally, although this is only a limited study
involving 44 cases, it does appear that the
combination of starch gel electrophoresis and gel
isoelectric focusing might be used to advantage in
monitoring benign or malignant paraproteinaemia,
particularly as there is a possibility that a number
of 'benign paraproteinaemias' may in fact represent
a pre-malignant phase.

REFERENCES

1. ZAWADZKI, Z.A. and BENEDEK, T.G., 'Rheumatoid
     Arthritis, Dysproteinaemic Arthropathy and
     Paraproteinaemia'. Arthr. Rheum., 12, 555-568
     (1969)
2. COMBINED STAFF CLINIC, 'Plasma Cell Dyscrasia.
     Current Clinical and Biochemical Concepts'.
     Amer. J. Med., 44, 256-269 (1968)
3. KOHN, J. and SRIVASTAVA, P.C., 'Paraproteinaemia
     in Blood Donors and the Aged: Benign and
     Malignant'. In: Protides of the Biological
     Fluids (20th Colloquium, 1972), Vol. 20, Ed.
     H. Peeters, Pergamon, p. 257 (1973)
4. AWDEH, Z.L., WILLIAMSON, A.R. and ASKONAS, B.A.,
     'Isoelectric Focusing in Polyacrylamide Gel
     and its Application to Immunoglobulins'.
     Nature, Lond., 219, 66-67 (1968)
5. LEABACK, R.H. and RUTTER, A.C., 'Polyacrylamide
     Isoelectric Focusing - a New Technique for the
     Electrophoresis of Proteins'. Biochem.
     Biophys. Res. Commun., 32, 447-453 (1968)
6. HOBBS, J.R., 'The Immunochemical Classification
     of Myelomatosis'. Brit. J. Haem., 16, 599-617
     (1969)
7. AWDEH, Z.L., 'Staining Method for Proteins
     after Isoelectric Focusing in Polyacrylamide
     Gel'. Science Tools, 16, 42-44 (1969)
8. NUSSENZWEIG, V. and BENACERRAF, B., 'Antihapten
     Antibody Specificity and L Chain Type'.
     J. Exper. Med., 126, 727-743 (1967)
9. FAHEY, J.L., 'Heterogeneity of Myeloma
     Proteins'. J. Clin. Invest., 42, 111-123 (1963)
10. SMITHIES, O., 'Zone Electrophoresis in Starch
     Gels; Group Variations in the Serum Proteins of

Normal Human Adults'. Biochem. J., 61, 629-641
(1955)

11. POULIK, M.D., 'Starch Gel Electrophoresis in a
Discontinuous System of Buffers'. Nature,
Lond., 180, 1477-1479 (1957)

12. AWDEH, Z.L., WILLIAMSON, A.R., and ASKONAS, B.,
'One Cell - one Immunoglobulin: Origin of
Limited Heterogeneity of Myeloma Proteins'.
Biochem. J., 116, 241-248 (1970)

13. RESSLER, N., 'A Systematic Procedure for the
Determination of the Heterogeneity and Nature
of Multiple Electrophoretic Bands'. Anal.
Biochem., 51, 589-610 (1973)

SECTION IV

Miscellaneous Applications

28. TOWARDS AN UNDERSTANDING OF
BEER HAZE FORMATION

D.J. Savage, C.C. Thompson and S.J. Anderson

28.1 INTRODUCTION

The haze which slowly develops in beer during long
storage has been the subject of much research.
Although the involvement of proteins in haze
formation has been established, the contribution
made by individual proteins has not yet been fully
determined because beer contains an extremely
complex mixture which is difficult to resolve.
Previous communications have described the
isoelectric focusing of beer proteins in thin layers
of polyacrylamide gel[1], and of beer hazes in similar
systems incorporating urea[2]. A technique was
developed to permit optical scanning of the gels,
thus enabling the separated fractions to be
quantitated. It was established that the proteins
with isoelectric points below pH 5.0 were important
in haze formation. Beer haze itself was
particularly rich in proteins with isoelectric
points below pH 5.0 (termed the 'acidic fraction'),
but in addition contained all but the most basic
proteins present in beer. The band pattern of the
'acidic fraction' of beer haze was identical with
that of the acidic components of beer itself and
appeared to contain no additional proteins.
The present study describes the further
application of isoelectric focusing to elucidate the
factors influencing the generation of the acidic
fraction during the brewing process.

28.2 MATERIALS AND METHODS

28.2.1 Laboratory Worts
Infusion mashes were prepared from finely ground
malt or barley using the EBC mill (Casela Ltd.,

329

London) according to the recommended method of the Institute of Brewing[4], at 65°C using tap water. The pH was adjusted to 5.0 at 65°C and was usually 0.5 units higher at 20°C.

'Hopped worts' were prepared by boiling the sweet worts with 40 mg/l of α-humulone (added as 30% (w/v) extract) for one hour under reflux, before cooling to 20°C and filtering.

28.2.2 Preparation of Samples

Wort and beer protein samples were prepared by precipitation with 70% saturated ammonium sulphate as described previously[3]. Barley and malt proteins were extracted under conditions which minimised enzymic degradation[3].

28.2.3 Isoelectric Focusing and Densitometry

Thin-layer polyacrylamide gel isoelectric focusing was carried out by the method of Awdeh et al.[5], modified to permit scanning of the focused protein bands. Urea was incorporated into the system to eliminate trailing of certain proteins insoluble at their isoelectric points. 2 M urea was optimal for barley and malt proteins, and 0.5 M urea for beer and wort proteins. The samples, which typically contained 1 mg protein, were dissolved in 50 µl of 1% (w/v) Ampholine (pH 3.5 to 10.0) containing urea at the appropriate concentration, and spread evenly as a 5 mm wide band over the entire length of the gel. On completion of isoelectric focusing, proteins were precipitated with 20% (w/v) trichloroacetic acid and the gel strips were scanned using a Joyce Loebl Chromoscan in the transmission mode. The integrated peak areas were expressed as a percentage of the total peak area. The bands with isoelectric points below pH 5.0 were grouped together and expressed as the 'percentage acidic fraction'.

Density gradient isoelectric focusing using pH 3.5 to 10.0 Ampholine was carried out in a U-tube and the gradient (15 ml) was stabilised by sucrose as described by Weller et al.[6]. On completion of the run, the gradient was passed through a u.v. recording spectrophotometer and 0.2 ml fractions collected. Polyphenols were determined by the method of McFarlane[7] and pH measurements were made using a microelectrode type M22DP from Activion Glass Ltd., Fife.

28.3   RESULTS

28.3.1 The Generation of the 'Acidic Fraction'
Protein extracts were prepared from a sample of
barley (variety Otter), the derived malt, and from
the sweet and hopped worts and beers produced in
the laboratory; these were subjected to isoelectric
focusing. The 'percentage acidic fractions' are
shown in Table 28.1.

Table 28.1   The generation of the 'acidic fraction'
             during the brewing process

	Barley*	Malt*	Sweet wort	Hopped wort	Beer
% Acidic fraction (pI <5.0)	6	8	25	24	24

*Extracted under conditions to minimise enzymic
degradation[3].

Barley contained only a small proportion of acidic
protein and the amount did not increase appreciably
during malting, although the isoelectric profile
increased in complexity. The acidic proteins were
principally generated during mashing.

28.3.2 The Influence of Polyphenols on the 'Acidic
Fraction'
It has been suggested that an equilibrium is
established between polyphenols and proteins during
mashing[8]. Moreover, the presence of polyphenols in
acidic material has previously been indicated[9]. The
acidic fraction may thus have been produced by the
interaction of more basic proteins with polyphenols.
The effect on the acidic fraction of mashing under
conditions which are known to influence the
polyphenol composition of worts was, therefore,
investigated.
      It has been shown that the aeration of the mash
promotes polymerisation of polyphenols and increases
their tanning power; in contrast, the addition of
diethyldithiocarbamate (DIECA) inhibits polyphenol
oxidase systems[8]. The effect of these treatments on
wort composition is shown in Table 28.2.
      Vigorous aeration of the mash resulted in a
change in the balance and composition of the
polyphenols and 'acidic fraction'. Aeration
resulted in a sweet wort with a lower polyphenol

Table 28.2 The influence of polyphenols on the 'acidic fraction'

Treatment of mash	Sweet wort			Hopped wort			% N lost on hop boiling
	Total N (mg/l)	Polyphenols (mg/l)	% Acidic fraction	Total N (mg/l)	Polyphenols (mg/l)	% Acidic fraction	
Aerated	728	55	23	551	77	13	24
4000 ppm* DIECA	720	164	37	540	56	48	18
Control	699	81	24	580	87	22	17

*Based on dry weight of malt.

content than the control, but the percentage 'acidic
fraction' was normal。 There was a greater loss of
nitrogenous material and particularly of the 'acidic
fraction' during hop boiling。 The presence of DIECA
gave a sweet wort with a high level of acidic
protein, which was further increased on boiling。
The rates of haze formation in the resulting hopped
worts are compared in Figure 28.1。

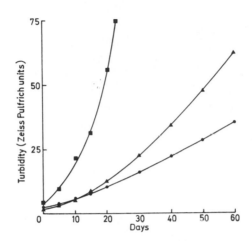

Figure 28.1   The development of haze in experimental
worts。 The preparation was incubated at 20°C and the
turbidity determined by means of a Zeiss-Pulfrich
photometer。 (—▲—), Control; (—●—), aerated; (—■—),
DIECA-treated

28.3.3 The Polyphenol Content of the 'Acidic Fraction'

Fractions obtained on isoelectric focusing of beer
protein in a sucrose density gradient were examined
for polyphenols. Figure 28.2 relates the polyphenol
content of the focused bands (Figure 28.2b) to the
densitometric tracing obtained when the same protein
sample was focused in a thin layer of polyacrylamide
gel followed by precipitation with trichloroacetic
acid (Figure 28.2a)。 Bound polyphenols predominate
in the acidic protein, but are present throughout
the profile。

28.4   DISCUSSION

Previous investigations have suggested that the
acidic proteins of beer may be implicated in haze
formation. Nummi et al.[10] separated acidic proteins
from beer haze by chromatography on DEAE cellulose,

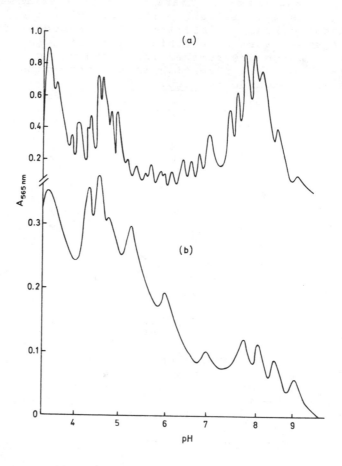

Figure 28.2 Isoelectric focusing of beer proteins.
(a) Beer 'proteins' resolved by isoelectric focusing
in thin-layer gel (densitometer trace). Beer
proteins were subjected to isoelectric focusing in a
thin layer of polyacrylamide gel containing 1% (w/v)
Ampholines (pH range 3.5 to 10.0). Proteins were
separated at a potential of 25 V/cm at 2°C for 18 h.
Protein zones were precipitated with 20% (w/v) TCA
and the gel scanned with a densitometer. (b) Beer
'protein' resolved by density gradient isoelectric
focusing (polyphenol profile). Beer proteins were
subjected to isoelectric focusing in a sucrose
density gradient and the polyphenol content of each
fraction determined. The $E_{280 \, nm}$ of the fraction was
similar to the polyphenol content and reflected the
absorbance of polyphenols rather than proteins

and demonstrated their greater tendency to induce
haze formation than the more basic fractions.
Partial removal of the 'acidic fraction' of beer by
tannic acid precipitation or partial degradation by
digestion with papain, considerably reduced the rate
at which protein haze forms during storage[1,2].

Grabar et al.[11], using immunoelectrophoretic
techniques, showed that the main protein components
of haze are derived from the native barley by
protein degradation. However, it has been
established that all the proteins in beer or in haze
separated by isoelectric focusing form precipitin
arcs with an antiserum prepared against a mixture of
barley and malt proteins (Savage and Thompson,
unpublished observations).

Barley contains only a small proportion of
acidic proteins, and this increases little during
malting. Mashing barley with a B. subtilis
α-amylase/proteinase preparation gave a wort with a
low level of acidic protein, suggesting that the
precursors of the acidic fraction and the enzyme
systems necessary for their generation develop
during malting.

Acidic proteins are generated principally
during mashing by the interaction of more basic
protein fragments with polyphenols. Thus the acidic
proteins contain much more bound polyphenol than
their more basic counterparts. The effect of
boiling on the amount of 'acidic fraction' depends
on wort composition, which in turn depends on the
mashing conditions. It appears that wort boiling
establishes an equilibrium between coagulation and
the formation of acidic haze precursors.

Changes in wort composition have been achieved
by aeration and by the inhibition of the polyphenol
oxidase system with diethyldithiocarbamate.

The findings described here suggest that
aeration of the mash promoted the oxidation and
polymerisation of the extracted polyphenols,
increasing their affinity for protein, so that on
boiling appreciably more protein, especially acidic
protein, was coagulated and removed from the wort
resulting in a low 'percentage acidic fraction'.
The rate of haze formation in this wort was
substantially reduced. A wort prepared in the
presence of diethyldithiocarbamate contained a much
higher level of unoxidised polyphenols, and a higher
proportion of soluble acidic protein. Boiling
promoted the further combination of 'simple'
unoxidised polyphenols with basic protein fragments
resulting in a further increase in the proportion of
the acidic fraction. No new protein bands were

formed, suggesting that the experimental conditions employed were not outside the ranges of the natural processes involved in mashing and wort boiling.

28.5 CONCLUSIONS

The acidic proteins (pI <5.0) are the immediate protein precursors of beer haze, and are principally formed by the interaction of more basic proteins with simple polyphenols during mashing. They contain the bulk of the bound polyphenols present in wort and beer.

The choice of mashing conditions, which alters the nature and quantity of polyphenols extracted, profoundly influences both the composition of the acidic proteins and their behaviour on wort boiling.

ACKNOWLEDGEMENTS

We thank the Directors of Whitbread and Co. Ltd., for their permission to publish this paper.

REFERENCES

1. SAVAGE, D.J. and THOMPSON, C.C., 'The Isoelectric Focusing of Beer Proteins in Polyacrylamide Gel'. J. Inst. Brew., 77, 371-375 (1971)
2. SAVAGE, D.J. and THOMPSON, C.C., 'Electrofocusing Studies on the Formation of Beer Haze'. J. Inst. Brew., 78, 472-476 (1972)
3. SAVAGE, D.J. and THOMPSON, C.C., 'The Nitrogen Status of Barley and Malt and its Influence on Beer Quality'. Proc. 14th Europ. Brew. Convention (Salzburg) 1973, Elsevier, Amsterdam, 33-42 (1974)
4. HOWARD, G.A., 'Recommended Methods of Analysis'. J. Inst. Brew., 77, 189 (1971)
5. AWDEH, Z.L., WILLIAMSON, A.R. and ASKONAS, B.A., 'Isoelectric Focusing in Polyacrylamide Gel and its Application to Immunoglobulins'. Nature, 219, 66-67 (1968)
6. WELLER, D.L., HEENEY, D.A. and SKOGREN, R.E., 'A Simple Apparatus and Procedure for Electrofocusing Experiments'. Biochim. Biophys. Acta, 168, 576-679 (1968)
7. McFARLANE, W.D., 'The Determination of Anthocyanogens'. J. Inst. Brew., 67, 502-506 (1961)
8. CHAPON, L. and CHERMARDIN, M., 'Dissolving and Oxidation of Malt Tannoids on Mashing-In'. Am. Soc. Brewing Chemists Proc., 244-257 (1964)

9. BATESON, J.B. and LEECH, A.A., 'Nitrogen Studies
    of Worts in Relationship to Beer Gravity'.
    Proc. 12th Europ. Brew. Convention (Interlaken)
    1969, Elsevier, Amsterdam, 161-171 (1970)

10. NUMMI, M., LOISA, M. and ENARI, T-M.,
    'Fractionation of Haze Forming Compounds in
    Beer'. Proc. 12th Europ. Brew. Convention
    (Interlaken) 1969, Elsevier, Amsterdam,
    349-356 (1970)

11. GRABAR, P., DAUSSANT, J., ENARI, T-M. and
    NUMMI, M., 'L'origine des troubles au froid'
    ('The Origin of Chill Hazes'). Proc. 11th
    Europ. Brew. Convention (Madrid) 1967,
    Elsevier, Amsterdam, 379-387 (1968)

29. CHARACTERISATION OF CELL SURFACES BY ISOELECTRIC EQUILIBRIUM ANALYSIS

G.V. Sherbet and M.S. Lakshmi

29.1 INTRODUCTION

The cell surface has been the subject of extensive investigation on account of the important part it plays in biological phenomena such as morphogenesis, neoplastic development and invasiveness; it is important also in the social behaviour of both normal and neoplastic cells in vitro[1,2]. The surface properties of cells are attributable in part to the nature of the ionisable groups present on the cell surface, and to their distribution. Much information about the cell surface has been obtained by means of free electrophoresis of cells. The aim of this paper is to discuss the scope of isoelectric focusing as applied to the study of cell surfaces.

29.2 DETERMINATION OF pI OF INTACT CELLS

The isoelectric points of intact cultured mammalian and Escherichia coli cells have been determined using a modified LKB 8101 column. A pH gradient of the required range is generated using Ampholines of the appropriate pH range. The cells under investigation are loaded into the column at a suitable point during the layering of the density gradient, or subsequently, after the pH gradient has been generated. The experimental methods have been described in detail previously[3,4]. The results are presented in Tables 29.1 and 29.2 .

29.3 THE INTERPRETATION OF SURFACE pIs

The isoelectric point of the surface of a cell
(i)   provides information about the kind of

338

ionisable groups present in the isoelectric
zone,
(ii)   allows one to calculate the number of such
         groups, in combination with experiments in
         which particular groups are chemically
         modified or excised by enzymatic treatments,
(iii)   allows one to calculate the electrophoretic
         mobilities of cells in buffers at
         physiological pH and ionic strengths.

29.3.1 <u>The Surface pI and Ionisable Groups</u>
The pI of a cell surface is determined by the pK
values of the different ionogenic groups that are
present and also by their numbers. For example,
polyoma-transformed BHK-21, Yoshida ascites and
Ehrlich ascites cells have a pI of between 5.6 and
6.4. This is compatible with the presence of
α-COOH and α-NH_2 groups, but excludes the
possibility of the occurrence of groups such as the
ε-NH_3^+ of lysine and guanidyl groups which have
high pK values. HeLa and rat liver cells have pI
values which are in a higher pH range, namely 5.8
to 6.7, and here one can also safely exclude the
presence of the highly acidic phosphate groups.

     Another approach to this problem may be made by
modifying the surface groups by appropriate chemical
treatments and determining the pI of the modified
cell. In this way one can estimate the overall pK
of particular species of ionisable groups. <u>E. coli</u>
cells have a pI of 5.6; the amino groups on the
surface of these cells can be modified by treatment
with formaldehyde. When this is done the pI value
of these cells decreases to 3.85 which reflects the
overall pK of the carboxyl groups. This pI is
indicative of the presence of carboxyl groups on the
cell surface and also excludes the presence of
phosphate groups: if phosphate groups were present
the pI value of the formaldehyde-treated cells would
be less than 3.0. If a value of 3.85 is accepted as
the overall pK of the acidic groups, one can
calculate from the equation $pI = -\log(\Sigma k'a \times k'w/\Sigma k'b)^{\frac{1}{2}}$
(see legend to <u>Table 29.1</u>) that the pK of the amino
groups should be about 7.5. When the carboxyl
groups are esterified with ethyleneimine, however,
a mean pK of 8.55 is obtained for the amino groups.
This discrepancy suggests that the <u>E. coli</u> cell
surface probably contains some weakly acidic groups,
such as thiols. The presence of thiols can be
confirmed by treating the cells (either unmodified
or ethyleneimine-treated cells) with
6,6'-dithiodinicotinic acid carboxypyridine
disulphide (CPDS). This compound specifically binds

Table 29.1 Isoelectric equilibrium analysis of some mammalian cell types

Cell type	Observed pI	Probable ionogenic groups in isoelectric zone*		Calculated pI†	No. of net negative charges per cell $\times 10^{-6}$††
		Present	Excluded		
Polyoma-transformed BHK - 21	6.40 ± 0.19	Sialic acid COOH, α-COOH; thiol; α-NH$_2$	ε-NH$_3^+$ of lysine; guanidyl groups	5.6 - 6.4	6.0
Yoshida ascites sarcoma	6.35 ± 0.19				36.4
Ehrlich's ascites	5.60 ± 0.01				100.7
HeLa	6.85 ± 0.11	Sialic acid COOH, α-COOH; thiol; α-NH$_2$	ε-NH$_3^+$ of lysine; guanidyl groups; phosphate	5.8 - 6.7	3.9
Normal rat liver	6.50 ± 0.10				27.9

Table 29.1 (contd.)

Cell type	Observed pI	Probable ionogenic groups in isoelectric zone*		Calculated pI†	No. of net negative charges per cell x 10^{-6}††
		Present	Excluded		
γ-Globulin-treated HeLa	6.36 ± 0.14				16.7

*The isoelectric zone is estimated to extend to a depth of 6.0 nm below the cell surface.

†pI values were calculated from surface pK of ionogenic groups corrected using the Hartley-Roe equation, pI = $-\log(\Sigma k'a \times k'w/\Sigma k'b)^{\frac{1}{2}}$ where k'a and k'b are corrected dissociation constants of the strongest anionogenic and cationogenic groups, respectively. k'w = 6.81×10^{-15} at $20^{\circ}C$.

††The number of net negative charges on the cell surface was calculated as described by Sherbet et al.[3] using the equation Q = $PDr^2K \times 3.3 \times 10^{-3}/e$, where Q is the number of net negative charges per cell. The potential, P, on the surface of the cells is estimated as the potential difference between a solution at neutral pH and a solution isoelectric with the cell surface and is given by (7 - pI) x $2.303RT/F$, where R is the gas constant (8.315 Joules/$^{\circ}C$), T the absolute temperature, F the Faraday (96 500 C). The value of $2.303RT/F$ = 0.0592 at $25^{\circ}C$. D is the dielectric constant of water (78.54 at $25^{\circ}C$), r the radius of the cell in cm, K the Debye-Hückel function ($0.327 \times 10^8 I^{\frac{1}{2}}$) at $25^{\circ}C$ where I is the ionic concentration due to Ampholines assumed to be 0.01 M, and e the electronic charge 4.8×10^{-10}e.s.u.

Table 29.2 Isoelectric equilibrium analysis of E. coli cells after different treatments

Treatment*	Observed pI	Probable ionogenic groups in isoelectric zone§		Calculated pI†	No. of net negative charges per cell x 10^{-6}††
		Present	Excluded		
E. coli cells (untreated controls)	5.60 ± 0.10	COOH; NH_2 pK ≈ 7.5	Acidic groups of pK <3.2; $\varepsilon-NH_3^+$ of lysine	5.38	0.37
AW-EI-E. coli	8.55 ± 0.04	NH_2 pK ≈ 7.5	NH_2 groups of phospholipids; phenolic -OH; guanidyl groups	8.7	+0.41
HCHO-E. coli	3.85 ± 0.06	COOH groups of glucuronic and neuraminic acids β-COOH of aspartic acid and γ-COOH of glutamic acid	Acidic groups with pK <3.2	3.5	0.84

Table 29.2 (contd.)

Treatment*	Observed pI	Probable ionogenic groups in isoelectric zone§		Calculated No. of net negative charges per cell x 10^{-6}†† at pI†
		Present	Excluded	
E. coli-CPDS	4.28 ± 0.05	As in E. coli control	Thiols¶	
E. coli AW-EI-CPDS	7.47 ± 0.18	As in AW-EI cells	Thiols¶	

*AW-EI-E. coli, acid-washed ethyleneimine-treated E. coli cells; HCHO-E. coli, E. coli cells treated with formaldehyde; AW-EI-CPDS, AW-EI cells treated with 6,6'-dithiodinicotinic acid (CPDS); E. coli-CPDS, E. coli cells treated with CPDS[4].

† and †† see Table 29.1

§ The isoelectric zone is estimated to extend to a depth of 6.0 nm below the cell surface

¶ The total number of thiol groups on the E. coli surface equals the number of net negative charges introduced by reacting them with 6,6'-dithiodinicotinic acid, which is approx. 0.35 x 10^6 groups. Only a proportion of these (less than 3%) are dissociated at physiological pH.

thiol groups and introduces, on the cell surface, one negative charge for each thiol group reacted; it has the effect of lowering the pI. In addition, the use of CPDS permits the number of thiol groups on the cell surface to be determined.

29.3.2 Calculation of Surface Charge and Estimation of Ionisable Groups

The numbers of the different kinds of charged groups can be calculated using the equation $Q = PDr^2K \times 3.3 \times 10^{-3}/e$ (see legend to Table 29.1). The derivation of this equation from general principles will not be attempted here. In Tables 29.1 and 29.2 data on the net negative charges of a variety of cell types, the probable numbers of anionogenic and cationogenic groups, and the number of thiol groups present on the surface of E. coli cells have been presented.

29.3.3 Calculation of Electrophoretic Mobilities from Isoelectric Data

It has also been found possible to predict electrophoretic mobilities of cells from isoelectric data. Sherbet et al.[2] found a linear relationship between charge densities calculated from pI values and their observed electrophoretic mobilities (EPM). Using this as a standard curve one could predict the mobilities of a variety of cell types. The predicted mobilities compared favourably (deviation less than 10% in 10 out of 14 instances) with the observed mobilities of these cells. It is also possible to calculate the EPMs of cells directly from their isoelectric data. Equations have been evolved for this purpose and will be published in detail elsewhere.

29.3.4 Assay of Surface Antigens Associated with Viral Transformation of 3T3 Balb/C Mouse Fibroblasts

The binding of antibodies to the charged groups on cell surfaces has been investigated before using the method of cell electrophoresis[5-8]. Woo and Cater[8] claim that they could detect the binding of anti-rat foetal liver antibodies to foetal liver cell and to rat hepatoma cell surfaces. The antiserum is reported to have reduced the electrophoretic mobilities of these cells by approximately 50%. However, cell electrophoresis does not seem to be a suitable method for assessing binding of antibody molecules to the cell surface. For, gamma globulin molecules have a thickness of approx. 4.0 nm and at physiological pH cell electrophoresis can probe the surface only to a depth of approx. 1.0 nm.

Forrester et al.[7] showed that the pH-mobility curves
for silica particles with adsorbed γ-globulin
molecules resembled the pH-mobility curves obtained
for γ-globulins themselves. Since the isoelectric
equilibrium method can explore the cell membrane to
a depth of about 6.0 nm[4] one may expect that the
changes in the surface charges induced by the
binding of the antibodies to be reflected accurately
in the isoelectric points of cells.

　　We have raised an antiserum in rabbits against
simian virus 40-transformed 3T3 fibroblasts
(SV-3T3), and have investigated the binding of this
serum before and after absorption with untransformed
3T3 cells, to a variety of virally transformed
cells, using the isoelectric equilibrium method. We
have shown that the isoelectric point of SV-3T3
cells is lowered when treated with the antisera.
From the differences in the isoelectric points
produced by two successive dilutions of the
antiserum we have estimated that about $8.6 \times 10^3/\mu^2$
transformation-associated antibody binding sites
occur on the SV-3T3 cell surface. The antisera are
also capable of binding 3T3 cells transformed by
polyoma virus. The effects of the antisera on the
pI of these cells have shown that they have the
same number and kind of transformation-associated
sites. Neither the unabsorbed nor the absorbed
antiserum affects the pI of simian virus-transformed
rabbit kidney cells. We have thus shown that the
surface antigens detected by the isoelectric
equilibrium method are host cell-specific and not
specific for the transforming virus[9].

ACKNOWLEDGEMENTS

This work was supported by grants from Tenovus, the
Medical Research Council, the Lord Dowding Fund for
Humane Research, and the Central Research Fund of
London University.

REFERENCES

1.　ABERCROMBIE, M. and AMBROSE, E.J., 'The Surface
　　Properties of Cancer Cells: A Review'. Cancer
　　Research, 22, 525-548 (1962)
2.　EASTY, G.C., 'Cell Surfaces in Neoplasia'. In:
　　Neoplasia and Cell Differentiation, Ed. G.V.
　　Sherbet, S. Karger AG, Basel (1974)
3.　SHERBET, G.V., LAKSHMI, M.S. and RAO, K.V.,
　　'Characterisation of Ionogenic Groups and
　　Estimation of the Net Negative Electric Charge
　　on the Surface of Cells using Natural pH

Gradients'. Exp. Cell Res., 70, 113-123 (1972)

4. SHERBET, G.V. and LAKSHMI, M.S.,
    'Characterisation of Escherichia coli Cell
    Surface by Isoelectric Equilibrium Analysis'.
    Biochim. Biophys. Acta, 298, 50-58 (1973)

5. COULTER, C., 'The Isoelectric Point of Red Blood
    Cells and its Relation to Agglutination'.
    J. Cell Physiol., 3, 309-323 (1921)

6. SACHTLEBEN, P., 'The Influence of Antibody on
    the Electrophoretic Mobility of Red Blood
    Cells'. In: Cell Electrophoresis, Ed. E.J.
    Ambrose, J. & A. Churchill, London (1965)

7. FORRESTER, J.A., AMBROSE, E.J. and STOKER, M.,
    'Micro-electrophoresis of Normal and
    Transformed Clones of Hamster Kidney
    Fibroblasts'. Nature, 201, 945-946 (1964)

8. WOO, J. and CATER, D.B., 'A Study of the Cell
    Surface of Tumour, Foetal and Lymph Node Cells
    by Cell Electrophoresis after Antibody and
    Enzymic Treatment'. Biochem. J., 128,
    1273-1284 (1972)

9. SHERBET, G.V., LAKSHMI, M.S. and COAKHAM, H.B.,
    'Surface Antigens Associated with
    Transformation of 3T3 Cells by Simian Virus 40
    assayed by Isoelectric Equilibrium Method'
    (in preparation)

30. ISOELECTRIC FOCUSING OF BIOLOGICAL MEMBRANES

J.C. Allen and C. Humphries

30.1 INTRODUCTION

The great asset of isoelectric focusing lies in its
ability to separate and concentrate protein mixtures
simultaneously; native conformations, and hence
activities, are usually retained. Paradoxically,
the focusing effect itself is also the technique's
greatest disadvantage: that components are
concentrated at their isoelectric points, often pH
values at which they are least soluble. Although
the ensuing precipitation can be reduced by, for
instance, reducing the sample size or increasing the
Ampholine concentration, such efforts are not really
satisfactory. It is probably for this reason that
the technique of isoelectric focusing has so far
found little application in the field of membrane
biochemistry. Although the water-soluble fraction
of human erythrocyte membrane has been fractionated
by isoelectric focusing[1] and some interesting
characterisations of cell surfaces have been
achieved[2] by isoelectric equilibrium analysis, the
insoluble nature of most membrane materials might
appear to rule out the widespread use of isoelectric
focusing for their separation.
    In the course of research on the structure and
function of the bovine milk fat-globule membrane, it
was decided to investigate the possibility of
adapting density gradient isoelectric focusing for
the separation of membrane components, by the
inclusion of a suitable surfactant in the sucrose
gradient. Results have proved encouraging, and this
paper records the general pattern of the separations
of milk fat-globule membranes and of an experiment
with human erythrocyte membranes, together with some
accompanying enzyme activities.

30.2 CHOICE OF SURFACTANT

Anionic or cationic surfactants are obviously
unsuitable for use in isoelectric focusing.
Non-ionic surfactants of high molecular weight did
not cause sufficient solubilisation of the membranes
in the media of low ionic strength necessary for
isoelectric focusing; experiments showed that
precipitation of the sample occurred readily during
the run, usually concurrent with the establishment
of the pH gradient.

These difficulties have been largely overcome,
however, by the employment of zwitterionic
surfactants such as:

$$R\!-\!\overset{\displaystyle CH_3}{\underset{\displaystyle CH_3}{\vert}}\!\!\overset{+}{N}\!-\!CH_2CO_2^{-} \qquad (R = C_{10} \text{ to } C_{16})$$

alkylbetaine type
(Empigen BB, supplied by
the Marchon Division of
Albright and Wilson Ltd.,
Whitehaven, Cumberland,
England)

$$\text{and } R\!-\!\overset{\displaystyle CH_3}{\underset{\displaystyle CH_3}{\vert}}\!\!\overset{+}{N}\!-\!CH_2CH_2SO_3^{-} \qquad (R = C_{12})$$

sulphobetaine type
(Sulfobetaine DLH, supplied
by Textilana Corp.,
Hawthorne, California,
U.S.A.)

Such compounds are very effective in the
solubilisation of membranes at low concentrations
(between 5 to 30 mM; 0.1 to 0.5% w/v) and under
exceedingly mild conditions, and have been used in
the agarose chromatography of membrane materials
(Allen and Humphries, unpublished observations).
Enzymatic activities are not, in general, destroyed
by the action of these surfactants (an exception is
erythrocyte acetylcholinesterase, which is
inactivated by Empigen BB but not by Sulfobetaine
DLH); this is in contrast to the denaturant effect
of anionic surfactants such as sodium dodecyl
sulphate[3]. These zwitterionic surfactants are

compatible with isoelectric focusing: only low concentrations are necessary, they are electrically neutral, and the pKa values of the charged groups lie either side of the pH range of 3 to 10 which is usually employed.

30.3 MEMBRANE PREPARATIONS

Haemoglobin-free human red blood-cell membranes were obtained by the method of Moldow et al.[4]. The cream-coloured material was treated with 0.1% (w/v) Sulfobetaine DLH for 18 h at $4^{\circ}C$ prior to isoelectric focusing.

Bovine milk fat-globule membrane was prepared by a method similar to that of Swope and Brunner[5]. Unwashed cream from pooled raw (i.e. unpasteurised) milk was churned, the buttermilk thus obtained made 0.1 M with respect to sodium citrate buffer, pH 6.8, and centrifuged at 12 000 g for 30 min at $4^{\circ}C$. The sediment was discarded and the supernatant centrifuged further at 25 000 g for 2.75 h at $4^{\circ}C$; the pellet of membrane material was re-suspended in distilled water and re-sedimented. Samples for isoelectric focusing were treated with either 0.1% (w/v) Empigen BB or 0.1% (w/v) Sulfobetaine DLH for 18 h at $4^{\circ}C$ to give a final protein concentration of 6 mg/ml before applying to the column.

Some of the milk fat-globule membrane preparation was treated with surfactant and subjected to agarose chromatography in the following manner. The membranes were suspended in 0.05 M Tris buffer, pH 8.0, containing 0.1% (w/v) Empigen BB, and the suspension left at $4^{\circ}C$ for 18 h. A sample containing 12 mg protein in 2 ml was chromatographed at $4^{\circ}C$ on a 450 x 25 mm column of Bio-Rad A-150m agarose, using 0.05 M Tris, pH 8.0, containing 0.1% Empigen BB as the eluting buffer. Two protein-containing peaks emerged: one at the void volume which was discarded, and the other, sharp and well separated, which represented the material of lower molecular weight which had been solubilised by the surfactant. This fraction, containing xanthine oxidase, alkaline phosphatase and 5'-nucleotidase, was dialysed for 18 h against a solution of 0.1% (w/v) Empigen BB, and then subjected to isoelectric focusing.

30.4 ENZYME ASSAYS

Xanthine oxidase was assayed by the increase in absorbance at 290 nm caused by the oxidation of xanthine to uric acid[6]. Acetylcholinesterase was

M*

determined by the hydrolysis of acetylthiocholine
according to Ellman et al.[7]. Alkaline
phosphatase was estimated by the hydrolysis of
p-nitrophenyl phosphate[8], ATPase was measured by the
production of inorganic phosphate from ATP and
5'-nucleotidase by the method of Belfield and
Goldberg[9].

30.5 RESULTS OF ISOELECTRIC FOCUSING EXPERIMENTS

The experiments were carried out using an LKB 8101
column, at 4°C, with 1% Ampholines and (usually)
0.5% (w/v) surfactant in the sucrose density
gradient. The voltage was maintained below 200 V,
and the current stopped and the column eluted when
the focusing bands showed signs of imminent
precipitation; most experiments reached this stage
after about 24 h. Control experiments showed that
absence of surfactant led to widespread
precipitation of the sample within two to three
hours. Also, the surfactant, when focused alone,
produced no fractions with significant absorbance
at 280 nm within the range pH 3 to 10.
  First results showed that only one or two
protein fractions focused above pH 7.0, and that
most of the protein, and the enzymes so far studied,
separate between pH 3 and 6. For this reason, the
experiments discussed below deal mainly with this
region of the gradient.
  Figure 30.1 shows the isoelectric focusing
pattern of the low molecular weight fraction from
the agarose chromatography of milk fat-globule
membrane; the sample, containing 5 to 6 mg of
protein, was focused in 0.5% (w/v) Empigen BB for
24 h using Ampholine of pH range 4 to 6. Absorbance
at 280 nm revealed three groups of peaks: at pH 4.2,
5.2 and 5.9. The xanthine oxidase activity was
concentrated in the middle group, with a maximum
value at pH 5.3; this coincides with the reported
value for the isoelectric point of the purified
enzyme[10]. The 5'-nucleotidase activity also
occurred in well defined fractions at pH 4.9 and
5.9, which may reflect the presence of two
isoenzymes[11], or may mean that the enzyme occurs in
two different subunits or 'domains'[12] of the
membrane, which are dissociated from each other by
the action of the surfactant and then separated by
isoelectric focusing. On the other hand, alkaline
phosphatase was present in most fractions with
activity tending to correspond to the protein
concentration. This suggests that this enzyme
occurs widely in the membrane and is not associated

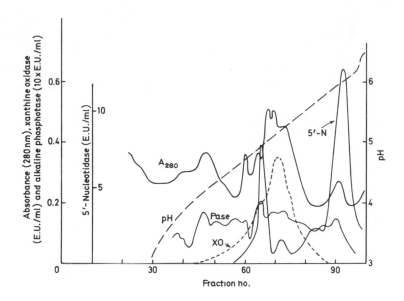

Figure 30.1 Isoelectric focusing of the lower molecular weight fraction from the agarose chromatography of bovine milk fat-globule membrane, using 1% Ampholines of pH range 4 to 6 and 0.5% (w/v) Empigen BB. The sample applied to the column contained 5 mg protein, and enzyme activities are expressed as µmols substrate converted per min, at 25°C and pH 7.5 for xanthine oxidase (XO), at 25°C and pH 10.4 for alkaline phosphatase (Pase) and at 37°C and pH 7.9 for 5'-nucleotidase (5'-N)

with one particular subunit.
  • The separation of human erythrocyte membranes is depicted in <u>Figure 30.2</u>. The protein bands, as indicated by absorbance at 280 nm, were well defined with a particularly sharp and intense peak at pH 5.3. Acetylcholinesterase activity was most apparent in the region pH 4.0 to 4.5 with a peak at pH 4.3. ATPase was found between pH 5.2 and 5.3, and appeared to reside almost entirely in a single protein fraction.
    The results of these exploratory experiments show that reproducible isoelectric focusing patterns of protein and enzymic activities can be obtained from surfactant-treated membranes and membrane fractions. It is hoped that closer examination of these active fractions will reveal details of the membrane structure from which they

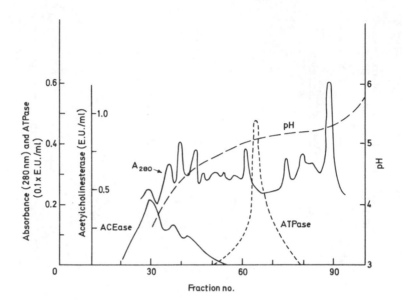

Figure 30.2 Isoelectric focusing of human red blood-cell membranes, using 1% Ampholines of pH range 4 to 6, and 0.5% (w/v) Sulfobetaine DLH. The sample applied contained 4 mg protein, and enzyme activities are expressed as μmols substrate converted per min at 25°C, at pH 8.0 for acetylcholinesterase (ACEase) and at pH 7.3 for ATPase

are derived; further work on the milk fat-globule membrane is now in progress.

ACKNOWLEDGEMENTS

The author wishes to thank Unigate Ltd. for the supply of raw milk, and Marchon Ltd. and the Textilana Corporation for the gift of zwitterionic surfactants. Thanks are also accorded to Miss Elizabeth Wilkie for skilful technical assistance.

REFERENCES

1.   HAMAGUCHI, H. and CLEVE, H., 'Properties of the Water Dissolved Membrane Proteins of Human Erythrocytes'. Biochim. Biophys. Acta, 233, 320-333 (1971)

2. SHERBET, G.V. and LAKSHMI, M.S.,
    'Characterisation of E. coli Cell Surface by
    Isoelectric Equilibrium Analysis'. Biochim.
    Biophys. Acta, 298, 50-58 (1973)
3. REYNOLDS, J.A., HERBERT, S., POLET, H. and
    STEINHARDT, J., 'The Binding of Diverse
    Detergent Anions to Bovine Serum Albumin'.
    Biochemistry, 6, 937-947 (1967)
4. MOLDOW, C.F., SUCKER-FRANKLIN, D., GORDON, A.,
    HOSPELHORN, V. and SILBER, R., 'Studies on the
    Succinylation of Erythrocyte Membranes'.
    Biochim. Biophys. Acta, 255, 133-147 (1972)
5. SWOPE, F.C. and BRUNNER, J.R.,
    'Characteristics of the Milk Fat Globule
    Membrane of Cow's Milk'. J. Dairy Science, 53,
    691-699 (1970)
6. KALCKAR, H.M., 'Differential Spectrophotometry
    of Purine Compounds by Means of Specific
    Enzymes'. J. Biol. Chem., 167, 429-443 (1947)
7. ELLMAN, G.L., COURTNEY, K.D., ANDRES, V. and
    FEATHERSTONE, R.M., 'A New and Rapid
    Colorimetric Determination of
    Acetylcholinesterase Activity'. Biochem.
    Pharmacol., 7, 88-95 (1961)
8. LOWRY, H.O., ROBERTS, N.R., WU, M., HIXON, W.S.
    and CRAWFORD, E.J., 'The Quantitative
    Histochemistry of Brain (ii) Enzyme
    Measurements'. J. Biol. Chem., 207, 19-37
    (1954)
9. BELFIELD, A. and GOLDBERG, D.M., 'Inhibition of
    the Nucleotidase Effect of Alkaline
    Phosphatase by β-Glycerophosphate'. Nature,
    219, 73-75 (1968)
10. AVIS, P.G., BERGEL, F. and BRAY, R.C.,
    'Cellular Constituents. The Chemistry of
    Xanthine Oxidase. Part II. The Homogeneity of
    Crystalline Metalloflavoprotein Fractions'.
    J. Chem. Soc., Part II, 1212-1219 (1956)
11. HUANG, C.M. and KEENAN, T.W., 'Preparation and
    Properties of 5'-Nucleotidases from Bovine Milk
    Fat Globule Membranes'. Biochim. Biophys.
    Acta, 274, 246-257 (1972)
12. CAPALDI, R.A. and GREEN, D.E., 'Membrane
    Proteins and Membrane Structure'. FEBS Lett.,
    25, 205-209 (1972)

Allen, J.C.   St. Bartholomew's Hospital
                         Medical College, University
                         of London, Charterhouse
                         Square, London EC1M 6BQ

Alper, C.A.   MRC Research Group on Serum
                         Complement, Department of
                         Immunology, Royal
                         Postgraduate Medical School,
                         London W12

Anderson, S.J.   See Savage, D.J.

Arbuthnott, J.P.   Department of Bacteriology,
                         University of Glasgow, Royal
                         Infirmary, Glasgow G4 OSF,
                         Scotland

Beeley, J.A.   Department of Oral Biology,
                         University of Glasgow Dental
                         School, Glasgow G2 3JZ,
                         Scotland

Beeley, J.G.   Department of Biochemistry,
                         University of Glasgow,
                         Glasgow G12 8QQ, Scotland

Catsimpoolas, N.   Laboratory of Physical
                         Biochemistry, Department of
                         Nutrition and Food Science,
                         Massachusetts Institute of
                         Technology, Cambridge,
                         Massachusetts 02139, U.S.A.

Caie, I.S.   See Talbot, P.

Cwynarski, M.T.   Department of Medicine, Guy's
                       Hospital Medical School,
                       London SE1

Davies, H.   LKB-Produkter AB, S-161 25
                       Bromma 1, Sweden

Fawcett, J.S.   Department of Experimental
                       Biochemistry, London Hospital
                       Medical School, Queen Mary
                       College, London E1 4NS

Gasparić, V.   Aminkemi AB, Box 20105, S-161
                       20 Bromma 20, Sweden

Haglund, H.   LKB-Produkter AB, S-161 25
                       Bromma 1, Sweden

Hobart, M.J.   See Alper, C.A.

Howard, C.R.   Hepatitis Research Unit,
                       Department of Microbiology,
                       London School of Hygiene and
                       Tropical Medicine, London
                       WC1E 7HT

Humphries, C.   See Allen, J.C.

Johnson, P.M.   MRC Rheumatism Research Unit,
                       Canadian Red Cross Memorial
                       Hospital, Taplow, Maidenhead,
                       Berkshire

Lachmann, P.S.   See Alper, C.A.

Lakshmi, M.S.   See Sherbet, G.V.

Leaback, D.H.   Biochemistry Department,
                       Institute of Orthopaedics,
                       Stanmore, Middlesex HA7 4LP

Lidström, P.-A.   Institute of Biochemistry,
                       University of Uppsala,
                       Uppsala, Sweden

MacGillivray, A.J.   The Beatson Institute for
                       Cancer Research, 132 Hill
                       Street, Glasgow G3 6UD,
                       Scotland

Matthew, M.   Microbiology Department,
                       Glaxo Laboratories, Greenford,
                       Middlesex

Maxey, C.R.	Ilford Ltd., Ilford, Essex, England
McNiven, A.C.	See Arbuthnott, J.P.
Milne, G.R.	See Templeton, J.G.
Palmer, M.R.	See Maxey, C.R.
Pettersson, S.	University of Gothenburg, 40220 Gothenburg, Sweden
Radola, B.J.	Institut für Chemisch-technische Analyse, Technische Universität München, D 8050 Freising-Weihenstephan, W. Germany
Rickwood, D.	See MacGillivray, A.J.
Righetti, A.B.B.	Institute of Occupational Health, Via Commenda 12, Milano, Italy
Righetti, P.G.	Department of Biochemistry, University of Milano, Via Celoria 2, Milano 20133, Italy
Rilbe, H.	Department of Physical Chemistry, Chalmers Institute of Technology, Gibraltargatan 5A, Gothenburg S, Sweden
Rosengren, A.	See Gasparić, V.
Savage, D.J.	Whitbread & Co. Ltd., Oakley Road, Luton, Bedfordshire
Sherbet, G.V.	Department of Biochemical Pathology, University College Hospital Medical School, University Street, London WC1E 6JJ
Smyth, C.J.	See Wadström, T.
Söderholm, J.	Statens Bakteriologiska Laboratorium (SBL), S-105 21 Stockholm, Sweden

Stevenson, S.M.   See Beeley, J.A.

Talbot, P.   Animal Virus Research
                         Institute, Pirbright, Woking,
                         Surrey GU24 0NF

Templeton, J.G.   Glasgow and West Scotland
                         Blood Transfusion Service,
                         Law Hospital, Carluke,
                         Lanarkshire ML8 5ES, Scotland

Thompson, C.C.   See Savage, D.J.

Vesterberg, O.   Occupational Health
                         Department, The National Board
                         of Occupational Safety and
                         Health, Fack, S-100 26
                         Stockholm 34, Sweden

Wadström, T.   Statens Bakteriologiska
                         Laboratorium (SBL), S-105 21
                         Stockholm, Sweden

Watkins, J.   Protein Reference Unit,
                         Immunology Department,
                         Hallamshire Hospital Medical
                         School, Beech Hill Road,
                         Sheffield S10 2RX

Williamson, A.R.   Institute of Biochemistry,
                         University of Glasgow, Glasgow
                         G12 8QQ, Scotland

Zuckerman, A.J.   See Howard, C.R.

Acidic fraction
  (see beer haze)
Acidic phosphate
  groups 339
Acidic proteins in
  brewing 335
Acid Phosphatase 155
Acrylamide
  (see polyacrylamide)
Additives 80-81
Adenovirus subunits 284
Adsorption of samples
  to filter paper 160-161
Aeromonas haemolysin 234
Aeromonas hydrophila 234
Agarose 170
Agarose overlayers
  165, 167
Aggregation 69
Alkaline Phosphatase 154
Alkali-processed
  gelatin 261
Alkylbetaine 348
L- and D-amino acid
  oxidase 154
Amino acid composition
  changes 15
Ampholine
  absorbance 8
  buffering capacity 18
  classical
    properties of 8
  conductivity of 11
  historical aspects 3
  ^{14}C-labelled 17, 18
    168, 178-181

Ampholine (cont.)
  low apparent molecular
    weight 178-181
  mixtures for gels
    103-104, 133-134
  molecular weight 17, 18
  molecular weights
    distribution of 181
  narrow range 25, 51
  pI distribution 18-20
  properties of 3-20
  protein interaction -
    chemical 14-16
  protein interaction -
    complex formation
    16-17
  ranges available 18-19
  removal of, from
    protein 36-37
  time of addition to
    polyacrylamide gels
    81-82
Ampholytes
  buffering capacity 5
  conductivity of 4-5
  partial protein
    hydrolysates as 6
  polyaminopolycarboxylic
    acids 8-9
α-Amylase 156,
  164-165, 243-244
Analytical isoelectric
  focusing 114-129
Antibodies 91, 291
Anti-D IgG Immunoglobulin
  313-318

Anti-D plasma 314
Anti-enzymes 294
Antimony microelectrode
     148-150, 243
Antrypol (EAC43) 307
Application of samples
     (see sample application)
Artefacts 167, 169
Autoradiography 255

Bacillus cereus 167
Bacteroides fragilis 166
Balb/C Mouse
     Fibroblasts 344
Barley and malt
     proteins 330
Barley 331
Beer haze acidic
     fraction 329-337
Beer protein 330
Bence-Jones protein 321
Bio-Gel 183
Biological
     membranes 347-358
Blood group
     antibodies 313
Bovine milk-fat
     globule membrane 347,
     349
Bowman-Birk proteinase
     inhibitor 61
Bromophenol blue 320
Buffering capacity
     5, 18

Capillary columns 125
Carbamylated
     haemoglobins 124
Carbamylation 232
Carbohydrate 284
Carbohydrate moieties
     232
Carbonic anhydrase 33-34
Catalase 206
Causes of multiple forms
     (see heterogeneity and
     multiple forms)
Cell surfaces 338-346
Cellulase 156
Cellulose acetate
     electrophoresis 207
Cephalosporin analogue
     (87 - 249), 312

Cephalosporinase
     (β-lactamase) 251
Cereolysin 234
C-gene 292, 299
Charge groups on cell
     surfaces
     α-COOH 339-343
     α-NH$_2$ 339-343
     -NH$_3^+$ 339-343
     acidic phosphate
          groups 339-343
     guanidyl groups
          339-343
Chromatin nonhistone
     protein 254-260
δ-Chymotrypsin 156
Clostridium botulinum
     type A toxin 229
     type B toxin 229
Clostridium perfringens
     (welchii)
     α-toxin 227, 228, 230
     α_A-toxin 230, 232
     α_B-toxin 230, 232
     θ-toxin 227, 228, 230
     collagenase (κ-toxin)
          227, 229
     enterotoxin 228
     hyaluronidase (μ-toxin)
          227, 229
     phospholipase C 232
Column - micro-quartz
     58-59
Complement 276, 295,
     306-312
     C2, C6, C7 276
     C6 306-312
     C6 allotypes 310
     genetic loci 308
Complex formation 16-17
Conductance 69
Conductivity 4-5, 11
Conformation changes
     69, 214
Conformers 214, 232
Continuous flow 40
Constant wattage 132
Constant wattage
     regulator 143-146
'Contact prints'
     (see zymograms)
Cooled metal block 259

Cooling 30, 35, 99-100, 117-119, 127, 134
Cooling temperature 109-110
Cooling through membranes 48-50
Cooling - vertical 44-56
Coomassie Blue 89
Coomassie Blue R-250 85, 111
Coomassie Violet R-150 184
Covalently linked structures 278
Cross-linking concentration (C) 79-80
Cystic fibrosis 308
Cytochrome C 19

Deamidation 232, 297
Defocusing 64-67
NAD/NADP Dehydrogenase 155
Denaturation 86
Density gradient columns capacity 51-56
    isolation of focused zones 26-28
    multiple 34-36
    recent designs 28-33
    short 44-56
    UV monitoring 27-28, 31, 58-59
Deoxyribonuclease 165, 227
Desalting - Diaflo ultrafiltration cell 240
Detection of enzymes (see zymograms)
Detection of protein - thin layer gels 89-90
Diamond patterns 320-322, 324
Diethyldithiocarbamate (DIECA) 331, 335
Differential refractometer 179-180
Diffusion 10
Diffusion coefficient 66-67, 69
Diffusion in polyacrylamide gels 69

Digital data processing 59-60
Diphtheria toxin 141
Dissociation 69
Dithioerythritol (DTE) 255, 258, 259
6-6'-dithionicotinic acid carboxypyridine disulphide (CPDS) 339
Dithiothreitol 284
DNP-binding antibodies 295
α-DNP-Decalysine 300
α-DNP-oligo-L-lysine 300
'Double Chamber' apparatus 183
Drying of gels 136
Drying of stained gels 111-112

Ehrlich ascites cells 339
Elastase 165
Electro-
    endosmosis 81
    endosmotic flow 12, 126
    endosmotic water flow 207
Electrodes
    palladium silver 45
    platinum 48
Electrode solutions 82, 106, 135
Electrode vessels 12-13, 15
Electrophoresis 90, 91
Empigen BB 349, 350
Endo-β-N-glucosaminidase 227
Endo-osmotic flow (see electro-endosmotic flow)
Enterotoxin 227
Enumeration of free thiol groups 276
Enumeration of polypeptide chains 276
Enzymes - detection on polyacrylamide gels (see zymograms)
Epididymal-α-N-acetate-hexosaminidase 208
Erythrocyte acetyl-cholinesterase 348

Erythrocyte membranes
  349, 351, 352
Esterase 154
Ethylene glycol 80
Ethyleneimine 276
Ethyleneimine -
  treated cells 339

Ferri haemoglobin 121
Ferritin 125
Focusing time 109-110
Focusing time -
  minimal 60-62
Focused zones - isolation
  of from density gradient
    columns 26-28
Foot and Mouth Disease
  virus 270-274
  12S subunit 272
Formaldehyde - treated
  cells 339

β-Galactosidase 294
Gelatin 261-269
  alkali-processed
    gelatin 261
  chemically modified 265
  gelatin - coated
    plates 261
  hydrogen bonding 264
  hydrolysis 265
  molecular weight 263
  multiple forms 263
Gel polymerisation
  102, 134, 169
Gel rods 241
Gel rods -
  advantages of 127, 168
Gel staining (see
  also stains) 135-136
Gel - surface rippling
  80, 108-109, 139-140
Gel swelling 108
Gel tubes - plastic 120
  quartz 120
Genetic polymorphism 310
Glass plates 102
α-Glucosidase 227
β-Glucuronidase 154
Glycerol 80
Glycoproteins 244

Gradient pore
  electrophoresis 201
  pore limits 201
Granulated Gels 183
  maximum load capacity
    189
  overloading 188
  recovery 192
  QAE Sephadex 259
  Sephadex 259
  Sephadex G50 258
  Sephadex G75 184
Guanidine hydrochloride
  259
Guanidyl groups 339

Haemoglobin 88, 109,
  121-125, 128, 208
Haemolysins 165, 167
Heating effects 116, 127
Heating 24, 110, 140-141
Heating - thin layer
  gels 86-87
Heavy chain subclass 321
Hepatitis B Antigen 281-287
  dissociation 284
  electronmicroscopy of
    281
  electrophoretic
    migration 281
  iodinated 283
  partial separation from
    serum components 282
Heterogeneity (see
  also multiple forms)
    259, 263, 277, 281,
    282, 291, 297, 324,
    335
High voltage 24
High voltage - preparative
  and analytical
    isoelectric focusing
    114-129
High voltage thin-layer
  isoelectric focusing
  with constant wattage
  132-141
High voltage thin-layer
  gels - heating 140-141
L-histidyl-L-tyrosine
  65, 67
Hopped worts 331

Horizontal trough
  apparatus 74-77, 270
Horseradish peroxidase
  183
Hyaluronidase 230

IgA immunoglobulin 207
  genetic loci 291
  multiband patterns 322
  post synthetic
    changes 297
IgG immunoglobulin
  202, 206, 207
  anti-D IgG 313-318
  κ chain type 321
  λ chain type 321
  monoclonal 202, 322
  monoclonal proteins
    319-325
  paraproteins 319-322
  sub classes 295, 315,
    317
Immunoglobulin
  isoelectric spectra
    291-305
Immunological detection
  procedure 90
Interactions 69
Interconversion
  interconvertible forms
    221, 272, 273
Iodinated purified
  hepatitis B antigen 283
Iodoacetoamide 276
Iodoacetic acid 276
Ion-exchange
  chromatography 207
Ion-exchange resins 36-37
Isoelectric
  equilibrium 345
Isoelectric
  precipitation 283
Isoelectric spectra of
  antibodies 291-305
Isoenzymes 153, 243, 279

Joule effect (see
  heating effects)
Joyce Loebl Chromoscan
  330

β-Lactamase 248-253

β-Lactamase (cont.)
  Enterobacter 251
  Klebsiella   251
  Proteus   251
  Salmonella   251
Lactate dehydrogenase
  154, 206, 279
β-Lactoglobulin
  47, 48, 61
Leucine aminopeptidase
  206
Lipoprotein 284
Loading capacity 23,
  33-34
β-Lysin (see
  sphingomyelinase C)
Lysozyme 244

Maleation 275
Mashing 335
Microelectrode 148-150
Milk-fat globule
  membrane 350
Minicon
  micro-concentrator 241
Molecular weight 232
Molecular weight of
  Ampholines 178-181
Monoclonal antibody
  spectra 298, 299
Monoclonal IgG
  immunoglobulins 202,
    206, 322
Mouse plasma cell
  tumour (5563) 296, 297,
    324
Multi-band patterns (see
  also heterogeneity and
    multiple forms) 322
Multiphor 98-102, 115, 158
  cooling 99-100
  electrode strips 98
  focusing time 109-110
  gel moulding 100-102
  heating of gels 110
  lid design 98-99
  polymerisation 102
  sample application 102
  voltage, power 109-111
Multiple forms (see
  also heterogeneity)
    220, 223, 225, 279

Multiple forms (cont.)
  causes of 213, 233
  deamidation 225, 226
  protein-protein
    interaction 232
Multiple myeloma 319
Myeloid leukaemia 308
Myeloma proteins 295, 296
  band patterns 296, 297
  cellulose acetate
    electrophoresis 207
  clinical inferences
    319-326
  gradient pore
    electrophoresis 201-207
Myoglobin - horse 32
  sperm whale 50
  whale 32

Neuraminidase 227, 230
Neurotoxins 227
NIP-BGG (4-hydroxy-3-
  iodo-5-nitrophenacetyl-
  bovine γ-globulin)
  299
Non-covalently associated
  subunits 279
5'-Nucleotidase 350

Oligomers of identical
  subunits 279
On:off ratio 116
Osmolarity 80
Ovalbumin 61
Overlayers (see also
  agarose overlayers) 158
Oxygen - labile
  haemolysins 233, 234
Oxyhaemoglobin 121

Palisade patterns
  320, 321, 322, 324
Paraproteinaemia 325
Paraproteins 322, 324
Parotid saliva 243, 244
Penicillinase 165,
  166-617
Pepsin 20, 156
Peptide separation 178-181
Peroxidase 155
pH gradient 136-138
pH gradient
  artificial 4

pH gradient (cont.)
  formation and stability
    of 106-108
  instability of 10
  linearity at right
    angles to the pH
    gradient 108-109
  measurement of 111
  measurements of in
    gels 147-150
  natural 4
  segmental 62, 68
  shallow 25
  stability and
    deformation 137-139
pH measurement 31-33,
  104, 241
  accuracy of 149
  antimony
    microelectrode
    148-150
  disadvantages of water
    elution of gel slices
    147-148
  temperature of 149
  thin layer gels
    88-89, 135
Phadebas^R amylase test
  164
Phosphatase 227
Phospholipase C 160-163,
  165, 227
Phosphorylated proteins
  255
Photopolymerisation 102
Phthalic anhydride 265
Physical constants -
  theoretical
    considerations 63-64
pI - apparent 62
Picornaviruses 272
Plastic plates 102
Plastic tubes 120
'Plateau phenomenon'
  features of 10-13, 81,
    106-108, 137
Polio virus 273
Polyacrylamide
  concentration (T)
    79-80
Polyacrylamide gels
  Ampholine composition
    of 103-104

Polyacrylamide gels (cont.)
  optimum gel
    concentration and
    degree of cross-linking
    79-80
  preparation of 103, 134
Polyacrylamide gel slabs
  thin-layer slabs 275
Polyacrylamide gels -
  thin-layer (see thin
  layer gels)
Polyacrylamide -
  polymerisation 82
Polyethylene glycol 179
Poly-L-lysine (PLL) 302
Polymerisation - of
  gels 115, 117, 134, 169
Polyoma - transformed
  BHK-21 cells 339
Polyphenols 331, 333, 335
Polyploidation (genetic
  polymorphism) 311
Post-synthetic charge
  alteration 324
Power supply
  Bosi 116
  pulsed 128
  voltage-limiting
    device 76
Precipitate 33, 34
Preparative isoelectric
  focusing 114-129
  recent developments
    23-41
Procarboxypeptidase A 154
Pronase E 183, 186, 188, 189
Pronase P 183, 186
Protease 158, 165
Proteases, crude
  bacterial 156
Protein - Ampholine
  complexes 169
Protein-bound
  oligosaccharides 325
Protein denaturation 14
Protein-protein
  interactions 226
Protein - separation
  from Ampholine 36
Protein structures 275
Proteins - oxidation
  of 15

Proteins - reduction
  of 15, 16
Proteolysis -
  heterogeneity 192
Proteolytic activity
  (see also zymograms)
  183
Pseudomonas aeruginosa
  protease 158
Pulse frequency 116
Pulsed power supply 116

Quartz tubes 120

Radioactive antigen 294
Radioactive detection
  procedure 90
Red blood cell
  membranes 349
Red cell haemolysate 34
Refocusing 64-66
Refractometer 179-180
Regulator for constant
  wattage with constant
  voltage or constant
  current power
  supplies 143-146
Resistance 143
Resolution maximum
  23-24
Resolving power 62
R-factor 248
Rheumatoid arthritis
  243
Rippling (see gel
  surface rippling)
Routine clinical
  analysis 128

Saliva 164-166, 241,
  244, 245
Salivary proteins 241
Sample application
  82-85, 102, 116, 135,
  158, 161-164, 169
Sample application -
  grade of filter
  paper 162-164
Self association 69
Separation of proteins
  from Ampholines
  36-37

Sephadex (see also
  granulated gels) 37-38,
  40, 184, 258, 259
Sephadex columns 37-38
Sephadex columns -
  for ampholine removal 37
Sephadex - for Ampholine
  molecular weight
  determination 179
Serum hepatitis virus 281
Servo motor - advantages
  of in wattage
  regulation 146
Short density gradient
  columns 44-56
Sialic acid 325
Simian virus 40
  transformed cells 345
Sjögrens syndrome 243
Sodium dodecyl sulphate
  284
Sorbitol gradient 19
Sphingomyelinase C 167
Stains
  bromophenol blue 320
  Coomassie blue 89
  Coomassie blue R250
    85, 111, 125
  Coomassie violet 183
  light green SF 185
  lissamine green 243
  PAS stain 243
Staining of gels 111,
  135-136
Staining procedures 89-90
Staphylococcal
  haemolysin 165, 167
Staphylococcal toxins
  α-toxin 214, 216,
    220-223
  β-toxin 214, 216
  γ-toxin 214, 216, 226
  δ-toxin 214, 217, 226
  enterotoxin A 215,
    217, 223
  enterotoxin B 217, 223
  enterotoxin C$_2$ 217,
    223, 225
  epidermolytic toxin
    215, 217, 226
Staphylococcus aureus
  protease 158

Staphylokinase 156
Starch slide
  zymograms 243
Steady state 58
Steady state - anomalous
  behaviour 69, 70
Streptolysin-O 234
Step-wise pH gradient 267
Storage of gels 111-112
Sublingual saliva 245
Sublingual glycoprotein
  245
Submandibular saliva
  241, 244
Substrate overlayers 158
Subtilisin - see also
  subtilopeptidase 160
Subtilopeptidase 156, 160
Sucrose as a gel
  additive 80
Sulphabetaine 348
Sulphatase 227
Surface antigens 344
Surface water 80
Surfactant, alkyl betaine
  type (Empigen BB) 348
  sulphabetaine 348
Sweet worts 331

Tandem duplication 311
Taurine 306
Thin-layer gels 78-92,
  97-112, 292
  advantages of 79,
    92, 97-98,
    167-168
  constant wattage
    132-141
  cooling 134
  detection of enzymes
    (see zymograms)
  electrodes 135
  focusing time 88
  heating 86-87, 110,
    140-141
  high voltage 132-141
  immunological
    procedures 90
  pH measurements 135,
    148-150
  radioactive procedures
    90

Thin-layer gels (cont.)
  resistance 143
  sample load 85
  staining 135-136
  staining procedures
    89-90
  voltage and wattage
    85-88
  zymograms 90
Toxinogram 167
Trace acetylation 275
Transamination 276
Transient state
  isoelectric focusing
    58-70
Tropocollagen 266
Trypsin 156
Two-stage isoelectric
  focusing 26

Unit charge change 275
Urea 80, 255, 258, 259, 330
  gradient 277
  solutions 277
  0.5M urea 284
  studies in 222, 232, 311
UV monitoring of density
  gradient columns
    27-28, 31, 58-59

Valmet - type apparatus
  38-40, 74-77
V - gene 292, 299, 300,
  303
Viral transformation 344
Viruses 77
Viscosity 69
Voltage 109-111

Wattage 109-110

Wattage - constant 132
Wattage - constant
  regulator 143-146
Wavy patterns (see
  gel-surface rippling)
Wedge patterns 320-322
Worts 330, 331, 335

Xanthine oxidase 349

Yeast hexokinase 206
Yoshida ascites cells 339

Zone convection 38-40
Zwitterionic surfactants
  348
Zymograms 90, 152-171
  α-amylase 164-166
  artefacts 169
  buffer equilibration
    of gels 168-169
  future developments
    170, 171
  general procedure
    153-158
  inhibitory effect of
    Ampholine 168
  penicillinase 165,
    166-167
  phospholipase C
    160-163, 165
  problems and artefacts
    167
  problems of sample
    application 169
  proteases 158
  removal of ions by
    chelation 168
  Staphylococcal
    haemolysins 165, 167